SYSTEMATICS
AND THE
ORIGIN OF SPECIES

SYSTEMATICS
AND THE
ORIGIN OF SPECIES
FROM THE VIEWPOINT OF A ZOOLOGIST

by ERNST MAYR

WITH A NEW INTRODUCTION BY THE AUTHOR

Dover Publications, Inc., New York

This Dover edition, first published in 1964, is an unabridged and corrected republication of the work first published by the Columbia University Press in 1942, to which has been added a new Preface by the author.

This work was first published as Number XIII of the Columbia Biological Series.

Library of Congress Catalog Card Number: 64-20884

Manufactured in the United States of America

Dover Publications, Inc.
180 Varick Street
New York 14, N.Y.

INTRODUCTION

A NEW AND SIGNIFICANT trend has become discernible in biology during the last decade. The excessive specialization which had prevailed in the recent past seems slowly to be giving way to a greater unity; a science of general biology appears to be emerging. In a way this trend represents a partial reversal of a historic tendency of much greater duration. For more than a century the field of biology was so extensive and growing so rapidly that no single investigator, no matter how broad might be his grasp, could keep abreast with the developments in all the numerous branches. The response of biology to this challenge was a sub-division of the general field into many disciplines, each endowed with its own materials, methods, and techniques. Instead of being biologists, most of us became systematists, physiologists, geneticists, embryologists, biochemists, pathologists, etc. Inevitably, secondary subdivisions have arisen in the course of time. Nobody could any longer be at home in, for example, the systematics of all animals or of all plants. The systematists split into mammalogists, ornithologists, entomologists, helminthologists, protozoologists, etc., and finally into specialists on separate families, genera, and even smaller groups. The genetics of, let us say, Oenothera threatened to become incomprehensible to those engaged in studies on the genetics of Drosophila or of man. This extreme compartmentalization of biological knowledge proved fruitful in that it led to an enormous accumulation of factual information; it has been deleterious in so far as it resulted in a lack of understanding between the representatives of the various disciplines and a consequent lowering of the efficiency of biological research. It stands to reason that the exigencies of the situation continue, and probably will continue, to demand that each biologist be a specialist in some small portion of the general field. During the last decade the conclusions reached by many of the specialists have begun to converge toward a set of general principles applicable to the entire realm of living matter. One can now hope that this will occur in increasing measure in the future. Biology, it seems, is no longer in its childhood; as a science, it is approaching maturity.

Obviously, it would be out of place to attempt to discuss here the results of the unifying trend in modern biology as a whole. Suffice it to say that Dr. Mayr's *Systematics and the Origin of Species* is one of the manifestations of this trend. Dr. Mayr is an outstanding zoological systematist; his specialty is ornithology, and he is the foremost authority on the birds of Oceania and Indonesia. The results of his preoccupation with the subject matter of his special investigations are amply evident in his choice of examples in many chapters of the book. Yet it is equally evident that this book has not been written from the point of view of a specialist on the systematics of a certain group of animals inhabiting a certain part of the world. It has been written by a general biologist. Although this book contains a critical reassessment of the evidence furnished by zoological systematics regarding the course and the mechanisms of the biological evolution, that is not what makes it unique. Such critical reassessments have been published from time to time by many systematists and they are undoubtedly interesting and necessary. But Dr. Mayr's chief accomplishment in this book has been to correlate the evidence and the points of view of modern systematics with those of other biological disciplines, particularly genetics and ecology. A correlation of this sort has been necessary for some time; even in the recent past there existed a notorious lack of mutual comprehension between the systematists on one hand and the representatives of the experimental biological disciplines on the other. That this lack of mutual comprehension was due in part to an unfamiliarity with each other's factual materials and methods, and in part to a sheer misunderstanding of the respective points of view, was felt by many systematists as well as by experimentalists. But it remained for a systematist of Dr. Mayr's caliber, possessing a wide familiarity with and a perfect grasp of the apparently conflicting disciplines, to demonstrate conclusively that this conflict is spurious.

TH. DOBZHANSKY

Mount San Jacinto, California
July, 1942

PREFACE TO DOVER EDITION

DURING the first three decades of this century disagreement among evolutionists reached its height. De Vries and other early Mendelians saw in mutation the moving force of evolution, and they thought of mutation as something so drastic that it could produce new species in a single step. There was no room in their conceptual framework for gradual changes and for natural selection. In the scheme of the naturalists, on the other hand, gradual variation and the effect of the environment were dominant, but they went to the extreme of seeing in the environment not only an agent of selection but also of direct induction (in the sense of Geoffroy St. Hilaire). The two schools were so far apart as to preclude effective communication.

Three developments in the 1920's made reconciliation possible. First, genetics showed that not all mutations are drastic, thereby eliminating the distinction between the (re-defined) mutation and the "small variations" of the taxonomists. Secondly, J. Schmidt for fish (*Zoarces*), Sumner for *Peromyscus*, and Goldschmidt for *Lymantria*, showed that the small and intergrading differences between local populations and geographic races have a genetic basis. They are not (or are only to a small extent) nongenetic modifications of the phenotype as had been claimed by the mutationists. Finally, Haldane and Fisher demonstrated mathematically that even very small selective advantages would in due time lead to genetic changes in populations and species. Unquestionably R. A. Fisher's *Genetical Theory of Natural Selection*, published in 1930 (Dover, 1958), was a milestone in this development.

In the meantime, quite unnoticed by the experimentalists, a rapid maturing of taxonomic concepts had occurred and, in particular, an application of population thinking to systematics. Three German publications by Rensch (1929, 1933, 1934) summarized much of this new thinking in systematics. These writings were not nearly as well known internationally as deserved, but fortunately two other biologists, Chetverikov (1926)[1] and Dobzhansky, both trained in

[1] (1926), Chetverikov, S. S. On certain aspects of the evolutionary process from the standpoint of modern genetics. J. Exptl. Biol. (Russian) A2:3–54. Eng. trans. (1961), Proc. Amer. Phil. Soc. 105:167–195.

Russia as insect taxonomists, facilitated the introduction of population thinking into genetics. The publication in 1937 of Dobzhansky's *Genetics and the Origin of Species* signalized the termination of the conflict between genetics and systematics.

In 1940, in a volume of essays by 22 authors on problems of taxonomy and evolution, J. S. Huxley, the editor, expressed the "hope for a new systematics." There is, indeed, a far greater stress on the biological aspects of systematics in that volume than in much of the conventional taxonomic literature. My own researches on speciation in birds, made possible by the extraordinary collections of the Whitney South Sea Expedition, led me to similar views. An invitation by Columbia University to give the Jesup Lectures for 1941 gave me an opportunity not only to confirm Dobzhansky's conclusions from the point of view of systematics, but also to formulate the new thinking emerging in animal taxonomy, now referred to as the "new systematics." *Systematics and the Origin of Species*, when published in 1942, was the first systematic presentation of the ideas of the new movement.

By 1950 I had undertaken a new work, intended to supersede *Systematics*, and I asked Columbia University Press to let the earlier work go out of print. However, the demand for it continued to be active even after *Animal Species and Evolution* was published in 1963, since there is much in *Systematics* that is not covered in the newer work.

A comparison of *Systematics* and *Animal Species* reflects some of the changes in thinking in the 21 years between 1942 and 1963. In 1942, it was most important to demolish the typologically defined species. The emphasis had to be on the subdivisions of the species, on subspecies and local races. This prepared the way for a treatment of geographic variation and of speciation. The conclusions derived from this approach are now so generally accepted that it has again become important to stress the unity of the genotype in a species, and this is the key concept of the 1963 volume.

The reader is warned that not everything in the 1942 volume represents modern thinking. For instance, phenotype and genotype are confused in the discussion on neutral polymorphism (p. 75) and the erroneous assumption is made that the absence of a selective advantage in the visible phenotype is an indication of selective neutrality of the genotype. In Chapter X, in the discussion of higher categories, there is occasional confusion of taxa and categories. It is evident in some other discussions that they were written in 1942 and not in 1963. As far as the discussion of geographic variation and of the polytypic species is concerned, *Systematics and the Origin of Species* is still valuable, especially with respect to birds. In particular, it contains a summary of the evolutionary results of the Whitney South Sea Expedition.

For these various reasons, and considering that much of the volume is still quite modern, it has seemed well justified to make it again available.

Museum of Comparative Zoology   ERNST MAYR
  Harvard University
  Cambridge, January, 1964

PREFACE TO FIRST EDITION

During the past fifty years animal taxonomy has undergone a revolution almost as fundamental as that which occurred in genetics after the rediscovery of Mendel's laws. It is true that the change from the static species concept of Linnaeus to the dynamic species concept of the modern systematist has not entirely escaped the attention of progressive students of genetics and evolution. However, the whole significance of the polytypic species, of the phenomena of geographic variation, of the differences between geographic and other forms of isolation are by no means as widely appreciated among students of evolution and even among taxonomists as they deserve. I have attempted in this book to summarize our knowledge in the field of systematics, and to subject to a searching analysis the principal concepts on which taxonomic work is based. Finally I have tried to present some of the evidence of the systematist on the question of the origin of species. A discussion of general evolution and of such specific subjects as the evolution of sex, degeneration, and parasitism has been considered outside the scope of this book. The extreme scattering of taxonomic literature makes it inevitable that some publications worthy of detailed discussion have been overlooked. Special emphasis has been placed on the most recent literature and on the field with which I personally am most familiar, the ornithology of the Pacific Islands.

This book is based on the Jesup lectures delivered at Columbia University in March, 1941. The writer presented the evidence of the zoologist, and Dr. Edgar Anderson, of Washington University and of the Missouri Botanical Garden, St. Louis, that of the botanist. The present volume includes only the material of the zoological lectures. Parts of the manuscript were read by Edgar Anderson, Charles M. Bogert, Mont A. Cazier, James P. Chapin, Kenneth Cooper, J. Eric Hill, George G. Simpson, Herman Spieth, George M. Sutton and John T. Zimmer, to all of whom I owe many valuable suggestions. A. E. Emerson, Julian Huxley, and other friends have discussed a number of problems with the author and have helped him in crystallizing his ideas. Most of all I am indebted to Th. Dobzhansky and L. C. Dunn, who aided in countless ways in the preparation of the manuscript and who encouraged and inspired me throughout. I dedicate this work to the army of taxonomists who have unselfishly devoted their lives to the task of describing and classifying the animals of the world.

ERNST MAYR

The American Museum of Natural History
New York, May, 1942

CONTENTS

INTRODUCTION BY THEODOSIUS DOBZHANSKY   vii

I   THE METHODS AND PRINCIPLES OF SYSTEMATICS   3

II   TAXONOMIC CHARACTERS AND THEIR VARIATION   18

III   PHENOMENA OF GEOGRAPHIC VARIATION   33

IV   SOME ASPECTS OF GEOGRAPHIC VARIATION   71

V   THE SYSTEMATIC CATEGORIES AND THE NEW SPECIES CONCEPT   102

VI   THE POLYTYPIC SPECIES, IN NATURE AND IN SYSTEMATICS   123

VII   THE SPECIES IN EVOLUTION   147

VIII   NONGEOGRAPHIC SPECIATION   186

IX   THE BIOLOGY OF SPECIATION   216

X   THE HIGHER CATEGORIES AND EVOLUTION   275

LITERATURE   299

INDEX   315

ILLUSTRATIONS

1. Localized Populations of *Achatinella mustelina*   34

2. Irregular Variation of *Cacatua galerita triton*   37

3. Geographic Variation of the Shape of the Tail in Birds   40

4. Subspeciation in the Whistler *Myiolestes megarhynchos*   42

5. Geographic Variation of the Anatomy of *Xerocrassa cretica*   44

6. Geographic Variation of Sexual Dimorphism in *Petroica*   49

7. Geographic Variation of *Pachycephala pectoralis* in the Solomon Islands   51

8. Parallel Evolution in the *Turdus poliocephalus* Group   58

9. Transient Polymorphism and Subspecies Formation (Diagram)   81

10. Geographic Variation in *Monarcha castaneoventris*   82

11. Geographic Variation in *Microscelis leucocephalus*   83

12. Variation of Phaeomelanin in *Parus atricapillus*   91

13. Variation and Hybridization in *Paradisaea apoda*   97

14. Polytypic Species of marine shells (Cypraeidae)   145

15. Speciation in the *Tanysiptera hydrocharis* Group   153

16. Stages of Speciation (Diagram)   160

17. "Genus" *Serresius*, a Member of the Superspecies *Ducula pacifica*   168

18. Double Invasion of Tasmania by *Acanthiza pusilla*   175

19. Overlap in a Chain of *Larus argentatus* Races   180

20. Allopatry and Overlap in the *Halcyon chloris* Group   181

21. Overlap in a Ring of Subspecies of *Phylloscopus trochiloides*   183

22. Overlap of Subspecies of *Peromyscus maniculatus*   184

23. The Superspecies *Zosterops rendovae*   227

24. Insular Ranges and Taxonomic Divergence in *Astrapia*   230

25. Isolation without Subspeciation in *Dichoceros bicornis*   231

26. Altitudinal Subspecies of Grassland Birds in New Guinea   233

27. Intergeneric Hybrids among Birds of Paradise (Diagram)   261

28. Stabilized Hybrid Populations in *Pachycephala pectoralis*   269

29. Diagram of Part of a Phylogenetic Tree   282

ACKNOWLEDGMENTS FOR ILLUSTRATIONS

I am deeply indebted to Mr. Roger T. Peterson for drawing the originals of Figs. 10 and 11. Science Press permitted the reproduction of Figures 2, 13, 17, 19, 20, and 23 from Mayr (1940a) (*The American Naturalist*) and supplied the cuts of Figures 2, 13, 19, and 23. This assistance is gratefully acknowledged. The American Museum of Natural History supplied the cuts of Figures 27 and 28. Figures 1, 3, 5, 12, 14 also are reproductions of previously published illustrations, the other 16 figures are original.

SYSTEMATICS AND
THE ORIGIN OF SPECIES

CHAPTER I

THE METHODS AND PRINCIPLES
OF SYSTEMATICS

THE RISE of genetics during the first thirty years of this century had a rather unfortunate effect on the prestige of systematics. The spectacular success of experimental work in unraveling the principles of inheritance and the obvious applicability of these results in explaining evolution have tended to push systematics into the background. There was a tendency among laboratory workers to think rather contemptuously of the museum man, who spent his time counting hairs or drawing bristles, and whose final aim seemed to be merely the correct naming of his specimens. A welcome improvement in the mutual understanding between geneticists and systematists has occurred in recent years, largely owing to the efforts of such men as Rensch and Kinsey among the taxonomists, Timofeeff-Ressovsky and Dobzhansky among the geneticists, and Huxley and Diver among the general biologists.

It was realized by these workers that only some of the problems of the origin of species can be solved by the geneticist, while other aspects are more accessible to such branches of biology as ecology and biogeography, paleontology, and taxonomy. A satisfactory understanding of intricate evolutionary phenomena can be attained only through the coöperation of all these disciplines, and systematics is willing and able to contribute its share.

The importance of systematics in the study of evolution was perhaps better realized in the last century than it is now. Darwin's conclusions in his *Origin of Species* were based largely on the results of contemporary taxonomic work, and I can see no reason why modern systematics should not yield even greater results. After all, systematics has grown tremendously since Darwin's day. The number of species of animals known to us, eighty years after Darwin, is probably tenfold and the number of specimens in collections a thousandfold. But not only the number of known species has grown; the degree to which they are known has also increased. With this vast body of material before us—and I might confess, from my own museum experience, with an equally large or even greater amount of work still to be done—it is very easy to lose sight of the final aims of such work. It is therefore necessary to pause once in a while in order to make a survey of its present status.

THE STATUS OF SYSTEMATICS

Systematics is in a more difficult position than most other sciences. It seems as if all the conclusions and generalized laws derived from a study of taxonomic material were dependent to a very high degree on the nature of this material and the background of the student. The result is that—partly from the variety of the material, too—we have an almost unlimited diversity of opinion in answer to such questions as: What is a species? How do species originate? Are the systematic categories natural? and so forth. There is no uniform point of view among taxonomists; in fact, in regard to many of these questions there may not even be a majority opinion. This situation is revealed rather clearly if we study the discussions of the twenty-two contributors to *The New Systematics* (Huxley 1940) or the various recent species and speciation symposia in *The American Naturalist* (1940, 1941). This is true not only for the plant taxonomist versus the animal taxonomist, or the parasitologist versus the zoölogist, but also for the opinions of the taxonomist of fresh-water organisms as compared with those of the student of terrestrial animals, or of the students of continental and insular faunas, and even of different taxonomic groups—let us say the opinions of the taxonomist of diptera and mollusca, as compared to those of the ornithologist. This situation indicates clearly that no one taxonomist can yet attempt a broad outline of the generalizations deducible from systematics that is acceptable to all his fellow taxonomists.

The reasons for this vast diversity of opinion are not yet quite clear. It is unquestionably true that species limits are strongly affected by ecological factors and that consequently parasites and other ecologically specialized forms show a taxonomic behavior and course of speciation different from that of widespread, polyphagous animals, such as birds. The influence of these ecological factors will be discussed in greater detail in a later chapter. However, equally or even more important for the opinions of a taxonomist on speciation is the degree to which the group with which he is working is known. It can be claimed without exaggeration that lasting generalizations can be based only on systematic groups that are well known. Recent work on the mosquitoes of the *Anopheles maculipennis* group, on fresh-water fishes, on "biological races" of certain plant pests, and the like have proven this point abundantly.

There is little doubt that birds are better known taxonomically than any other class of animals and that in consequence taxonomic interpretation in ornithology has reached a degree of refinement which is not equaled in any other group. It is estimated that less than 2 percent of the total number of species of birds of the entire world remain still unknown. Nearly every species is well represented in one or another museum, and for the last forty years most of the work has centered on a study of infraspecific groups. A few genera of mammals, butterflies, beetles, mollusks, and so forth are as well known as the most thoroughly studied avian genera, but our knowledge of most systematic groups of animals is very incomplete; this is particularly true of most invertebrates.

How little we know of certain groups of animals is best indicated by the many recent discoveries in the field of systematic zoölogy, such as the living Coelacanthid fish, *Latimeria* (1939), or the new class of animals, the Pogonofora (Johansson 1937). But in addition to these spectacular novelties, new discoveries are made daily, even in comparatively well-explored areas. A striking illustration of this is presented by Remane's work on the microscopic marine fauna of the Kieler Bucht, an area previously considered to be exhaustively known (Remane 1933). By thorough search and with the application of new methods, Remane found in ten years 300 new species, including representatives of 15 new families. Among them were several entirely new types. In a revision of the small red mites (Amystidae) that are so common in gardens, Oudemans (1936) added 10 new genera to the known 5, and 14 new species to the well-known 12; 24 additional species of the family are insufficiently known, and nobody knows how many species are still undiscovered. In his monograph on the South American weevil genus *Conotrachelus*, K. Fiedler (1940) lists a total of 547 species, of which 404 (74 percent) are described by him as new. A reviewer of the work (Marshall) estimated that this amounted to approximately one-fourth of the probable 2,000 species of this genus. Kinsey (1936) added to the known 50 species of a subgroup of American Cynipid gall wasps no less than 36 additional species during two collecting trips. Dr. Gertsch, of the American Museum, has described some 500 new species of North American spiders during the last eight years and he, as well as three or four other arachnologists, find every year some additional new species, even in such well-worked areas as New England or New Jersey. He estimates that altogether less than 25 percent of the spiders of the earth have so far been described. In the fruit fly genus *Drosophila* only 28 Nearctic species were known in 1921, as compared to more than 75 known today. Of the 44 species which are known to occur in Texas only 7 were known in 1921, the other 37 being discovered during the last four years, and no less than 21 of these were new to science (Patterson in litt., Feb., 1941; see also Patterson 1942). Had not this genus such prominence in genetics, we would not even suspect this abundance of species. There are many large taxonomic groups, such as the parasitic hymenoptera and certain families of flies and of minute tropical beetles, in which the number of known species is estimated to be less than 10 percent of those probably existing.

The specialist who deals with such groups is happy if he can keep step with the unworked material that continues to pour in. Only seldom does he have time to go beyond the purely descriptive phase of work and try his hand at putting some order into the growing "heap" of species. Newly discovered species are likely to upset his ideas any day. He is forced by necessity to do "old" systematics.

THE OLD AND THE NEW SYSTEMATICS

Huxley recently introduced the happy term "New Systematics" (Huxley 1940: Foreword) and even though he says: "the new systematics is not yet in being: before it is born, the mass of new facts and ideas which the last two or three decades have hurled at us must be digested, correlated, and synthesized," I feel that the outlook and the technique in the more mature taxonomic groups might well be characterized by the term "new systematics."[1] Naturally, there is no sharp line of demarcation between the two, for no taxonomic work is all old or all new systematics. The two are always mixed in varying proportions.

If we had to characterize the differences between old and the new systematics, we might do it as follows:

The old systematics is characterized by the central position of the species. No work, or very little, is done on infraspecific categories (subspecies). A purely morphological species definition is employed. Many species are known only from single or at best a very few specimens; the individual is therefore the basic taxonomic unit. There is great interest in purely technical questions of nomenclature and "types." The major problems are those of a cataloguer or bibliographer, rather than those of a biologist.

---

[1] The terms systematics and taxonomy are considered by me as approximately synonymous. In America the term taxonomy seems to be preferred, in the rest of the world the term systematics seems to be more widely used. The expression "new systematics" had been used by Hubbs (1934) already 6 years earlier.

The new systematics may be characterized as follows: The importance of the species as such is reduced, since most of the actual work is done with subdivisions of the species, such as subspecies and populations. The population or rather an adequate sample of it, the "series" of the museum worker, has become the basic taxonomic unit. The purely morphological species definition has been replaced by a biological one, which takes ecological, geographical, genetic, and other factors into consideration. The choosing of the correct name for the analyzed taxonomic unit no longer occupies the central position of all systematic work and is less often subject to argument between fellow workers. The material available for generic revisions frequently amounts to many hundreds or even thousands of specimens, a number sufficient to permit a detailed study of the extent of individual variation.

Nobody can foresee what refinements of technique and what changes in point of view the future may have in store. What we consider as new systematics in the year 1941 may, indeed, be very old systematics fifty years hence. The trend which I have tried to express by comparing the characteristics of old and new systematics is, however, unmistakable. It is primarily characterized by the fact that the new systematist tends to approach his material more as a biologist and less as a museum cataloguer. He shows a deeper interest in the formulation of generalizations, he attempts to synthesize and to consider the describing and naming of a species only as a preliminary step of a far-reaching investigation. Whether a worker will apply the methods of the old or the new systematics to his own work depends as much on the available material and the degree of knowledge attained in his group as on his training and point of view. One of the finest entomological monographs, Hubbell's (1936) revision of the cave cricket genus *Ceuthophilus* shows this very clearly. Hubbell has modern ideas and tries to apply modern methods, but more than 50 percent of the treated forms are described as new by him in the revision and some of them from single specimens or from single localities. No collections at all were available from vast stretches of North America. No wonder that only the beginning was made of a study of geographical variation and that the interrelationship of many forms remains obscure. The outlook of a systematist is correlated very closely with the amount of material he has examined.

The material available for taxonomic work.—Even in well-worked orders and classes, as for example birds, new species and subspecies are occasionally described on the basis of a single or just a few specimens. In general, however, every species is represented by a series that is sufficiently large to illustrate the principal trends of variation. The Ameri-

can Museum of Natural History in New York has what is probably the
largest and most complete bird collection in the world. This collection
comprises about 800,000 skins, or about 100 skins per species, and
about 30 specimens per subspecies. This is the material of a single
museum, but, if a specialist wants to examine a genus critically, he can
draw on the resources of sister institutions and borrow their material.
He will rarely find it difficult to gather 500 specimens or more of a polytypic species. For his recent monograph of the difficult warbler genus
Phylloscopus, with 66 forms in 30 species, Ticehurst (1938a) examined
9,300 specimens, that is, an average of 140 specimens per form; and
A. H. Miller (1941) examined 11,774 specimens of the 21 forms of the
genus *Junco*, including 4,552 birds from the breeding grounds.

There are, of course, certain groups of nocturnal or otherwise secretive
or rare species of which it is impossible to obtain large series of specimens. In general, the conclusions of the bird taxonomist are founded on
the basis of abundant material coming from localities throughout the
range of the species. The same can be said for some invertebrate groups.
Müller and Kautz (1940) based their study of the two sibling butterfly
species *Pieris napi* and *bryoniae* on over 50,000 specimens. Kinsey
(1936) reports that he examined 35,000 insects and 124,000 galls in 165
(sub-)species of *Cynips*, an average of 214 insects and 755 galls per
(sub-)species. Crampton (1932), in his study of the *Partula* snails of
Moorea, examined 116,166 specimens of 10 species, and the more common and more variable European snails are present in collections by the
thousands. I have quoted these figures to indicate, first, that such copious
material permits the introduction of biometric and other modern methods and, second, that the systematic categories in such well-worked
groups are based on ample material and not on single aberrant specimens. The modern taxonomist often has as much material at his disposal
as the geneticist has in breeding experiments. Our discussion on variation in the following chapter will make it very clear why the systematist
needs such copious material.

THE FUNCTIONS OF THE SYSTEMATIST

There is considerable doubt in the minds of some taxonomists and
even more in the minds of most nontaxonomists as to what the real
functions of the systematist are. Some laboratory men and ecologists
seem to think that the taxonomist should content himself with identifying material and with devising keys. Beyond that he should keep his
collections in good order, describe new species, and have every speci-

men properly labeled. According to this view systematics is the mere pigeonholing of specimens. No taxonomist will deny that these particular tasks are part of his job, and the worker in the less-known groups may not be able to go beyond the cataloguing phase of taxonomic work. The systematist of the better-known groups, however, will not be satisfied with such a limitation; for him systematics is more than an auxiliary science. He inquires not only into the "What?" but also as to the "Why?"

After all, it must not be forgotten that the average taxonomist is more than the mere caretaker of a collection. In most cases he collects his own material, he studies it in the field, and develops thereby the technique and point of view of the ecologist. Furthermore, most of the younger systematists have had a thorough training in various branches of biology, including genetics. This experience, both in field and laboratory, gives the well-trained systematist an excellent background for more ambitious studies. It is only natural that he cannot and will not content himself with being merely a servant to some other branch of biology. Systematics is for him a full-fledged science.

We can therefore say that systematics has both a practical side, pertaining to the identification and classification of specimens, and a theoretical one, inquiring into the origin and nature of the units with which it works. The field of activity of the systematist can perhaps be subdivided under three headings:

Identification (*analytical stage*).—It is the basic task of the systematist to break up the almost unlimited and confusing diversity of individuals in nature into easily recognizable groups, to work out the significant characters of these units, and to find constant differences between similar ones. Furthermore, he must provide these units with "scientific" names which will facilitate their subsequent recognition by workers throughout the world.

Even this "lowest" task of the taxonomist is of tremendous scientific importance. The entire geological chronology hinges on the correct identification of the fossil key species. No scientific ecological survey should be carried out without the most painstaking identification of all the species of ecological significance. Even the experimental biologist has learned to appreciate the necessity for sound, solid identification work. There are a great number of genera with two, three, or more very similar species. Such species very often differ more conspicuously in their physiological traits than in their morphological characters. It has happened again and again that two workers have come to different conclusions concerning the physiological properties of a certain species because, in fact, one worker was working with species A and the other worker with species B, or with a mixed stock of A and B. Every biologist will recall such cases in his own field.

Classification (synthetic stage).—The recognition and accurate description of the species is the first task of the systematist. But should he stop there, he would soon be confronted with a chaotic accumulation of species descriptions. To prevent this, the systematist must try to find an orderly arrangement of the species; he must create and arrange higher categories; in other words, he must devise a classification. This is the second task of the taxonomist. The devising of a classification is, to some extent, as practical a task as the identification of specimens, but at the same time it involves more speculation and theorizing. The taxonomist must decide whether two similar forms should be considered one species or two. He must also determine whether the similarities of two species are due to convergence of habitus or to close phylogenetic relationship. There is the question whether the higher categories represent phylogenetic groups or not. Do genera and families have an objective reality or are they artificial creations of the taxonomist?

Such are the questions that confront the systematist who is trying to classify the bewildering multitude of organisms and inevitably they lead to a study of the factors of evolution.

Study of species formation and of the factors of evolution.—Work in this field comprises the third task of the systematist. It is here that he comes into closer contact with the other branches of biology, with genetics and cytology, with biogeography and ecology, with comparative anatomy and paleontology. All these sciences pursue the study of evolution in their own way, with their own questions and with their own methods. One of the principal differences, for example, between the systematist and the geneticist is that the geneticist can test his conclusions by experiment, whereas the systematist relies on the implications of observed data. He can therefore say very little either on the origin or the mode of inheritance of taxonomic characters. On the other hand, the geneticist has difficulties in duplicating in the laboratory the conditions under which speciation proceeds in nature. Many animals cannot be kept in a laboratory, and others will not reproduce in captivity. Furthermore, the enormous time which the thorough genetic analysis of a species requires (it is still very far from complete in the two best-studied organisms, the fruit fly *Drosophila melanogaster* and the corn plant *Zea mays*) makes it impossible for the geneticist to study more than a very small proportion of the known organisms. Up to the present time only about one five-hundredth of one percent of the known species of animals has been studied with any degree of thoroughness by geneticists. It is therefore obvious that the systematist can and will have to fill many gaps. But there is a more basic difference between the approach of the geneticist and the taxonomist to the problems of evolution. The geneticist, in his analysis, seeks the "biological atoms," the genes and other basic units. The taxonomist, on the other hand, works with much more comprehensive entities: with the carriers of taxonomic characters, with individuals, populations, species. There is, of course, some overlapping of the two methods, but the difference is striking enough to lead to a considerable difference in outlook and sometimes even in conclusions.

The systematist who studies the factors of evolution wants to find out how species originate, how they are related, and what this relationship means. He studies species not only as they are, but also their origin and changes. He tries to find his answers by observing the variability of natural populations under different external conditions and he attempts to find out which factors promote and which inhibit evolution. He is helped in this endeavor by his knowledge of the habits and the ecology of the studied species.

THE PROCEDURE OF THE SYSTEMATIST

A discussion of the principles of systematics is not a suitable initiation for the beginner into the practical methods of taxonomic work. Even though there is not available, in the English language, a good introduction to the methods of systematics, comparable to Rensch's *Kurze Anweisung für zoologisch-systematische Studien* (Rensch 1934), Ferris's book (1928) can be recommended, and Schenk and McMasters (1936) also give some useful hints, although mostly on questions of nomenclature. The best textbook in most systematic groups is some particularly good monograph in that group which, by its thoroughness and lucid treatment, sets an example of method. If none is available, a work in some related group can usually be used to advantage. In addition to the short preliminary papers (species descriptions, and the like), there are two principal categories of taxonomic publications: faunistic papers and generic (or species or family) monographs. The results of expeditions are usually presented as faunistic reports, and the resident naturalist of a certain region also favors this kind of work ("local list"). Such papers may be a mine of information for the biogeographer and the ecologist, but the student of evolution usually finds more of interest in monographs of single systematic groups. As the collections in the museums of the world grow, it becomes increasingly possible to prepare such monographs, and their number constantly grows.

But before our knowledge of a species reaches the point where it can be included in a monograph, it has to be subjected to a definite process of study, of which I will now give a short outline.

The collecting of material.—The time is past in which the taxonomist depended completely on random collections made by expeditions or by all-round collectors. The modern museum worker attempts to collect at least part of his own material. Admiral H. Lynes, who is interested in the African warbler genus *Cisticola*, with some forty species, made a whole series of collecting trips to nearly every corner of Africa in order to get the kind of material he needed for his painstaking monographic studies of these birds. He combined his collecting with a detailed study of the ecology and the habits of these birds, of their song, nest construction, and so forth. The result is that the genus *Cisticola*, formerly the despair of the bird taxonomist, is now well understood (Lynes 1930). A. C. Kinsey applied himself in a similarly diligent manner to the gall wasps of the genus *Cynips*. In numerous collecting trips, extending as far as Mexico and Guatemala, he explored the majority of the favorable habitats of species of this genus and returned with literally hundreds of thousands of specimens for study (Kinsey 1936: 18–21). Collecting activities were, in these cases, limited to certain genera; in other cases they were restricted to geographical regions. The most ambitious undertaking along these lines was probably the Whitney South Sea Expedition, operated under the auspices of the American Museum of Natural History in New York, with funds donated by the Harry Payne Whitney family. This single expedition visited practically every island in the South Seas, obtaining nearly complete bird collections and fair collections of other material. It operated continuously from 1921 to 1934, and its work was continued by single collectors into 1940. The student of such collections has the gratifying feeling that it is unlikely that his findings will be upset by future discoveries. A considerable portion of the subsequent discussions are based on the magnificent material of the Whitney South Sea Expedition, which I was fortunate to be able to study.

Identification.—The first step in working out such a collection is the sorting out of individuals into groups which the worker considers to belong to different species; the second step is the identification of each of these species. Identification means comparison with all other known similar forms until one is found with which it seems to agree. If such a form can be found, this first task is completed; the species has been identified. Very frequently, however, particularly in less well-known groups of animals, some of the investigated specimens do not agree with any described species. Here is where the difficulties of the conscientious systematist begin. Before he can proceed to describe his specimens as a new species, he must eliminate a number of other possibilities.

There is considerable individual variation in most animals. Perhaps his specimens are just extreme variants? Or there may be an undescribed sex or age class, or an unknown ecotype. A study of the equivalent variants of the already known species of the genus generally answers such questions. If not enough material is available the taxonomist often must hazard a guess. Even an experienced worker may make the wrong decision in such situations. If all the other possibilities have been eliminated and there is no more doubt possible that the unidentifiable specimens belong to a previously unknown species, the systematist must prepare a scientific description.

The description.—The primary purpose of a description is that it shall serve as a diagnosis. It is therefore requisite that a description include all the information which will guarantee the identification of the species (or whatever taxonomic group is involved) to which it refers. On the other hand—and this is an important point which beginners and unskillful workers often overlook—the description of species in well-known groups should not be burdened with superfluous information. The description of a new species of *Drosophila* does not and should not contain a reference to any character that is common to all known species of this genus. One of the principal advantages of the binary system is that it permits the omission from the description of all characters common to the genus, family, and higher categories. To include these "higher" characters in the species diagnosis would only obscure the true diagnostic features. A subspecies diagnosis is likely to be even shorter, since the number of characters that vary within the species is generally smaller than that of the characters differentiating two good species. "Like the typical race, but wing 84–94 mm., instead of 72–82 mm." may be a sufficient diagnosis of a new subspecies of bird. The diagnosis should include a direct comparison with the nearest relative. This is, in fact, required by the emended International Rules of Zoological Nomenclature,[2] to make a description valid.

[2] "Article 25c.—No generic or specific name, published [as new] after December 31, 1930, shall have any status of availability (hence also of validity) under the Rules, unless and until it is published either

1.—with a summary of characters (seu diagnosis; seu definition; seu condensed description) which differentiate or distinguish the genus or the species from other genera or species; etc."

The workers in each taxonomic group have their own conventions as to how descriptions are to be prepared and what characters should be discussed. Ferris (1928) gives some valuable suggestions on this point. In many groups of insects and other invertebrates only an illustration either of the entire animal or of its genital armature can supply sufficient information to insure correct identification. Not even the lengthiest description can replace this. In brightly colored animals, such as certain coral fishes, butterflies, birds, and so forth, colored plates are desirable.

A detailed and complete description is needed if a very distinct species or a new genus is involved. Likewise we should demand detailed species description in all those genera and families in which only a minor portion of the probably existing number of species has as yet been described. It is obvious that it is impossible in such groups to decide which of the many characters of an animal will serve to distinguish it from its nearest (still unknown) relatives. In actual taxonomic practice it turns out that descriptions of new species in such insufficiently known groups are, unfortunately, generally very sketchy and not in the least diagnostic. This is particularly true for many entomological species descriptions. Such species will eventually be identifiable only by the reëxamination of the type specimen. Hence the importance of types.

The diagnosis should not be based merely on the type specimen, but rather on the entire topotypical series. Individual variation should be mentioned and should be described and treated statistically, if pronounced. If there are color phases, their exact proportion in the available material must be stated, and if there are specimens which do not fit the diagnosis they should not be ignored or suppressed, but treated in particular detail. When the information is available, it should be stated concisely whether or not intergradation or hybridization occurs with neighboring races or species, also where this occurs, and how large a percentage of the population is affected. If populations are included with a subspecies which differs slightly from the topotypical population, such differences should be described. If possible, the description should contain a series of measurements, including both minimum and maximum, as well as the mean. In birds, for instance, the length of the wing is the standard measurement and to some extent an index of general size. We would state, for example: Wing, 12♂ 117–130 (122.7), 9♀ 105–115 (111.2) mm. These measurements have numerous advantages, such as the possibility of exact comparison and that of treatment by statistical methods, if sufficient material is available. For a detailed treatment of biostatistics, see Simpson and Roe (1939). See also p. 135.

I might summarize these remarks by saying that the principal feature of the description of a new species is not its naming, but rather the working out of the characteristic attributes which will enable us to identify and classify it.

Types.—Descriptions are often ambiguous, and the describers of new species frequently fail to state the basic diagnostic characters. As later authors discover "new" species in the same group, a question always arises as to which of the two or three species the first author had before him. This can be decided quickly if the original, the "type," material is still available.

Formerly, the specimens on which the original description of a species was based were designated as the cotypes. Modern authors select a single specimen and designate it as the type (holotype), in order to eliminate a possible source of trouble. This is necessary, because it frequently happens in difficult or insufficiently known groups that two or more similar forms or even species are mixed in the original type series. Every worker is able to cite such mistakes in his own field; they happen occasionally even to the most careful specialists. For example, the species in the bird genus *Collocalia* (cave swiftlets) are exceedingly similar, and the foremost student of this genus had two different species in the type series (paratypes) of at least three of his new species. Fortunately, in every one of these cases only a single specimen was designated as the type, and no confusion of names resulted when the puzzle was finally solved.

The one and only function of a type is to fix the correct name to a definite individual and thus to the species or subspecies to which this individual belongs. It has nothing to do with the validity of a species or with its limits. It is not necessarily the most typical specimen of the species (such probably does not exist), and therefore it should not form the sole basis of the description.

The type is typical of nothing. It is only an indication of which groups of individuals must be associated with a particular specific name. It is the final court of appeal for purposes of nomenclature only. . . . There can be no possible reason for having any other type except a single one for each species name [Williams 1940].

If the characters of a form are better expressed in the female or in a larval stage, it is advisable to choose a female or larval stage as type. The type should, if possible, be chosen from the locality which the author considers to be inhabited by the most representative population of the species or subspecies. By choosing a single type specimen, the author at the same time fixes a definite type locality. Material subsequently collected in the same locality is called topotypical. Such material is important because the populations of no two localities seem to be exactly alike, and therefore only material from the type locality has the typical characteristics of the subspecies or species.

What should be named.—Only such subspecies or species should be named as are really distinct from others. This admonition may sound superfluous, but if it were so we would not have so many synonyms for most of our species. The first rule, which cannot be emphasized often enough, is that we should name populations, not individuals, even though an individual be chosen as type. Therefore, no individual color variations or other aberrations should be named. In the case of subspecies, it is a good convention that at least 75 percent of the individuals of one subspecies (or of the available specimens) should be separable, on the basis of their diagnostic characters, from the specimens of the most similar subspecies. Ecological variants that are likely to be merely phenotypic modifications should not be named. At any rate the author of a new name should always keep in mind Bather's very true words (1927): "A name once published is irrevocable, a permanent addition to the labour of future investigators. Let us beware of adding needlessly to the burden of posterity!" The quality of a taxonomist's work is measured not so much by the number of new forms which he describes as by the percentage of synonyms among them. The works of the really great taxonomists prove that the making of synonyms can be avoided to a large degree. The taxonomist should never lose sight of the fact that he does not have "the species *a*" before him, but only a small and inadequate sample of the natural population which it represents.

Nomenclature.—Each animal has its scientific name. The application of this name is subject to an elaborate set of regulations, the "International Rules of Zoological Nomenclature," published as a supplement to the Proceedings of each International Congress of Zoology. They are explained in more detail by Schenk and McMasters (1936). The basic purpose of these rules is to insure stability of nomenclature and to prevent authors from being too arbitrary in their choice of names. It was thought by the originators of these rules that this end could best be attained if the name first given an animal be chosen as its permanent designation. This admirable law of priority works very well in theory, but it has proved to have certain practical drawbacks. It happens not infrequently that the earliest name of an animal was published in an obscure booklet, where it has escaped detection for a hundred years or more, or that the original description was misinterpreted for two or three generations. The unhappy consequence of such situations is not only that familiar names had to be changed, but, what is worse, that the basic principle of the rules, that of stability and permanence, has been sacrificed to the purely arbitrary rule of priority. An additional weakness of the rules is that too much leeway is permitted certain unscrupulous authors, who derive pleasure from unsettling current nomenclature by arbitrary actions. There is a strong sentiment among the saner taxonomists that something should be done to minimize these difficulties, but no agreement has yet been reached. It has been suggested, for example, that much name-changing could be prevented if there were a few simple exceptions to the rules of priority: for example, that no name in general use for thirty years or more could be replaced by an older synonym (*nomen oblitum*), or that no name which has been generally applied to one unit (for ten or more years) could be transferred to a different one (see Heikertinger 1935, for similar suggestions). The majority of the zoölogists are in favor of a few simple restrictions of this kind, which would not basically interfere with the generally adopted and otherwise sound rule of priority. It will be one of the most important tasks of the next International Zoological Congress to adopt such modifications and to rewrite some of the obscure passages of the code. Fortunately, in some groups, as, for example, birds, the unearthing of old names and other major nomenclatorial upheavals is largely a matter of the past, and a condition of comparative stability has been attained.

The systematic category.—In Linnæus's day an author did not have much difficulty when it came to choosing the lower category in which to place a new animal (or plant); it was either a new species or a new variety. With the refinement of modern systematic terminology, it is no longer sufficient to point out that the animal in question is different from all others that have been described before. It must also be determined whether it is really a good species, a geographic or ecological race, or merely a hybrid or an individual variant. These questions will be discussed in more detail in later chapters, as will also the question of the higher categories and their meaning and the significance of biological classification in general.

CHAPTER II

TAXONOMIC CHARACTERS AND
THEIR VARIATION

THE SYSTEMATIST who wants to establish the identity of an animal and find its place in the system must have some clues. These clues are the taxonomic or species characters. They are the building stones with which the structure is erected which we call "the natural system." A special chapter devoted to their discussion seems to be justified.

TAXONOMIC CHARACTERS

The primary value of taxonomic characters is diagnostic. Beyond this, they present some excellent clues to the paths of speciation. Simple taxonomic characters often have a simple genetic basis, and by tracing the fate of the taxonomic characters we can derive certain conclusions concerning underlying genetic factors. But let us first look at taxonomic characters from a purely practical viewpoint and study their diagnostic value.

Diagnostic characters.—If we accept a recent estimate, we might assume that a higher animal may have in the neighborhood of 10,000 genes, while the number of characters is limited only by the patience of the investigator. Even two related species of the same genus may differ in from 400 to 600 characters. Zarapkin (1934) in a study of two races of the beetle *Carabus cancellatus* studied 166 characters, but these were only features relating to the sculpture and the proportions of the chitinous shell. In addition to such morphological characters, there exist all sorts of physiological differences, particularly threshold differences and rates of growth and development, as well as inherited ecological adaptations and psychological reaction norms such as differences in instinctive behavior.

It would require more than a lifetime to prepare an exhaustive species description which would contain references to all these characters. And then it would be so voluminous that no one would be willing to publish it. But not only is such a complete species diagnosis impractical, it is also unnecessary, since even a small fraction of the morphological differences is sufficient, in most cases, to insure the correct diagnosis. In fact, the inclusion of physiological differences in a diagnosis is actually undesirable, since most identifications have to be made from dead specimens. The most practical diagnostic characters are those that relate to some easily visible structure with low variability. This character may be, and very often is, of no particular importance to the species, but it serves as a marker to the taxonomist. To illustrate this point I might make the following comparison: If I want to direct a person to one of two houses on a street, I need not go into a detailed description of all of its features; I merely say: "It is the white, not the red one!" Color is a rather superficial attribute of a house. Actually the white house may be built of wood, the red one of stone or brick; the white one may have six rooms, the red one ten rooms, and so forth. Even if I paint the red house white, it would remain basically different from the other white house. The relationship of the diagnostic characters of an animal to its other species characters is frequently of an equally superficial nature. It is necessary to emphasize the biological insignificance of many of the "key characters" or "diagnostic characters," because this is not sufficiently realized by taxonomists, or by nontaxonomists. If one of two related genera of insects is diagnosed as having two extra bristles on the thorax, this does not mean in the least that this is *the* basic difference between these genera. It may be the least important one, but it may be the one which can be recognized most quickly by the taxonomist.

The taxonomist's viewpoint is much like that of the *Drosophila* geneticist who prefers to work with conspicuous mutations affecting easily distinguishable characters of external morphology, in the conviction that the really important physiological mutations follows the same genetic laws. In both fields the conspicuous character is preferred to the cryptic one, and there is much evidence from both fields that this choice of the worker is permissible, since no underlying difference has been found in regard to the genetic basis and the physiology of the two kinds of characters.

Summarizing this discussion, we might say that the species characters consist of a few diagnostic and many other characters. The geneticist should remember that the genetic analysis of the few diagnostic characters of a species by no means completes the genetic analysis of the species. The taxonomist, on the other hand, should not forget that two populations are by no means identical just because they do not differ in any obvious characters. Certain differences have been found between all populations subjected to a really thorough genetic or bio-metric analysis.

What is a taxonomic character?—We understand by taxonomic char-acter any attribute of an organism (or better, of any group of organisms) by which it may differ from other organisms. Such characters are, in general, morphological ones, that is, they refer to size, proportions, structure, coloration, or color pattern. These are the characters that are most convenient for the taxonomist, because they are generally pre-served in the dead specimens with which the taxonomist usually has to work. However, now that the systematic categories are better known, it has been found that these often rather superficial morphological char-acters are generally correlated with a considerable number of physiologi-cal and biological characters. In modern taxonomic publications we find more and more references to characters which are not purely morphologi-cal, such as ecological requirements, migratory status, pairing habits, sea-sonal occurrence, vertical distribution, and so on. In fact, these biological differences are often more striking than the morphological ones. "The courtship behavior, the general habits, and the range of habitats of *Cepaea hortensis* [as compared to the very similar species *C. nemoralis*] are just as diagnostic as are the shape of its spire, the structure of its radula or the number of its mucous glands" (Diver 1939). The slugs are a group of animals which, although morphologically very similar, tend to have color phases and varieties, most of which had originally been described as good species. No two taxonomists could agree as to which of these forms were good species and which were not. In a study of the pairing behavior of these slugs, Gerhardt (1939) showed that the dis-plays that lead up to copulation are exceedingly complicated and con-sequently highly specific. In the genus *Limax* six definite pairing types could be determined, which apparently correspond to six good species. Many of the other described "species" of this genus are probably noth-ing but color varieties. In related genera (for example, *Agriolimax*) a similar clarification of the system was made possible by a study of the copulation types. In the Old World warblers it is very difficult to sepa-rate the genera *Sylvia* and *Phylloscopus* on the basis of morphological characters. *Sylvia nana* and *Phylloscopus collybita* are much more alike than some of the species of *Phylloscopus*. But according to Ticehurst (1938a), "it seems that the genus *Phylloscopus* is differentiated from *Sylvia* more by the habits and breeding economy than by any structural differences." The nest of *Phylloscopus* is always domed and at or near the ground, while that of *Sylvia* is cup-shaped and off the ground. "There is one further distinction: so far as I have seen in the genus *Sylvia* the newly hatched chick is devoid of down, whereas, so far as I have seen, in *Phylloscopus* down is always present." In other cases differences or similarities of the ecto- or endoparasitic fauna of two forms have helped in determining their relative taxonomic status. Emerson (1935) found morphological differences between two highly similar species of termites only after he had received a clue as to their distinctness by differences in the termitophile beetle fauna of their respective nests.

In conclusion it may be said that, although most of the taxonomic characters are morphological ones, the refinements of taxonomic technique and our increasing knowledge of the living animals have made almost any attribute of a species (or other category) usable as taxonomic character.

Taxonomic characters and classification.—Any system or classification is based on the proper evaluation of taxonomic characters. The more characters two animals have in common, the closer we generally group them in the system. Systematic categories are usually formed by uniting lower categories that share certain characters. We shall not, at this time, enter into a philosophical discussion concerning the validity of this procedure, but we shall treat some of the practical difficulties which confront us in the evaluation of taxonomic characters (see also Rensch 1934:88–96).

Linnæus and most of his followers for almost a century classified birds by purely adaptational characters. Birds with webbed feet were put into one category, birds with a hooked bill into another, and so on. Eventually it was realized that characters that were adaptations to one specific mode of living were not only subject to rapid changes by selective forces, but also could be acquired in different unrelated lines. Such characters have only a limited value in taxonomic work. Instead, we must search for characters that tend to remain stable, characters that are phylogenetically conservative.

It will usually be found, on closer examination, that good characters are correlated to a number of other characters. Where there is a break between two systematic categories, this break will generally affect a whole group of different characters. It is thus important to base systematic categories and classification schemes on as many characters as possible. The fewer the characters used, the greater is the danger that mistakes in the classification will be made.

It happens not infrequently in animals that a character which is quite constant over a number of genera or families behaves aberrantly in a single species or genus. A study of all the other characters of the aberrant form proves that it is very closely related and that it would be a mistake to place too much weight on the single character. It can therefore be said that, even though a certain character is widespread in a certain taxonomic group, this does not prove that all forms that lack this character do not belong to this group. Rensch (1934:94) illustrates this with the following examples:

(1) The genera of Clausiliidae (Snails) are characterized by the folds in the shell mouth. The number, direction and length of these folds is of such constancy, that this character is frequently sufficient even for the identification of species. Similar folds have a much lower taxonomic value in the closely related family of the Pupillidae, and in some species (for example *Vertigo arctica*) the number of folds may vary between one and four. One would have to split *Vertigo arctica* into four species if one were to give the folds a taxonomic value equivalent to that in the Clausiliidae.

(2) The presence of a cleaning apparatus on the hind legs is a taxonomically very important character in the hymenoptera, on the basis of which they are divided into two major groups, the diplocnemata (with) and the haplocnemata (without the apparatus). This character breaks down in the family of the Methocidae, which have the apparatus, even though it is indisputable from all the other taxonomic evidence that this family belongs to the mutillids, a subgroup of the haplocnemata.

Rensch quotes a number of other cases (and many additional ones are recorded in the literature), all of which show that a character which is of the greatest taxonomic value in one group is not necessarily of equal value in other closely related groups. This is the reason why it is so important that all classifications be based on the greatest possible number of different characters. Such a procedure will offer the best guarantee against artificial systems. Every systematist knows cases in the history of his own special group in which neglect of this principle has resulted in serious mistakes.

THE VARIATION OF TAXONOMIC CHARACTERS

Taxonomic characters have been treated by us, to this point, as constant and absolute. Such an assumption is an unjustified simplification of the existing facts, based on the equally erroneous assumption that all the individuals of a taxonomic unit are identical. A careful analysis of natural populations will show that there is a considerable degree of variability, grouped around a mean which is typical for the particular taxonomic category. It is obvious that no single individual can represent, at the same time, the minimum, the maximum, and the mean of such variation, but it is possible to represent this variation fairly accurately, if an adequate sample of the population is available. This is the reason that a representative series, a sample of the population, has replaced the individual as the working unit of the systematist and this is also the reason that the collecting of adequate material is such an important part of his activities.

The study of the variation of taxonomic characters—and, since any character may be a taxonomic character, we might simply say the study of variation—has one eminently practical aspect. It informs the taxonomist as to the reliability of his tools, as to the existence or nonexistence of border lines between the taxonomic units, and other aspects of strictly taxonomic work. But beyond that, the study of variation is of the greatest scientific importance. It was Darwin who pointed out in the most convincing manner that evolution was not thinkable without variation and that therefore the study of the facts of variation was an integral part of the study of evolution.

The words "speciation" or "origin of species," which cover a considerable part of the field of evolution ("microevolution"), include two different aspects of evolution. One part of the process of speciation is the establishment of discontinuities, that is, the establishment of isolating mechanisms and their perfection to the point where reproductive isolation is accomplished and the "parent species" breaks up into two or more daughter species. This aspect of speciation will be discussed in two of the later chapters (Chapters VII and VIII). The other aspect of speciation is the establishment of diversity and divergence, that is, the origin of new characters and their differential distribution in various populations. The workings of this process can best be studied if we analyze variation. The study of variation is therefore not only of practical importance to the taxonomist, but should also yield significant results concerning the factors and processes of evolution.

TYPES OF VARIATION

Numerous attempts have been made to gather, to catalogue, and to classify the various phenomena of variation in nature (Philiptschenko 1927; Robson and Richards 1936; et al.). The taxonomist is keenly interested in this, since 90 percent of his work consists in the study of variation. Among the various possibilities of subdividing the fields of variation, one is particularly useful to the taxonomist; it is the distinction between *individual variation*, that is, variation within a population, and *group variation*, that is, variation between different populations within the species. Geographical variation, that is, variation between geographically localized populations, is the most common form of group variation encountered by the taxonomist.

The population concept, which has been used in these definitions and which will play an important part in many of our subsequent discussions, is based on the practical experience of the taxonomist, but it is difficult to define it adequately. The concept is based on a certain genetic similarity and on the possibility of interbreeding. It is therefore obvious that a population includes males and females, young and adults, workers and sexual animals (in social insects). In fact, the term population connotes, in general, a geographical coexistence. According to Webster's *Collegiate Dictionary* a population is: "(1) The whole number of people or inhabitants in a country, section or area. (2) Act or process of populating. (3) The body of inhabitants of a given locality. (4) *Biol.* The organisms, collectively, inhabiting an area or region." The population concept seems perfectly clear on the basis of these definitions, although normally the "population" is more or less an abstraction because there is a considerable interchange of individuals between neighboring populations, owing to the absence or incompleteness of physical barriers. Under ideal conditions a population consists of a small group of individuals clearly separated from other individuals of the species by a physical barrier. Examples of such isolated populations would be those on islands in the sea, or in oases of the desert, or on mountain tops, and the like. The term population, as used in taxonomic and speciation literature, refers in most cases to a "local population," that is, the total sum of conspecific individuals of a particular locality comprising a single potential interbreeding unit.

There exists one difficulty in nature which cannot be eliminated by even the most careful definition. In some species different groups of individuals coexist in the same localities, more or less effectively separated by ecological barriers. Such groups may be seasonal forms, or host or habitat specialists. If several of such groups form one reproductive continuum, that is, if no reproductive isolation exists between them, they are not considered separate populations. Conversely, groups of individuals that are, at least to some extent, reproductively isolated must be considered separate populations, even though they coexist in the same localities. Most of the cases that fall into this latter category have been insufficiently analyzed; they will be discussed later (Chapter VIII).

INDIVIDUAL VARIATION

Every individual of a sexually reproducing species is, in general, genetically different from any other member of the species, provided they are not identical twins. This enormous potential variability is expressed in a certain amount of visible morphological variability within the populations of a species. It is only rarely possible to say that this or that individual of a population is "more typical" than some others. The characters of a population are determined by the characters of the sum total of the individuals of which it is composed. If we want to compare a form or species with another one, we compare samples ("series" of the taxonomist), we do not compare individuals; this is one of the basic principles of modern systematics. It is therefore the first task of the taxonomist to study the variation within the population, the so-called individual variation, in order to determine the characteristic attributes of that population.

The various kinds of individual variation, which are encountered by the taxonomist may be classified as follows:

> *Nongenetic (Phenotypical) Variation*
>> Individual variability in time
>>> Age variation of the same individual
>>> Seasonal variation of the same individual
>>> Seasonal generations
>> Habitat forms
> *Hereditary (Genotypical) Variation*
>> Sex differences and alternating genetic generations
>> Individual genetic variability

NONGENETIC VARIATION

Some of the differences which we encounter between individuals of the same population are not due to genetic factors. Such nongenetic differences may not be of much significance in the study of the origin of species, but they are of considerable importance in practical taxonomic work. We must therefore devote some consideration to this type of variation. Furthermore, such passing stages in the life cycle of certain species sometimes give us valuable clues to the past course of evolution in these species.

INDIVIDUAL VARIABILITY IN TIME

Age variation.—Few species of animals are born in such advanced condition that they already resemble their parents. Animals, whether they are born more or less developed or whether they hatch from an egg, in general go through a series of juvenile or larval stages in which they are more or less dissimilar to the adults. The name lists of any group of animals is full of synonyms which are due to the failure of taxonomists to recognize the relationship between the various age classes of the same species. Fortunately for the taxonomist, there are many families in which species cannot be identified by larvae (*Drosophila*, for example) and in which all descriptions and names are based on adults only. The differences between adults and immatures are generally not very striking in terrestrial vertebrates. In many cold-blooded animals, and in particular in marine forms, the larval stages may have externally not the faintest resemblance to the adult form. One has only to be reminded of the floating larvae of some sessile coelenterates, of echinoderms and crustaceans, as compared to the adult stages of these species. In many fishes we find similar conditions, and endless numbers of juveniles have been described as belonging to different species and genera from the adults. Even more difficult of determination are parasitic species in which different stages occur in different hosts. Such stages are often so unlike that it seems hardly conceivable that they have the same germ-plasm basis.

It has not always been easy to unmask these age classes. Only by finding intermediate stages or by breeding such animals in the laboratory has it been possible to piece together the fragments of the life cycle of the species. All this makes for practical difficulties, but the taxonomist is well on the way toward their solution.

Seasonal variation.—Every naturalist knows the varying hare, the ermine, and the ptarmigan, animals that wear a white dress during the winter and a more or less brownish one in the summer. Many birds have a bright nuptial dress which they exchange at the end of the breeding season for a dull eclipse plumage. The same individuals wear in all these cases different dresses in different seasons. This type of seasonal variation is particularly common among vertebrates, with their elaborate hormonal apparatus.

Seasonal generations.—Many species of short-lived invertebrates, particularly insects, produce several generations during the various seasons of one year, and it is not uncommon that the individuals hatched in the cool spring are quite different from those coming forth in the summer, or that the dry-season individuals are different from the wet-season population. In butterflies, particularly, this situation has caused considerable confusion and much complication of nomenclature. The practical difficulty of deciding what individuals belong to one species is increased by the fact that distant populations frequently differ from one another in the same characters by which the seasonal variants of one locality differ. In such cases only by breeding experiments is it possible to decide whether or not such differences are nongenetic modifications. There are, fortunately, a number of indications which enable the experienced systematist to determine which of the two possibilities is the right one. Modern authors list such seasonal forms simply as the "spring form" or the "autumn form" of species A, instead of speaking of var. *milleri* or var. *variegata* of species A, as is done by some of the old-fashioned workers. The use of definite scientific names (with possible nomenclatural standing) for different forms of one subspecies leads to a number of undesirable complications which can be avoided by the use of descriptive terms in the vernacular.

Even more troublesome are cases in which the second generation of one year is not the descendant of the first, but that of a generation of the preceding year, as for example, in mayflies. Genetic differences may be involved in such cases. When there is a definite time gap between the breeding seasons of such generations, it is not unlikely that such a process may play an important role in speciation.

HABITAT FORMS (ECOPHENOTYPES)

That various habitats harbor different even though genetically identical forms of the same species is generally known. Corals that grow in a quiet lagoon have a rather different form from those that grow in the surf. Dall (1898) gives a very good account of the variations he observed in a study of the oyster, *Ostrea virginica*.

The characteristics due to situs may be partially summarized: When a specimen grows in still water it tends to assume a more rounded or broader form, like a solitary tree compared with its relatives in a crowded grove. When it grows in a tideway or strong current the valves become narrow and elongated, usually also quite straight. Specimens which have been removed from one situs to another will immediately alter their mode of growth, so that these facts may be taken as established. When specimens are crowded together on a reef, the elongated form is necessitated by the struggle for existence, but, instead of the shells being straight they will be irregular, and more or less compressed laterally. When the reef is dry at low stages of the tide, the lower shell tends to become deeper, probably from the need of retaining more water during the dry period. . . . When an oyster grows in clean water on a pebble or shell, which raises it slightly above the bottom level, the lower valve is usually deep and more or less sharply radially ribbed, acquiring thus a strength which is not needed when the attachment is to a perfectly flat surface which acts as a shield on that side of the shell. Perhaps for the same reason oysters which lie on a muddy bottom with only part of the valves above the surface of the ooze are less commonly ribbed. When the oyster grows to a twig, vertical mangrove root, or stem of a gorgonian, it manifests a tendency to spread laterally near the hinge, to turn in such a way as to bring the distal margin of the valves uppermost, and the attached valve is usually rather deep, the cavity often extending under and beyond the hinge margin; while the same species on a flattish surface will spread out in oval form with little depth and no cavity under the hinge.

The characters that seem to be of the most value in this group are the form of the beaks and the hinge margin, the sculpture of the inner margins of the valves, particularly at the hinge and immediately on either side of it, and the form and position of the muscle scar. In fresh water snails and mussels such habitat forms are particularly common. The upper parts of rivers, with cooler temperatures and a more rapid flow of water, have different forms from the lower reaches, with warmer and more stagnant waters. In limestone districts the shells are heavy and of a different shape from those which grow in waters poor in lime. This dependence of certain taxonomic characters on environmental factors was, curiously enough, entirely overlooked by some of the earlier workers, a fact which resulted in completely absurd systematics. Schnitter (1922), who largely cleared up the situation, describes these absurdities as follows:

The last step in the splitting of the fresh-water mussels of Europe was done by the malacozoologists Bourguignat and Locard. According to the shape and the outline of the shell they split up the few well-known species into countless new ones. Locard lists from France alone no less than 251 species on *Anodonta*. On the other hand, two mussels were given the same name, if they had the same outline of the shell, even though one may have come from Spain and the other from Brittany. It seems incredible to us that it never occurred to these authors to collect a large series at one locality, to examine the specimens, to compare all the individuals and to record the intermediates between all these forms. It is equally incomprehensible that these people did not see the correlation between environment and shape of the shell, even though they spent their entire lives in collecting mussels.

All these "species" of *Anodonta* are today considered to be habitat forms of a single or at most of two species (Adensamer 1937; Haas 1940). The range of phenotypical plasticity is genetically determined. Even within a species there may be much difference in this respect between various geographic races (Boycott 1938).

Poikilothermal animals are, as a rule, much more subject to this environmental variation than the warm-blooded ones, which carry their own self-made and self-regulated environment with them. Many taxonomic characters are the result of physiological processes (growth rates, pigment formation) which are very susceptible to temperature influence. The great variability of cold-blooded animals, particularly land invertebrates, as compared to birds or mammals, is the immediate result of their variable environment and is therefore not surprising.

The practical effect of this difference is that the taxonomist of poikilothermal animals encounters much greater difficulties than the ornithologist or the mammalogist. In many species of birds, for example, there is less than 8 percent difference between the linear measurements of the largest and the smallest adult of a population, and it makes no visible difference how much or how little food the individual receives during its growth period. It seems that a bird, unless he received too little food to survive, will eventually reach the genetically fixed "standard size" of the form to which he belongs. In insects, on the other hand, there may be differences of several hundred percent between certain measurements of the largest and the smallest individual of a population.

The castes of the social insects should also be mentioned in this connection. There is no genetic difference between workers and soldiers in ants and termites, so far as is known at present. The existing differences of the adults are modifications of the same genetic material through trophic influences (food differences) during the growth period.

It may be mentioned parenthetically that the working taxonomist must not neglect a type of change, in certain samples, which in its effect closely resembles individual variation. The bird which has just completed his molt or the butterfly which has just emerged from the chrysalis usually has a rather different appearance from worn members of the species. The taxonomist always has to keep this in mind, particularly since he works with museum material which is frequently not well dated. This process of wear may be needed to produce the full nuptial plumage of the species. In the starling (*Sturnus vulgaris*), for example, the freshly molted bird of October is covered with white spots and all the feathers show whitish or buffy margins. During the winter these edges and margins wear off and in the spring, at the beginning of the breeding season, the whole bird is a beautiful glossy black. A similar process of wear brings out the beauty of the plumage in the males of the linnet, the snow bunting, the house sparrow, and many other birds.

Many colors deteriorate in museum specimens. Extreme cases among birds are the twelve-wire bird of paradise (*Seleucides ignotus*), whose plumes are a deep orange yellow in nature, fading to a pale lemon; or the Chinese jay (*Cissa chinensis*), whose plumage is green in life, but which turns blue in collections, owing to the loss of the yellow volatile component. To a lesser degree the same is observed in a great many animal specimens. A comparison of fresh material with that which has been in the collection for a long time has led to many mistakes. In general, such changes are of taxonomic importance only in groups in which colors and patterns are used as diagnostic characters.

HEREDITARY (GENOTYPICAL) VARIATION

In all cases of variation mentioned above the same individual is subject to a change in appearance. In other words, all of these changes were phenotypic, with no change of genetic characters involved. But the taxonomist must also cope with a genetic variation within the population. This in turn can conveniently be subdivided as follows:

Sexes, generations, and so forth.—These infraspecific categories have one feature in common, namely, that they consist of groups of individuals which may be identical in their genetic constitution with other groups of individuals of the same species, except for the single factor (or group of factors) which determines to which sex or generation they belong. The actual differences, as encountered by the taxonomist, are often very striking indeed, as, for example, between the male and female in birds of paradise, or between the haploid and diploid generations in certain hymenoptera and hemiptera. In many cases the different sexes or generations were described originally as different species, and the actual relationships became apparent only after much painstaking work by naturalists. A celebrated case is that of the king parrot (*Larius [Eclectus] roratus*), in which the male is green with an orange bill, the female red with a black bill. The two sexes were considered different species for almost one hundred years (1776–1873), until naturalists proved conclusively that they belonged together. The males of the African ant *Dorylus* are so unlike other ants that they were not recognized as such and were considered for a long time to belong to a different family. Hymenoptera are particularly rich in such cases of striking difference of appearance in the sexes. No layman, on seeing the wingless pygmy female and the winged large male of a mutillid wasp would believe that they could possibly belong to the same species. In the genus *Cynips* (gall wasps) the agamic generation is so different from the bisexual one that it is quite customary to apply different scientific names to the two (Kinsey 1930).

Individual genetic variability.—A close scrutiny of the individuals of a population (excepting identical twins, clones, and similar cases) reveals both to the taxonomist and to the geneticist that no two individuals are ever identical, no matter how similar they may appear. The differences are in general slight, corresponding, let us say, to the differences between the inhabitants of a village. Sometimes rather distinct variants are observed, which may be very confusing. Every taxonomist will be able to recall such cases from the groups in which he specializes. The shape and the internal sculpture of the shell mouth has been used extensively as a taxonomic character in the snail genus *Pagodulina*. Klemm (1939) found, however, that nearly every one of the shell-mouth types was represented in a large number of specimens of one of these species of snails collected in the small area of one square meter. The species of the snail genus *Melania* have been largely described on the basis of shell characters, such as the presence or absence of spikes, diagonal and spiral ribs. However, spined and spineless specimens occur in the species *M. scabra, M. rudis, and M. costata*, and sculptured and smooth specimens in *M. granifera*, and so forth. In a recent revision of this genus no less than 114 "species" were found to be nothing but individual variants and had to be added to the synonymy of other species (Riech 1937). Every hunter knows of the surprising individual variability of the antlers in the deer family. In the moose (*Alces alces*) two distinct types of antlers are distinguishable, a palmated and a rounded.

The differences between individuals of a population are, in general, slight and intergrading. In certain species, however, the members of a population can be grouped into very definite classes, determined by the presence or absence of certain characters. Some authors have attempted to contrast such polymorphism with ordinary individual variation, but the work of the geneticist has shown that there is no basic difference between the two. Polymorphism will be discussed in a subsequent chapter.

But even in the species in which no such striking individual variability is found, there are always some differences in regard to size, proportions, and color shades, if the various individuals of a population are compared. In a careful study of the variation of the various parts of the body in a species of the mouse *Peromyscus*, Clark (1941) showed that the tail was the most variable part of the body. The various body parts, arranged in order of their decreasing percentage of variation, were: tail (6.66 ± 0.27), body (4.52 ± 0.21), femur (4.08 ± 0.12), foot (3.06 ± 0.06), mandible (2.67 ± 0.09), skull length (2.44 ± 0.10), and skull width (2.31 ± 0.09).

The important practical lesson is that confusing situations can be disentangled only by the study of a large series of specimens. The larger the series available from a certain locality, the greater is the chance that it includes all of the major variants and the extremes of size and coloration.

THE IMPORTANCE OF INDIVIDUAL VARIATION

We have thus seen that all the individuals of which each population is composed are by no means identical in their physical characters. A study of individual variation is therefore of great practical importance to the working taxonomist. It will enable him to determine which characters of an animal may safely be used in taxonomic studies and which are too variable to be used for this purpose. But beyond this purely practical interest, the study of individual variation is of considerable significance in the study of evolution.

It has become increasingly clear in recent years that all or nearly all geographic variation, or any differences between infraspecific categories are compounded from individual variants. Taxonomic work, unfortunately, tends to obscure this fact, since most taxonomists unconsciously minimize the bridge which individual variation builds between geographical races. Miller's *Junco* monograph (1941) is a notable exception.

Other, earlier authors had come to the conclusion that individual variation had, in most cases, very little to do with the variation processes that lead to species differences. In support of this argument, Rensch (1933:48) tabulates the percentage frequency of various variants in the garden snail, *Cepaea hortensis*. His figures demonstrate that neighboring populations often have rather different compositions, while the populations of widely separated localities are sometimes remarkably similar. Furthermore, the same color variants are found in the related species *C. nemoralis* and in other species of the genus, while the actual differences between these species concern characters which are not subject to much individual variation. Similar observations have been made in beetles, bumblebees and many other animals which are subject to much individual variation.

Rensch overlooked the fact that he was dealing with a very special case. The variation in color patterns, such as bands in snails and spot patterns in lady beetles are, by themselves, obviously of very insignificant selective value. Furthermore, *Cepaea hortensis* is a very common and widespread species, with almost unlimited possibilities for the rapid spread of genetic characters in neighboring populations. There is the further very important possibility that some of the small colonies which were examined had been established by single fertilized snails and that the similarity of the individuals was due to their close blood relationship.

We might say, in conclusion, that the differences between geographic races are frequently foreshadowed in the individual variation within these races, but that not all individual variation will be compounded into racial differences.

CHAPTER III

PHENOMENA OF GEOGRAPHIC VARIATION

SINGLE INDIVIDUALS are, at least in sexually reproducing species, rarely the immediate ancestors of completely new species. Speciation is, in general, not such a cataclysmic process. It is now becoming more certain with every new investigation that species descend from groups of individuals which become separated from the other members of the species, through physical or biological barriers, and diverge during this period of isolation. The concept of the isolated population as incipient species is of the greatest importance for the problem of speciation. It is for this reason that the study of group variation (Philiptschenko 1927) deserves detailed analysis. The variation between different local populations of one species, the socalled geographic variation, is the form of group variation which is most commonly studied by the taxonomist. The study of group variation complements the study of individual variation, because only by comparing different populations can we determine how and to what extent the differences between individuals are molded into the differences which exist between races and species.

DIFFERENCES BETWEEN LOCAL POPULATIONS

Every single locality on the earth, even the smallest geographic district, is somewhat different from other neighboring ones in the nature of its environment. The soils differ, as do vegetation, microclimate, topography, and other features. Add to this biological factors, such as the absence or the greater frequency of enemies, parasites, or competitors, and we have a formidable array of selective agencies which will shape each population of a species to fit into the particular geographical and ecological niche in which it has been placed. It is therefore only natural that the inquiring taxonomist finds differences between samples of local populations from the different parts of the distributional range of a species.

Recent studies indicate that actually no two populations are identical, provided a minute analysis is undertaken. Dice (1940b) summarizes

his experiences as follows: "In *Peromyscus* . . . each more or less isolated intrabreeding local population actually constitutes a local race,
for Sumner and myself have shown that no two local populations of
Peromyscus ever have exactly the same characters," this being true at
least for size, proportions, and coloration. the same phenomenon has

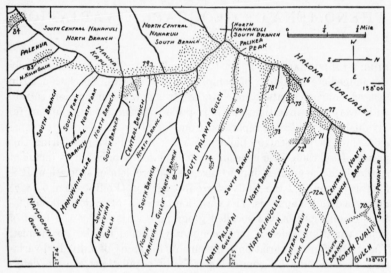

FIG. I. Map of a section of the range of the snail *Achatinella mustelina* on
Oahu, Hawaiian Islands. Dotted areas with numbers indicate the more or less
isolated populations of this species. (From Welch 1938.)

been found in nearly all species of animals when large enough series from
various localities were measured and compared. The most extensive
studies of this sort have been carried out on snails, since they are both
highly sedentary and locally abundant. Alkins (1928) collected a series
of one hundred or more specimens of the two sibling species *Clausilia
rugosa* and *cravenensis* at each of nineteen stations within an area seven
miles in diameter. In *Cl. rugosa*, when a comparison was made between
shells of different stations, a statistically significant difference was found
in regard to the altitude of the shells in 36 percent of the cases and in
regard to the major diameter in 53 percent of the cases. The respective
figures for *Cl. cravenensis* were 72 percent and 67 percent. Very extensive figures for the variation of color patterns exist for the common
European garden snails, *Cepaea hortensis* and *C. nemoralis* (Rensch
1933). These studies prove likewise that adjacent populations (colonies)
may show considerable differences in their genetic make-up. The exact

plotting of the different populations was possible in the case of the Hawaiian snail *Achatinella mustelina* (Welch 1938), which occurs in more than one hundred races on the Waianae Mountains of Oahu. The attached map (Fig. 1) indicates how small the ranges of some of the morphologically well-characterized races are. A comparison of 204 lady beetles of the species *Adonia variegata* from Styria, with 504 individuals of the same species from Hungary, deserves attention for the careful statistical analysis of the eleven points in which the two populations differ (Strouhal 1939). This local variability is not restricted to land animals, but is found in marine organisms as well. A biometric analysis of one Norwegian, two British, and eight New England populations has proved this for the marine snail *Littorina obtusa* (Colman 1932).

There are species that show very little visible morphological variation, and some authors have therefore come to the conclusion that the various populations of such species are identical. This may be true as far as taxonomically useful characters are concerned. On the other hand, whenever a genetical analysis of such similar populations has been undertaken, it has been proved invariably that such populations differ in their genetic characters. The most convincing study of this kind is probably Dobzhansky's analysis of the Californian *Drosophila pseudoobscura* populations (Dobzhansky 1941b; Dobzhansky and Wright 1941). Physiologists likewise found considerable differences in regard to physiological characters in many species when they compared geographically separated, but morphologically indistinguishable populations. All these findings confirm our contention that in most species of animals and probably of plants every local population differs genetically to a lesser or greater degree from every other population of the species. It is therefore self-evident that the systematist is confronted by phenomena of geographic variation in every careful taxonomic study in which material of one species is available from several localities. The study of geographical variation occupies, therefore, an ever-increasing share of the attention of the taxonomist of the better-known groups, such as birds, butterflies, mammals, snails, and others. The average taxonomist does not have sufficient time to carry out painstaking studies, such as the ones just quoted, since his collection cases are filled with undescribed genera and species.

The study of geographic variability leads not only to purely practical questions, such as how to group local populations into systematic categories (subspecies) and how to delimit these with regard to each other, but it also produces much relevant material on the subject of speciation. We should not forget that a study of geographic variation gave both Wallace and Darwin some of their most valuable inspiration concerning the course of evolution. An analysis of this subject therefore seems timely.

There are various ways of examining geographical variation of taxonomic characters. We might ask, for example, what attributes of an animal are subject to geographic variation, and how geographic variation originates and what is its genetic basis. We shall try to answer these questions in the present chapter. But there are additional aspects and manifestations of geographic variation, which lead to questions such as how taxonomic characters are influenced by various environmental factors, whether there is evidence for non-adaptive variation, and how geographic variation is influenced by the population structure. These questions will occupy us in the next chapter. There is naturally some overlapping between the two chapters, since there are many taxonomic situations which permit a number of different approaches. Still, an attempt has been made in the following chapters to present a well-organized discussion of the phenomena of geographic variation.

WHAT CHARACTERS ARE SUBJECT TO GEOGRAPHIC VARIATION?

The taxonomic characters are different in every group of animals. Color patterns and degrees of pigmentation are very important in birds and butterflies, as are the presence, form, and length of spines on the legs in certain crustaceans, certain features of the internal anatomy in worms, and the length of the tail and the structure of the teeth in mammals, to mention just a few of an unlimited variety of characters. Let us examine them and see whether they are subject to geographic variation and if so to what extent.

MORPHOLOGICAL CHARACTERS

Size.—Absolute size is an important taxonomic character only if it is not subject to too much individual variation. It is therefore of more value in homoiothermal animals, such as mammals or birds, than in poikilothermal animals, whose size tends to be much influenced by the environment. The amplitude (range) of variation of the wings of birds, for example, rarely varies in adult males or females by more than 10 percent of the mean length. This wing length is determined rather accurately by measuring to the tip of the longest wing feather after the completion of the growth period, a measurement which is, in birds, a much more reliable unit of comparison than weight or total body length.

If we compare the wing length of different populations of one species, we find, in general, that the means of no two populations are identical. Sometimes such differences are quite conspicuous. Measurements were made of the wing length of twenty-three populations of the subspecies *triton* of the cockatoo *Cacatua galerita*, which occurs throughout New Guinea and the neighboring islands (Mayr 1938a) (Fig. 2). No two

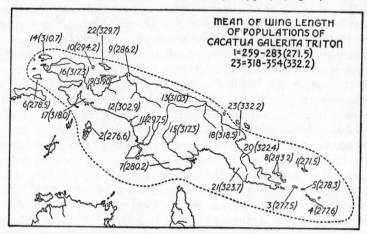

FIG. 2. Irregular variation within the range of one subspecies (*Cacatua galerita triton*). The smallest and the largest of 23 populations are very different, but the gap is bridged by intermediate populations. (From Mayr 1940a.)

populations had exactly the same mean, and the largest bird of the smallest-sized population was considerably smaller than the smallest bird of the largest-sized population. Equally pronounced size variations have been found in the honey eater *Foulehaio carunculata* (Mayr 1932a, 1940a), in the starling *Aplonis gigas* (Mayr 1931c), in the parrot *Psittrichas fulgidus* (Mayr 1938a), in the frogmouth *Podargus* (Mayr 1937), and in many other birds. The variation is geographically irregular in all of these cases, and there is so much overlap between the larger and the smaller populations that it would be unwise for the taxonomist to separate them subspecifically. It would be impossible to decide what names to apply to all the populations with intermediate-sized birds. This "checkerboard" type of variation is particularly common in tropical archipelagos or among desert animals where soils of different colors are distributed in an irregular manner (Hall and Hoffmeister 1942). Where environmental gradients are present, they tend to sort out these variants in an orderly way, with the result that in subtropical and temperate zones the size variants are usually arranged in the form of clines (see below, p. 94).

Of particular interest are the cases in which a small and well-isolated population deviates considerably in size from the rest of the species. This happens particularly on islands or on mountains. It was formerly believed that insular forms were invariably smaller than mainland forms, but this is by no means true. The only generalization we can make is that island forms are often different in size from the other populations of the species. Of the fifty-seven species of land birds which occur on Biak Island and are also represented on the mainland of New Guinea, the Biak race has smaller measurements than the New Guinea race in twenty-six species, larger measurements in only four species. In twenty-seven species there is no size difference (mostly widespread species) or else the material is insufficient to justify conclusions (Mayr and de Schauensee 1939). Several widespread species of birds have developed races of very small size on isolated Rennell Island, for example, *Phalacrocorax melanoleuca brevicauda* (tail 124–143 mm., against 150–165 in the nominate race), *Threskiornis moluccus pygmaeus* (culmen 132, against 170–196 in *moluccus*), and several others with less pronounced size differences. None of the Rennell Island species shows larger measurements than the corresponding species on the Solomon Islands, which in this case take the place of the nearest continent (Mayr 1931b). Birds on arctic islands and archipelagos are, if there is any difference of size, nearly always larger than their relatives on the neighboring mainlands. This is true, for example, in Greenland, Spitsbergen, Commander, and Bering Islands. Increase of size is sometimes also found in nonarctic insular populations. I have already mentioned the four species of Biak Island, but there are many other cases. Of the eight species of land birds on the Juan Fernandez Islands, at least two are distinctly larger than their closest relatives on the neighboring coast of Chile (*Spizitornis fernandezianus* as compared with *S. parvulus*, and *Thaumastes fernandensis*, as compared with *Th. galeritus*).

Equally pronounced or even more striking differences are found between representative populations on tropical mountain ranges, shown in Table 1, which gives the size variation of New Guinea honey eaters. The big *Melipotes ater* of the Huon Peninsula is about twice as heavy as the small *Melipotes gymnops* from the Arfak Mountains. Some of this variation seems to be entirely fortuitous, being caused by the possibility of rapid evolutionary changes in small isolated populations. In some cases, however, selective influences must have been active, as is indicated by the fact that we find an identical trend in many species of a particular island. This will be discussed in the next chapter.

TABLE I

SIZE OF ADULT MALES IN TWO SUPERSPECIES OF
NEW GUINEA HONEY EATERS

	ARFAK WEST NEW GUINEA	LOW ALTITUDE SOUTHEAST NEW GUINEA	HIGH ALTITUDE SOUTHEAST NEW GUINEA	HUON PENINSULA, NORTHEAST NEW GUINEA
Melidectes leucostephes group (wing mm.)	125–136	139–144	147–153	154–172
Melipotes gymnops group (wing mm.)	115–120	108–117	...	151–163
Melipotes weight (gr.)	58–62	...	...	114–142 (128)

Some of the above-quoted examples illustrate well the fact that the size differences between large and small-sized races of the same species can be considerable. The larger races of a species are often two or three times as heavy as the smaller ones. Unfortunately, the exact weight is rarely known in birds, but the wing measurements give some clue to the possible degree of difference. The extent to which a large and a small race of one species may differ is illustrated by the following additional wing measurements (in millimeters):

> *Bubo virginianus* (Great Horned Owl)
>> *mayensis* (Yucatan), ♀ 315
>> *wapacuthu* (Arctic North America), ♀ 385–390
> *Lampribis olivacea* (Glossy Ibis)
>> *bocagei* (San Thomé), 247.8
>> *olivacea* (West Africa), 330
>> *akeleyorum* (East Africa), 360

Even more striking size differences have been reported between geographic races of mammals.

Proportions.—Not only is absolute size subject to geographical variation, but also the proportions of the various organs and body structures. Prominent parts, such as the tail, the ears, the feet, and so forth, may be proportionately longer in some races than in others. These differences are frequently quite striking and are used by the taxonomist to distinguish related forms. For example, the tail of the bird of paradise, *Paradigalla carunculata*, from the Arfak Mountains is 89–92 percent of the wing length (in adult males), while it is only 32–34 percent of the wing length in the geographic representative *Paradigalla brevicauda* from the mountains of central New Guinea (Fig. 3).

One might expect that such body appendages would be subject to allometric growth and this is true to a limited extent. Mayr and Ripley

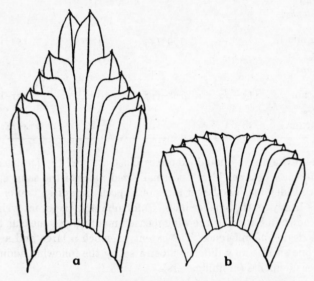

Fig. 3. Geographic variation in the structure of the tail of the bird of paradise *Paradigalla carunculata*. a = *P. c. carunculata* (elongated tail); b = *P. c. brevicauda* (square tail). (From Strese-mann, J. Ornith., 1925:152.)

(1941) found that in the superspecies *Lalage aurea* the tail is relatively shortest (68 percent) in the smallest species (*sharpei*), and longest (86 percent) in the largest form (*leucomela*). In general, the species *maculosa* has a short tail (69–73 percent), the *aurea-atrovirens* group a medium-sized tail (76–82 percent), and the species *leucomela* a long tail (80–86 percent), although there are forms of comparable wing length in each group. Thus special size factors modify basic allometric tendencies. Clark (1941), in a careful statistical study of a number of species and sub-species of *Peromyscus*, likewise found that the proportions of various selected body parts cannot be attributed primarily to general size factors and to allometric growth. Differences in the length of the tail, body, foot, femur, mandible, skull, and the width of the skull are due primarily to special size factors. Birds with very long tails are particularly favorable material for such studies. The racket-tailed kingfishers of the genus *Tanysiptera* have tails that are two to three times as long as their wings. Five forms of the superspecies *T. galatea* have the following mean values for wing length: 102.7 (*riedeli*), 108.7 (*galatea*), 109.4 (*carolinae*), 109.7 (*rosseliana*), 114.0 (*vulcani*); the corresponding mean values for tail-length are: 181.4 (*carolinae*), 188.3 (*riedeli*), 238.4 (*rosseliana*), 278.5 (*vulcani*), 280.9 (*galatea*). The sequence of the relative tail length (in terms of wing length) is thus: *carolinae* (length of tail equals 165.8 percent of wing-length), *riedeli* (183.4 percent), *rosseliana* (217.3 percent), *vulcani* (244.3 percent), and *galatea* (258.4 percent) (Mayr, unpublished). Similar computations on several other long-tailed species have been made by the writer and all conform to this principle. Linsdale (1928) showed that the geographical races of the Fox Sparrow (*Passerella iliaca*) differ in the proportions of the individual bones of the skeleton. Kattinger (1929) showed the same for a number of species of hawks and Rensch (1940) for tropical as compared to temperate zone subspecies. The differences between extreme subspecies of one species are frequently of the same magnitude as the differences between allied species. Nearly every species of snails that has been studied biometrically has shown geographical variation in the proportions of its shell. Allometric growth is frequently involved, since the height of the shell tends to increase more rapidly than the width (Crampton 1916, 1932; Fuchs and Käufel 1936).

The relative length of prominent body parts (as bill, ear, tail, and so forth) is subject to considerable environmental molding and will therefore have to be considered again in connection with a discussion of adaptation (Allen's rule, p. 90).

Epidermal and chitinous structures.—Almost any epidermal structure of an animal may be subject to geographic variation. In birds, this includes not only the shape of individual feathers, especially the ornamental plumes of hummingbirds and birds of paradise, but also wattles, crests, the casque on top of the hornbill's beak, and all the skin structures that are secondary sex characters of the male. In mammals, the horns and antlers of the Ungulates are geographically variable. This has been studied in African antelopes, in the reindeer (*Rangifer*), and in the deer group (*Cervus*). In reptiles the number of scales is subject to strong geographic variation (Mell, Klauber, and others), although some of this variation seems to be phenotypical.

Beetles are particularly satisfactory material for the study of the geographic variation in sclerotized structures, such as the sculpture of the elytra and the size and shape of special hornlike processes, and so forth. A number of valuable contributions have been published lately, of which I shall mention Endrödi's monograph of the beetle genus *Oryctes* (1938) and various monographic papers on the genus *Carabus*. In crustaceans the number, shape, and size of taxonomically important spines seem to vary geographically, but the analysis of most of these cases is still incomplete.

Patterns of coloration.—These play an important role in bird and butterfly classification, as well as in that of many other groups of animals. It is sometimes remarkable how many different pieces seem to combine to form the pattern of coloration and how these elements seem to vary independently from one another. Dobzhansky (1941a:71) has reproduced a tabulation of characters of the Melano-Polynesian races of the bird *Pachycephala pectoralis* (from Mayr's data). A similar though less striking case is presented by the *Lalage aurea* group (Mayr and Ripley 1941). In some butterflies many of the colors of the spectrum seem to be utilized to provide an almost endless array of differences between races (Seitz 1906ff; Eller 1936).

General pigmentation.—Such clear-cut pattern differences between geographic races are the exception, rather than the rule. The color dif-

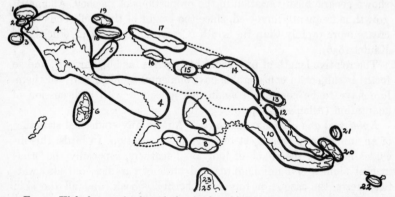

Fig. 4. High degree of subspeciation in the whistler *Myiolestes megarhynchos* on New Guinea and surrounding islands. Dotted lines indicate presumably continuous ranges. Each of the 25 numbers refers to a distinct subspecies.

ference is usually one of tone or of degree. The description in such cases does not read: head white or gray or black, but rather, head darker olive or more grayish olive or more yellowish olive. The student of geographic variation is generally confronted with this type of difference.

For example, in one of the plainest-looking New Guinea birds, *Myio-lestes megarhynchus* (Fig. 4), no less than twenty-five races have been described from the mainland of New Guinea and the neighboring islands. The entire range of differences, which is rather slight, is best expressed by the diagram:

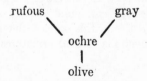

The basic type is a dull ochre, which turns more rufous in some races and more grayish or more olive in others. The bill is either pale horn-colored or black, and there is a slight difference in size, but otherwise all the races are alike.

These races are not arranged in any particular pattern; they are not darker in the south and paler in the north, or vice versa. There are occasional specimens which cannot be identified if isolated from the rest of the material, but if an entire series from one locality can be examined, there is never any doubt as to which subspecies it belongs. Geographic variation of coloration is often of this *Myiolestes* type.

Genital armatures.—In the taxonomy of certain groups of insects and other arthropods, the study of the genital armatures plays an important part. It has been found that the sclerotized parts of the male copulatory organ and of its accessory structures, and of the female sex aperture, often show specific differences. A study of the genital armatures is frequently the simplest and sometimes the only way of identifying species, particularly in certain genera in which many similar and variable species exist. I am not concerned here with the question of the possible importance of the differences in such structures for speciation. Exaggerated claims in this respect have been rejected by Dobzhansky (1941a) and Goldschmidt (1940:123–126). What concerns us here is simply the practical value of these structures to the taxonomist. An examination of the vast entomological literature on the subject reveals that the taxonomic value of these structures differs considerably in the different families and genera. In some genera there is great uniformity of the structures within each subspecies, but each species and subspecies can, with certainty, be identified on the basis of the genitalia. In other families not even the genera show any differences in regard to this character. This fact should not be overlooked by the entomologist.

Rensch (1934), with good reason, objected to the procedure of one author, who refused to separate two species, which were clearly defined in every other respect, simply because he could not find any differences in their genital armatures. Of course even the practical value of these features should not be overrated. They are not always as constant as has been claimed in the past. Kerkis (1931), in a study of the genitalia of the bug *Eurygaster integriceps*, found them to be no less variable than the external characteristics of this species. Summarizing this evidence one might say: The genitalia (sexual armatures) of insects and other

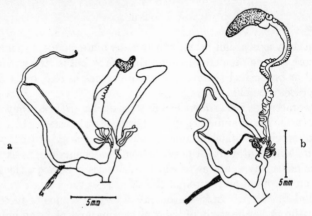

FIG. 5. Geographic variation of the anatomy of the genital tract in the Mediterranean snail *Xerocrassa cretica.* a = *adusta;* b = *seetzeni*. There are characteristic differences in the length of penis and vagina, in the shape of the seminal vesicle, and the structure of the accessory glands. (From Fuchs and Käufel 1936.)

arthropods often show specific characters with comparatively little individual and considerable geographic variation. They are therefore useful in taxonomic work, although their importance is frequently no greater and sometimes less than that of other structural characters.

Internal structures.—Internal structures have rarely been examined with sufficient thoroughness to reveal proof of geographical variation. The best evidence exists in the human anatomical literature in regard to differences in muscle formation, skin structures, and the like between Europeans, Negroes, and Japanese. Zoölogical evidence is scanty. Fuchs and Käufel (1936) showed that there is a considerable degree of geographical variation in the genital tract of the Mediterranean snail *Xerocrassa arctica* (Fig. 5). Further studies will probably show that this applies to other widespread species as well. The pituitary of two races of the domestic pigeon is quite different (Rost 1939), and it is to be expected that comparable differences will be found between geographic races, as was already done for the thyroid of various *Peromyscus* subspecies (Yocum and Huestis 1928).

Cytological structures.—In some cases where no subspecific characters could be found in either the external or the internal structures, striking differences were found in the chromosomes. There are several good recent accounts on *Drosophila* to which I have nothing to add (Muller 1940; Dobzhansky 1941a; Patterson 1942). Similar chromosomal differences between subspecies have been found in other animals, particularly in other insects and in worms. The European race of the turbellarian worm *Mesostoma ehrenbergii* differs from the American race (*wardii*) by its larger size, position of the penis, character of the ductus ejaculatorius, and musculature of the bursa copulatrix. Ten chromosomes are found in *ehrenbergii* and eight in *wardii*. At metaphase, in the primary spermatocytes of both animals the maximum number of bivalents is three. At least two univalents in *wardii* and four in *ehrenbergii* are always found at this stage. There are apparently additional subspecies of this species in northern Europe, in Asia, and in South America (Husted and Ruebush 1940). Geographic variation of chromosome number is also known in other turbellarian species.

PHYSIOLOGICAL CHARACTERS

Recent work has proven abundantly that physiological thresholds and the capacity to react to external stimuli are as much determined by genetic factors as are structural characters. It is therefore to be expected that species and subspecies should differ in physiological characters, in addition to the morphological ones. The technique of the taxonomist, who generally works with dead material, is, as a whole, not suited for the detecting of such characters, but both the naturalist and the experimental laboratory worker have gathered some relevant material. Small physiological differences between populations, subspecies, and species are often more important biologically than the accompanying structural differences. The latter may have adaptive value, but more often they appear to be mere by-products of evolution. Those cases in which morphologically identical populations show well-defined physiological differences are particularly interesting.

Temperature tolerance and preference.—One of the physiological characters of an animal that is most easily studied in the laboratory is its reaction to temperature. We have perhaps more data on geographic variation of physiological characteristics referring to temperature than for any other factor. Timofeeff-Ressovsky (1935) studied the relative viability of *Drosophila funebris* flies from twenty-four different populations of the western Palearctic at three different temperatures (15°, 22°, and 29° C.). It was found that the flies belong to three different temperature races: a northwestern race, which is resistant only to low temperatures; a southwestern race, which is resistant only to high temperatures; and an eastern race, which shows marked resistance to both high and low temperatures. An obvious correlation exists in this case with the climatic requirements of the respective regions. Banta and Wood (1927) showed that in *Daphnia* certain mutational changes may produce a considerable difference in temperature tolerance. Herter (1941) invented an experimental set-up in which an animal can choose an environment with an optimum temperature (V.T.). The V.T. of each species is closely correlated with its habits and habitat. Among the Palearctic reptiles, for example, he found that *Anguis fragilis*, which lives in shady forests in northern Germany, is at one end of the scale (V.T. = +28.38 ± 0.29° C.), and that some of the rock-dwelling reptiles of desert countries are at the other end, for example, *Agama stellio* from Egypt, with a V.T. of +45.59 ± 0.33° C. In the lizards *Lacerta vivipara* amd *L. sicula* there was a definite difference between the V.T. of lowland and high-altitude populations. Krumbiegel (1932) examined a number of European populations of the beetle *Carabus nemoralis* with the same technique. The V.T. was 26.1° ± 0.30 at Dresden (central Germany), 27.1° ± 0.76 in the Rhön Mountains (western Germany), 27.9 ± 0.39 at Münster (northwestern Germany), 29.3° ± 0.74 at Coblenz (western Germany), 29.4° ± 0.46 at Paris (central France), and 29.7° ± 0.37 at Olargues (southern France). The temperature preference is roughly parallel to the climates of the above-mentioned localities. Temperature races are also found in marine animals. Runnström (1930) found three different temperature races in *Ciona intestinalis*, an Arctic, an Atlantic, and a Mediterranean one. J. Moore has worked on the comparative physiology of the temperature requirements of various species and races of North American frogs. Little difference was found between the adults of various species, which can tolerate temperature ranges of nearly 40°, but the eggs and early embryological stages showed clear-cut climatic adaptations. The more northerly species are more resistant to low temperatures and develop more rapidly at low temperatures (Moore 1939). *Rana pipiens* populations from Quebec, Vermont, Pennsylvania, and Wisconsin have approximately the same rate of development and temperature tolerance. Those from southern Florida, however, differ markedly. The rate of development is slower at low temperatures, the eggs are much smaller and can tolerate a higher temperature, but are less resistant to lower temperatures (Moore, unpublished).

Physiology of sex and reproduction.—Recent investigations have revealed that certain physiological factors which pertain to sex and reproduction are particularly subject to geographic variation. In various species of frogs geographic races occur in which some of the males may be hermaphroditic or even show a predominance of female characters. Witschi (1930) has summarized the evidence, as far as the European grass frog (*Rana temporaria*) is concerned. Races occur in the Alps and along the Baltic in which the males obtain their male characters at an early embryological stage (differentiated races). In other localities populations occur which, at the time of metamorphosis, consist of females only (or females and a few hermaphrodites), and in which the genetic males acquire their male characters (via a hermaphroditic condition) during or after the first year of life (so-called undifferentiated races). A third group of races shows an intermediate condition, that is, the changing over of the genetic males into phenotypical males occurs earlier, starting even before metamorphosis. Witschi concludes that the present distribution of the three sex-races is a result of the colonization of central Europe after the end of the glaciation. It is unknown whether or not these differences in the time of sex differentiation have any selective value. Similar sex races have been reported for other European amphibians, for example *Rana esculenta* and *Bufo bufo*, as well as for the American spotted salamander (*Ambystoma maculatum*). J. A. Moore tells me (unpublished work) that in adult males of *Rana pipiens* in the cooler parts of the range (New England, Canada, and parts of the Rocky Mountains) the oviduct persists, whereas it is absent in the more southern part of the range. The males without the oviduct also have a larger vocal sac, a secondary sex character in this species. E. R. Dunn (1940) found that the seven geographic races of *Ambystoma tigrinum* differ not only in morphological characters, but also in physiological traits. Neoteny occurs only in some races, and eggs are laid singly in some races and in masses in others.

In the well-known European turbellarian worm *Planaria alpina*, A. Thienemann (1938) found that there are two very distinct subspecies, the typical alpine race and a northern race (*septentrionalis*) found in northern Germany and in Scandinavia. The alpine subspecies (*alpina*) has normal sexual reproduction, while *septentrionalis* reproduces entirely by asexual division. This difference has a strictly genetic basis, and specimens of *alpina* retained their sexual type of reproduction even after transplantation into northern brooks.

A rather different situation exists in regard to the sex races of the gypsy moth *Lymantria dispar*, a case which was exhaustively analyzed by Goldschmidt (1934). These sex races are characterized by different valences of their sex determiners, so that crosses between different sex races upset the sex-determining mechanism. If, for example, a "weak" female is mated with a "strong" male, she will produce only sons due to to sex reversal of the daughters; a "half-weak" female will produce inter-sexual daughters. These sex-races are distributed in a strictly geographic pattern. Most European races are weak, most races from continental Asia are half-weak, while on the main island of Japan (Hondo) strong races occur. The Tsugaru Strait of northern Japan separates the strong-est of all the races (northern Hondo) from the weakest of all the races (Hokkaido). The evolutionary significance of this situation is at once evident. If the islands of Hondo and Hokkaido should become connected by some geological event, or if one of the two races should venture to colonize the other island, it would result in a hybrid population of much reduced viability. Geographic variation seems also to affect the sex ratio in some species of insects and crustaceans (Vandel 1934).

PHYSIOLOGY OF PLUMAGE AND PLUMAGE CHANGE IN BIRDS

The plumage of birds is an accurate indicator of small differences of genetic background and physiological potentialities. The study of birds is therefore a particularly fertile field for the student of geographic variation.

Sexual dimorphism.—One of the important physiological character-istics of birds is that in some species male and female are colored alike, as for example in the familiar catbird (*Dumetella carolinensis*) of our gardens, while there is a decided sexual dimorphism in many other species (birds of paradise, pheasants, hummingbirds, and so forth). The degree of difference between the sexes is variable, sometimes being slight, sometimes very pronounced. What interests us in this connection is that the degree of this dimorphism varies geographically in some species.

In the widespread small whistler *Pachycephala pectoralis* the males are handsomely colored in a bright yellow, black, white, and olive color pattern, while the females are generally of a dull yellowish ocher-olive. On Rennell Island a race (*feminina*) occurs, in which the male has lost his ornamental plumage and is indistinguishable from the female. In-dependently, the same process has been repeated on Norfolk Island (*xanthoprocta*).

Conditions are even more interesting in the species *Petroica multi-color*. This Australian species has colonized many of the South Sea Islands, where it occurs in thirteen races (Mayr 1934). Normal sexual dimorphism characterizes the Australian parent race and eight races of the South Seas. In two places, however, the males have lost their bright plumage and wear a feminine one, while on San Cristobal in the Solomon Islands and in Samoa the females have become masculine and

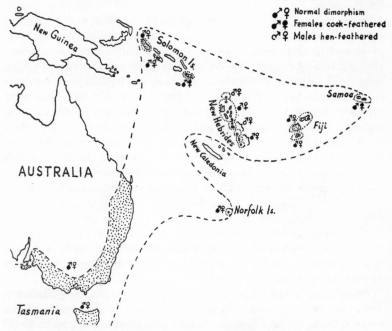

FIG. 6. Geographic variation of sexual dimorphism in an Australonesian fly-catcher (*Petroica multicolor*).

wear a plumage which resembles that of the male (Fig. 6). The occurrence of similar conditions in various species of birds has been reported by other authors (Hartert 1903–1938; Bateson 1913; Murphy 1938).

Six or seven additional cases of geographical variation of sexual dimorphism in birds could be added, but they all follow the pattern described above for *Pachycephala* and *Petroica*. It is important to emphasize the fact that loss of sexual dimorphism through feminization of the male plumage seems to develop only in well-isolated and rather small populations. The genetic "drift" may overcome, under such conditions, the effect of sexual selection. It might also be mentioned that such a breakdown of the male nuptial plumage seems to occur only in localities where no other similar species exist, i.e., where a highly specific male plumage is not needed as a biological isolating mechanism between two similar species. There is no doubt in all these cases that the males lost their bright plumage secondarily.

Geographic variation of sexual dimorphism has also been described in insects and has been analyzed in detail in a species of scorpions (Meise 1932).

Heterogynism is a term in the ornithological literature (Hellmayr 1929) for situations in which the female of a species shows stronger geographic variation than the male. It occurs most often in species in which the male is black or otherwise very intensely colored, whereas the female is brownish or grayish. The obvious explanation for this phenomenon is that the male has reached an intensity of pigmentation which is far above the threshold at which pigment formation is influenced, while the females in their less intense coloration are in a sensitive zone. In Hellmayr's original paper many cases of such heterogynism are quoted; Zimmer (1931ff.) added several more in the same genera. In *Pachycephala pectoralis* the Solomon Island races *bougainvillei, orioloides*, and *cinnamomea* are indistinguishable in the male sex, while the females are very different (Mayr 1932c). In *bougainvillei* the females are grayish-olive, in *orioloides* they are bright orange yellow with a more or less strongly developed rufous wash, and in *cinnamomea* they are pale gray with a rufous wash (Fig.7). Cases of heterogynism are rather rare, since in most birds geographic variation is equally pronounced in both sexes or more conspicuous in the male sex.

Occasionally we find that there is no difference in the adult plumages, but that the immatures vary geographically. The same is found for other animals. De Beer (1940a) quotes a number of cases in which larval stages show more differences than the adults. However, in most of his cases the differences are between good species.

Geographic variation of plumage changes.—Birds do not gradually change individual feathers after they have become old and worn, but rather change large parts of the plumage during a short molting period. All the members of the same species, with few exceptions, go through the same molts at about the same seasons. In fact, the general principles of these molts are often the same for entire genera and families. Exceptions to this rule, so far as they are subject to geographic variation, are of much interest, as a few examples will show. The adult birds of all the species of the tropical family Campophagidae have a single annual molt, with the one exception of the white-winged triller *Lalage sueurii tricolor* from Australia, which has a double molt. In one of these molts (January-February) the male acquires a femalelike dull-colored brownish plumage (eclipse plumage), and in the other molt (August-September) it acquires a beautiful glossy-black nuptial plumage. The subspecies *Lalage s. sueurii* from Timor and the Lesser Sunda Islands has only the "nuptial" plumage and only a single annual molt (Mayr 1940d). Somewhat similar

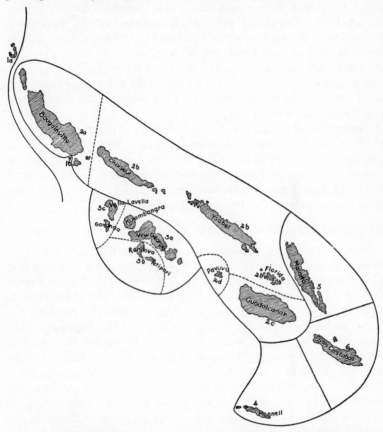

FIG. 7. Geographic variation of *Pachycephala pectoralis* in the Solomon Islands. 1a = males white-throated; 2, 3, 5; 6 = males yellow-throated; 1b = hybrid population between 1a and 2a; Males 2a, 2b, 2c indistinguishable, females vary geographically (heterogynism); 3a, 3b, 3c, a series with increasing tendency to melanism; 5 = males without black breast band; 4 = males hen-feathered. Many of these insular representatives stand on the threshold of specific distinctness.

conditions have been found among members of the Old World genus *Cisticola* (Sylviidae, warblers). Some tropical species of this genus have only a single plumage—a nuptial plumage—while most species, in particular the subtropical ones, have two plumages, a summer (or breeding) plumage, and a winter (or eclipse) plumage (Lynes 1930). There are, however, some four or five species known in which some subspecies have two molts and plumages and others have only one. This is correlated with the fact that these species have a wide latitudinal distribution, including both tropical and subtropical countries. In the duck *Anas castanea* the temperate zone race *castanea* from southern Australia has sexual dimorphism and a male nuptial plumage; in the other subspecies male and female are colored alike throughout the year (Ripley 1942). A similar geographic variation of the number of the molts seems to occur in other species of birds, for example in *Vireo olivaceus*, but the evidence is still somewhat contradictory.

The number of molts in the larvae of *Lymantria dispar* is also subject to geographical variation (Goldschmidt 1940:42). Both male and female may have four or five molts, or the two sexes may behave differently in regard to the number of molts. The mode of inheritance has been worked out in this case. Undoubtedly many similar cases will be found in other groups of animals as they become better known.

Geographic Variation of Other Physiological Characters

Every physiological character that was seriously studied was found to show geographical variation. This is not surprising if we consider that such characters have nearly always an adaptive value. We owe a great deal of information in this field to Goldschmidt, who determined in *Lymantria dispar* such factors as the length of time of larval development, the number of larval instars, the length of the diapause, and so forth (Goldschmidt 1934, 1940). Speyer (1938) studied the hatching time of the winter moth (*Cheimatobia brumata*), which roughly coincides with the time of the first fall frosts, but is subject to striking local variation. At one valley locality (Neuenkirchen) the moths appeared a month earlier than in the neighboring villages on low hills, even though no climatic differences were noticeable. However, most of this valley is flooded by the fall rains, and this had apparently resulted in the development of an early flying race, through the drowning of all the late-hatching pupae. The early hatching date was proved to be genetically fixed, since it was retained in the laboratory. It was possible to shorten the larval stage of a laboratory population through a period of years by selecting early flying individuals as the breeding stock. Hovanitz (1941b) showed likewise that the geographic variation in the time and length of æstivation and hibernation of the Californian races of a butterfly had a genetic basis. Müller and Kautz (1940) showed that the low-altitude races of *Pieris bryoniae* had two broods per year, the high-altitude races only one brood. The one-broodedness was retained by the high-altitude form, even when kept in captivity at high temperatures. Krumbiegel (1932) found that the geographic races of *Carabus nemoralis* differ in their phototaxis. The more northern races are strictly nocturnal, the southern races more or less diurnal.

Microgeographic races of fresh-water snails (*Lymnaea*) differ in regard to a number of physiological characters such as egg production, length of fertile period, age of maturity, growth rate, and longevity (Baily 1939; Forbes and Crampton 1942). Considerable differences are to be expected when the same species ranges all the way from the tropics to the temperate zone. Rensch (1931) showed that this affects a number of physiological processes and correlated organs, including the circulatory system (relative heart weight) and the intestinal tract (relative length of intestines and of cæca).

HABITS AND LIFE HISTORY

In the preceding paragraphs such physiological differences between races were discussed as expressed themselves in structural differences, or at least in growth processes and rates of development. There are others which express themselves in habits or ecological preferences.

Important as such characters are, as contributory factors in speciation, they are difficult to interpret. The principal trouble is that we never know to what extent such characters have a genetic basis. Let us demonstrate this by one example. The Yellow Wagtail (*Motacilla flava*) of Europe is nearly always a ground-nesting bird. About 1915 Schiermann (1939) found a little colony of these birds in which all the individuals (eight or nine pairs) had built their nests off the ground on Artemisia plants. The birds came back year after year and built the same kind of nests, until the habitat was destroyed. It is extremely unlikely in this case (and many similar ones) that some sort of mutation had occurred which resulted in the changed habit. It is much more likely that one bird started the new fashion and the others "learned" from him, until the entire population had "acquired" the new habit. Such new habits are usually lost as quickly as they are acquired, unless they add measurably to the survival value of the species. But we cannot rule out the possibility of a genotypical basis in many other cases. The Peregrine Falcon or Duck Hawk (*Falco peregrinus*), for example, generally nests on cliffs. There are extensive geographic areas in which only cliff nests are known. In other districts, for example the north German and Baltic plains, the birds reproduce in tree nests and are thus able to reach a much higher population density than is possible in the cliff districts. Still, in a fully populated cliff district birds will attempt to occupy an unsuitable cliff nesting site, rather than shift to a tree (Hickey 1942). This may be due to the conditioning of the young to the cliff nests, but it may also have a genetic basis.

The song races of birds may also belong to this category. It has been known to the field ornithologist for a long time that in some birds the song varies from district to district. Chapman (1940) lists, for example, differences in the song of various races of *Zonotrichia capensis*, a widespread South and Central American bunting. The isolated race *antillarum* from Santo Domingo has a song which is widely different from that of the other races of the species and resembles, in fact, that of some species of the genus *Melospiza*. The song of the Spanish race (*ibericus*) of the Chiffchaff (*Phylloscopus collybita*) is not at all like that of the other European races of the species from which it received its vernacular name, but is rather a lengthy sequence of soft whistles, much like the song of another species (*trochilus*) of the genus (Ticehurst 1938a). J. P. Chapin (personal communication) found striking differences between the song of the various subspecies of the South Sea Island warbler (*Acrocephalus*). On some islands the song was very beautiful, on others rather unmusical, while on Pitcairn Island no song at all was heard, even though the island was visited during the breeding season. The most remarkable geographic variation in song and call-notes that has been described occurs in the European chaffinch (*Fringilla coelebs*). Promptoff (1930) called attention to the fact that this species tends to break up into a number of geographic song races. Sick (1939), who gives a general survey of the literature on geographic variation of song, found that the so-called "rain-call" of the chaffinch is subject to an even more remarkable localization. This call, whose exact biological significance is still somewhat obscure, is uttered by the male within his breeding territory. In the township of Stuttgart, southern Germany, three sharply characterized rain-calls occur, of which one is restricted to the three-hundred-year-old park which extends along the valley floor for a distance of three kilometers. The second call is restricted to the hills to the west, and the third to the hills to the east of the town. A "hybrid-zone" is found where two of these dialect districts meet, but distributional barriers, such as railroad yards, prevent such hybridization in other places, so that the districts of pure call notes approach each other occasionally within a distance of only five hundred meters. Much circumstantial evidence indicates that these call notes are not genetically fixed, but conditioned. The young chaffinch learns these call notes from his father and from the neighboring males and he either stays at or always returns to the locality where he was born. The exact history of the parks of Stuttgart is known, and it is evident that a period of three hundred years was available for the development of the striking "park dialect." The significance of such nongenetic changes as contributory factors to isolating mechanisms is evident (see also Cushing 1941).

In other cases the song of various populations is remarkably alike, even in widespread species. In the genus *Phylloscopus* the *trivirgatus* group of species is widespread in the Indo-Australian archipelago. Not the slightest difference in song could be detected by me between five subspecies which are so different in color, pattern, and size that they are classed in three separate representative species by most ornithologists. The song of these forms, which range from westernmost New Guinea to the easternmost Solomon Islands, is decidedly more conservative than a number of size and color characters. The thrushes of the genus *Turdus* can be recognized by their song in whatever part of the world a species is encountered. There is also no question that the song of parasitic cuckoos must have a strictly genetic basis, for the young cuckoo is obviously more exposed to the song of his foster father than to that of his own. It is therefore likely that genetic factors enter into the formation of song races in birds, even though conditioning may play a major role.

Geographic variation (on a genetic basis) of the feeding habits or of food preferences may occur, but, in all the cases that have been reported in the literature, the difference is much more probably due to local conditioning and therefore phenotypical. So many sudden changes in the feeding habits of a population have been reported that considerable caution in their interpretation seems advisable.

It would be extremely valuable to get some information on the geographical variation of courtship patterns, display postures, and so forth. These differences must exist; otherwise we would not find such striking differences between good species. That such variation is possible is evidenced by the geographic variation which Venables (1940) reports in the begging postures of young mockingbirds in the Galápagos Islands. While begging for food the young droop the tail in *melanotis* (Chatham Island) and raise it in *macdonaldi* (Hood Island) and *baueri* (Tower Island).

Migratory movements.—The presence or absence of migratory movements in birds belongs as much to the genetic characteristics of a race or species as does size or color patterns. There are numerous species of birds in which some races are migratory, while others are sedentary. In the South American bunting *Zonotrichia capensis* (Chapman 1940) all the races are sedentary except the Patagonian subspecies *australis*. In the cuckoo *Chalcites lucidus* the races on the tropical islands (*harterti* and *layardi*) are sedentary, while the subtropical or temperate zone races (*lucidus* and *plagosus*) are migratory (Mayr 1932b). In the humming-bird *Selasphorus alleni* the race *sedentarius* Grinnell from the Californian islands of San Clemente and Santa Barbara is sedentary, while the bird from the opposite mainland of North America migrates south to Mexico (Grinnell 1929). These are but a few examples of literally hundreds of similar cases. Sometimes it is possible to find a population in which some individuals are migratory, others sedentary. Nice (1937) investigated this situation in a song sparrow population from central Ohio, but she was unable to establish the mode of inheritance of this trait. Similar differences in migratory behavior undoubtedly occur in insects and marine animals, but little has been recorded. Of two closely related species or subspecies of *Pieris* (butterflies), one (*napi*) is strongly migratory, while the other (*bryoniae*) is strictly sedentary (Müller and Kautz 1940).

Habitat preference.—It is an old and often-tested experience of the naturalist that similar species can be better identified in many cases by their habitat association than by morphological characteristics. This has led some authors to the assumption that such habitat requirements are constant in species, both in space and time. Consequently, whenever there was doubt as to whether or not two forms were conspecific, their habitats were examined. If they were found to be identical, the two forms were considered as only subspecifically different; if the habitats were different, the two forms were recognized as full species.

Reinig (1939) postulates, on the same basis, that by knowing the present-day ecology of a species, its history can be largely reconstructed. Both beliefs are partly correct, but are not without exceptions. Many cases have been described in recent years in which even populations of the same subspecies may occur in rather different habitats. The savanna sparrow (*Passerculus sandwichensis savanna*) is a common bird of the salt marshes of the Atlantic Coast of eastern North America from southern New Jersey to Canada, but it is also found in a very different plant association, on dry hillsides, from the Catskills to New England, and in many additional habitats in other parts of North America. The golden warbler (*Dendroica petechia*), which is a bird of the mangroves throughout its range, was found by Wetmore (1927) to occur on Puerto Rico not only in the mangroves, but also in gardens and other inland localities up to several hundred feet above sea level. Hile and Juday (1941) found that the depth of water inhabited by a single species of fish in the highland lakes of Wisconsin varies rather widely from one lake to another. Different species that live at the same depths in one lake may inhabit different depths in another. In most cases, however, such habitat differences are strictly associated with subspecific characters.

The fantail *Rhipidura rufifrons* of the Australian region is preëminently a bird of the lowlands, coast, mangroves, and of small islands, but the race *brunnea* (Malaita, Solomon Islands) is absent from the lowlands and is not found below 600 meters altitude, reaching its maximum abundance at 1,000 meters. In the thrush *Turdus poliocephalus* the subspecies on New Guinea, on Goodenough Island, and on Bougainville and Kulambangra Islands (Solomons), are high-mountain birds, usually not found below 2,000 meters. But other races of the species occur in the lowlands or even on small coral islands, such as the races on St. Matthias Island, Rennell Island, and on some of the islands of southern Melanesia and central Polynesia (Fig. 8). Some subspecies of the doves *Ptilinopus rivolii* and *solomonensis* live on small coral islets, others in the mountain forest of New Guinea or the Solomon Islands. In *Megapodius freycinet*, likewise, some subspecies are restricted to the mainland, others to small offshore islands (Mayr 1941a).

New Guinea presents abundant illustrations of this phenomenon. Species which in all other parts of the island are restricted to the mountains have isolated colonies at sea level near the lower Fly and Oriomo Rivers in southern New Guinea. This is true, for example, for the species *Coracina caeruleogrisea*, *Sericornis beccarii*, *Microeca griseoceps*, *Tregellasia leucops*, *Ailuroedus viridis*, *Zosterops novaeguineae*, as well as others (Mayr 1941a). Other New Guinea species are restricted to the lowlands or even to the coast, but one race (as for example the subspecies *balim* in *Pachycephala pectoralis*) is found far inland, or more than 1,000 meters high in the mountains. In some cases, and this is particularly true for widespread species, the various subspecies may be at home under extremely different conditions. The most striking case that comes to my mind in regard to birds is the raven (*Corvus corax*), who is equally at home in coldest Greenland and in the hottest parts of the Sahara, in the quiet forests of the Baltic region and in the precipices of the Alps.

The full significance of the extensive material on the geographic variation of morphological, physiological, and ecological characters will become more evident in some of the later chapters. At the present I shall limit myself to emphasizing two points. The first is that all the characters which have been described as good species differences have been found to be subject to geographic variation, whenever they have been

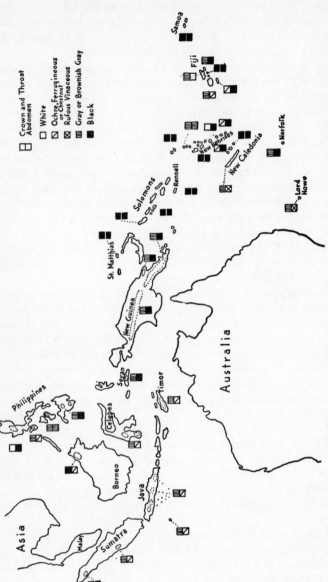

FIG. 8. Parallel evolution in the *Turdus poliocephalus* group. Subspecies from neighboring islands are sometimes more distinct (e.g., Fiji Islands) than those from the opposite ends of the range. All the western subspecies are found only above timber line. Some of the populations in the Melanesian and Polynesian Islands, as on St. Matthias, Rennel, some of the New Hebrides, and other islands, are found at sea level.

Legend:

Crown and Throat / Abdomen

☐ White
▨ Ochre, Ferrigineous or Chestnut
⊠ Rufous Vinaceous
▦ Gray or Brownish Gray
▬ Black

examined from such point of view. Rensch (1938b) looks at it from a slightly different angle, but means the same thing when he says "The characters, by which subspecies are distinguished, are of the same kind as the characters which separate 'valid' species living side by side."

The other point, which is intimately associated with the first one, is that geographic variation not merely helps in producing differences, but that many of these differences, particularly those affecting physiological and ecological characters, are potential isolating mechanisms, which may reënforce an actual discontinuity between two isolated populations (see Chapter IX). Geographic variation is thus capable of producing the two components of speciation, divergence and discontinuity.

THE GENETICS OF GEOGRAPHIC VARIATION

We have established, in the preceding discussion, the facts that geographic variation is of very common occurrence among animals and that it affects, so far as known, all taxonomic characters, that is, all the actual and potential differences between species. The study of geographic variation is thus of the greatest importance to the student of species formation. But such variation can be significant only if it affects the genetic basis of the visible characters, since the differences between species have a genetic basis. We must ask ourselves, therefore, if the differences between geographic races are phenotypical or genotypical, and what the genetic basis of geographical variation is.

THE GENOTYPICAL CHARACTER OF GEOGRAPHIC VARIATION

We have learned in the discussion of phenotypical individual variation (p. 27) that environmental influences are capable, under certain conditions, of changing individual animals considerably. It is only natural that the conclusion should have been drawn by many investigators that geographic variation was due entirely to the phenotypical adaptability of animals. This point of view was strongly endorsed by some plant ecologists, who observed a striking adaptability of plants to local conditions. To consider geographic variation merely a modification process was, perhaps, the prevailing belief among biologists, excepting the taxonomist, toward the end of the last and the first twenty years of the present century. However, a study of zoölogical-garden animals and, more recently, the genetic analysis of geographic populations led to a complete change of opinion, and for a while every difference between local populations was considered as entirely due to genetic factors. A healthy reaction has set in against this extreme, and a natural balance is being reached. We are now beginning to realize that, although there are many genotypical differences between local populations, not all geographic differences are genotypical, particularly in poikilothermal animals. It might be useful to summarize some of the evidence on which these conclusions are founded. I am somewhat handicapped, as an ornithologist, in the discussion of these phenomena, since birds with their highly uniform internal environment (homoiothermy) exhibit a minimum of changeability through external causes.

Phenotypical changes in birds.—No case is known to me of any population of birds having changed from one year to the next on account of an unusually strong influence (let us say, a particularly hot or dry season). The variation of the phenotype, in birds, is exceedingly narrow. Many species that have been bred in captivity for generations are in no way different from the wild type unless obvious mutations have occurred. The normal phase of the budgerigar (*Melopsittacus undulatus*), although bred in captivity for more than a hundred generations, is externally still the same as the wild bird in Australia. The house sparrow (*Passer domesticus*) was transplanted from Europe to North America about one hundred years ago, but no visible change has yet occurred (Lack 1940c). Several species of European birds were transferred to New Zealand during the nineteenth century, but no differences seem to have developed.

As far as wild birds are concerned, I know of only two doubtful exceptions. The British goldfinch (*Carduelis carduelis britannica*) was transferred to Bermuda and was supposed to have developed there into a different race (*bermudiana* Kennedy). Recent authorities, however, deny the existence of any differences. The second case concerns the Hawaiian house finch. A number of pairs of the Californian race (*Carpodacus mexicanus frontalis*) were taken after 1870 to several of the Hawaiian Islands (Oahu, Molokai) and have since developed into a thriving population. Grinnell found that Hawaiian birds differed from those of California by having all crimson colors replaced by yellow or orange and described, on this basis, a Hawaiian race *mutans*. Certain birds have pigments that are subject to captivity and food influences, and the red of the Purple Finch group is one of them. It is therefore probable that we have in this case a true phenotypic change of a wild population of birds, as Phillips (1912) has pointed out. In captivity a small number of birds are known to change the color of the plumage, in particular finchlike birds and pigeons. Crossbills and Purple Finches nearly always lose in captivity the red of their plumage, which is replaced by greenish-olive. Beebe (1907) produced considerable changes in the plumage of captive birds by subjecting them to darkness or to a particularly humid atmosphere.

Dr. H. Friedmann, who kindly gave me permission to quote this unpublished work, experimented with white-throated sparrows (*Zonotrichia albicollis*) in the Washington Zoological Park. Three groups of these birds, totaling between forty and fifty, were studied through three successive molts. One group was kept in the warm, humid atmosphere of the crocodile house, a second group in the dry, warm finch room, and a third group of controls out of doors. Neither gross inspection nor microscopic examination of the feathers revealed any change in the pigmentation of either of the experimental groups. Rensch (1933) has summarized most of the pertinent literature. The antlers of the Red Deer, which was introduced from the British Isles to New Zealand, are reported to have changed considerably and the hinds have been reported to come into breeding condition one year earlier (G. M. Thomson 1922). The fur of several of the Australian marsupials that were acclimatized on New Zealand is reported to have become denser in the cooler climate (Le Soueff).

Phenotypical changes in cold-blooded animals.—Phenotypical changes of taxonomically important characters are rare in warm-blooded animals, but common in cold-blooded ones and in particular in insects. This adds to the difficulties in studying geographic variation of invertebrates and cold-blooded vertebrates. It is in most cases impossible, without breeding experiments, to state whether a particular variant is genetic or not. Sometimes definite conclusions can be reached by a study of the ecological conditions. If, for example, all the animals of one stream system belong to one variant, and all the animals of another stream system to another variant, it is rather obvious that true subspecies are before us. If, on the other hand, the same variant occurs in the muddy mouth of both streams, another variant a little higher in both streams, and a third variant of the same species in the rapid waters near the source, the possibility cannot be excluded that these variants are merely phenotypic responses to specific environmental conditions, such as oxygen content, turbulence, calcium content of the water, and the amount of available food. It is distressing and embarrassing to the conscientious taxonomist to have to admit how many "new species" are created by less conscientious colleagues on the basis of nongenetic habitat forms. The taxonomy of fresh-water mussels and snails has been simplified tremendously through the elimination of so-called species which were nothing but phenotypic variants. We have mentioned already how Locard's 251 different species of *Anodonta* from France have recently been reduced to a single one. The same has been found in quite a number of species of fresh-water shells. There is a definite correlation in marine mollusks between the size and thickness of the shell and the temperature

and salinity of the water (Shih 1937). It is not known whether this variation is purely phenotypical or whether it has a genetic basis.

The final proof as to whether a certain habitat form has a genetic
basis or is entirely phenotypical can be found only through experiments
(see also Rensch 1932, 1937, Boycott 1938). "A population of the pond
snail *Limnaea peregra* from Leeds (England) was in its natural state a
well grown, large mouthed form with a short, sharply pointed spire.
Brought into the standard conditions of culture, it rapidly became more
elongated and smaller mouthed" (Diver 1939). Oldham took populations of *Helix pomatia*, *Arianta arbustorum*, and other species of snails
and reared one half of the individuals on a diet rich in lime, the others
on a diet poor in lime. The shells of both batches reached about the same
size, but the lime-fed individuals had a thick and heavy shell, while the
shells of the lime-starved individuals were extremely thin (Diver, *loc.
cit*). R. Woltereck (1921) in numerous experiments proved the extreme
plasticity of *Daphnia*. A normal culture of *Daphnia cucullata* from Denmark was transferred to an artificial pool in southern Italy, where the
temperature was higher and food conditions were particularly favorable.
After a number of generations (eight months) the Italian stock had
changed considerably; the average size was larger, the spine thicker, the
head ventrodorsally broadened, the helmet broadened, lower, and in old
females even curved forward. A transfer of individuals of this stock to
aquarium tanks in Leipzig (Germany) with standard conditions showed
a retention of the characters for from 3 to 4 generations, followed by a
gradual return to a habitus resembling the original one. Similar changes
may be caused by seasonal cycles, without any geographic transfer of
populations. The reader should consult Coker (1939) for a recent summary of this phenomenon, which has been termed cyclomorphosis. It has
been impossible, so far, to segregate in the genus *Daphnia* true geographic variation from these phenotypical changes.

Fresh-water fish are prone to the formation of local races. The work
of Hubbs, Gordon, and others indicates that a considerable portion of
this variability has a genetic basis, but some authors have gone too far
in considering as racial characters all the differences which they found
between local populations. W. Koelz (1931), in a taxonomic study of the
whitefish *Leucichthys artedi*, divided this species into a considerable
number of geographic races on the basis of size, proportions, numbers of
fin rays, gill rakes, and so forth. More recently Hile (1937) undertook an
analysis of the populations of this fish in four lakes in northeastern Wisconsin. These lakes are situated within a few kilometers of each other,
but show significant differences in regard to water temperature, pH,

bound CO_2, and other chemical and physical constants. A biometric analysis showed that the four populations of *L. artedi* in these lakes were significantly different from one another. It developed that the morphological characters of the four fish populations run in a parallel series, if the lakes are arranged in a graded series according to their physicochemical properties. One of the most striking discoveries was that the fish of Muskellunge Lake of the 1928 class (hatched in 1928) were quite different from the 1929 class of the same lake (examined in 1931 and 1932). An added complication in this species is that certain proportions were not only correlated with age and size, but also with growth rate. The populations with the most rapid growth had shorter heads, maxillaries, paired fins, and dorsal fins, wider bodies, and a smaller eye diameter. The growth rate, in turn, was largely dependent on the available food supply. It is obvious that the morphological characters of populations of this species depend to a large extent on nongenetic environmental factors and are thus phenotypical. The same is evidently true for the closely related European genus *Coregonus*, about the classification of which no two workers agree. Experiments in transplanting members of this genus indicate that all the taxonomic characters which have been employed in this genus are highly susceptible to environmental influences (Hile, *loc. cit.*). To what extent food can influence the morphology of a fish is demonstrated forcefully in Wunder's (1939) comparative analysis of starved and overfed carp (*Cyprinus carpio*). The hunger form of this species is long, low, with a big head and long fins, while the well-nourished form is stubby, high-backed, with short head and fins.

There is frequently one good indicator which permits us to differentiate phenotypical from geographic-racial characters. The geographic race has, in general, a fairly wide range, including a number of different habitats. The phenotypical variant, on the other hand, usually has a rather small range at any one locality, but crops up again and again wherever the same or a similar combination of environmental factors occurs. Unfortunately, this is also true for geno-ecotypes; in fact, as we shall later see (p. 194), no line can be drawn between subspecies and genetically characterized ecological races.

The genetic nature of geographic variation.—The above-cited phenomena of adaptive responses to specific environments has led many biologists to believe that the subdivisions of the species, local populations, and geographic races or subspecies were merely transient and nongenetic responses to the environment. That this view is not correct has been proven by all geneticists who have worked with geographic races. All these workers, Sumner and Dice on *Peromyscus*, Gordon, Hubbs, and others on fish, Goldschmidt on *Lymantria*, to mention only a few, found that the characters which the taxonomist had been using in separating geographic races, had, with few exceptions, a strictly genetic basis. A summary of this evidence has been given by Dobzhansky (1941a).

This result had been foreshadowed by a number of transplantation experiments (see p. 60). Even some races of the otherwise plastic freshwater animals proved to be genetically fixed. Individuals of an Irish population of *Limnaea peregra* were, in comparison with a stock from Leeds, England, of a strikingly different shape, being subinvolute, high-shouldered and laterally compressed. They also differed in the color and texture of the shell and in the distribution of body pigment. These differences proved to be heritable, and the race preserved its peculiarities in their entirety through at least ten generations of culture. A genetical analysis showed that these differences were due to a considerable number of genetic factors (Diver 1939). Recent genetic work has, furthermore, shown that subspecific differences are usually not due merely to one or two gene mutations, but apparently to a great many mutational steps as well as additional chromosomal rearrangements. As a matter of fact, it now appears that the genetic differences are invariably more extensive than the few superficial morphological ones would indicate. Genetic differences are often present, even where morphological ones are completely or nearly absent. This is particularly true in the genus *Drosophila*. Such genetic differences are sometimes expressed in the ecology or physiology of the various populations, a situation which puts the taxonomist in a dilemma because his technique was developed for the detecting of morphological differences, not of the deep-seated physiological ones, often equally or more important. The fact should therefore be emphasized that a species does not necessarily lack geographic variation, because the taxonomist cannot find it by his methods. On the contrary, all the recent work seems to indicate that all species (except those with very small ranges) are composed of groups of genetically different populations, even where visible differences are too slight to be noticed by the taxonomist.

The Genetic Basis of Species Formation

Modern genetics is a science which is so intricate and specialized that it seems impossible for an outsider to add anything to the excellent recent discussions of Dobzhansky (1941a), Timofeeff-Ressovsky (1940a), and Muller (1940) on genetics and the origin of species. Much of this literature, however, is rather technical or unknown to the average taxonomist for other reasons, and it may, therefore, not be entirely useless to make a few comments from the point of view of the taxonomist. They may contribute toward straightening out the differences between taxonomists and geneticists and may help to close the gap between the two sciences. But even the geneticists themselves have been unable to agree as to how to fit the known pieces of evidence together, and how to fill the gaps in our knowledge by interpretation. The fact that an eminent contemporary geneticist (Goldschmidt) can come to conclusions which are diametrically opposed to those of most other geneticists is striking evidence of the extent of our ignorance. If we are ever to arrive at a mutual agreement on the genetics of speciation, we must first segregate the generally accepted theories from the hypothetical assumptions. The two most fundamental and most widely accepted theses of genetics are:

(1) *Nearly all genetic factors are located in the chromosomes.*

(2) *Normal individuals of sexually reproducing species have two homologous chromosome sets, one each from either parent. The gene contents of two homologous chromosomes present in the same individual do not merge or blend, but segregate at the time of gamete formation*(disregarding, for the sake of simplicity, all the more complicated situations of haploidy, polyploidy, and so forth). These two simple facts are the reason for Mendelian inheritance; indeed, they explain basically most genetic phenomena. Only very few authors would take exception to these two statements.

A third statement of the geneticist, namely that the divergence in nature is due to mutations, was flatly rejected by most taxonomists during the first twenty-five years of this century. The reason for this becomes obvious if we look back over the history of the term mutation. "The mutation concept has had a tortuous history. Not only has the term changed repeatedly in meaning, but even now it is being used in at least two different senses" (Dobzhansky 1941a). The term, as such, is as old as natural science and was used in a more or less neutral sense up to the middle of the last century (Cuénot 1936, Remane 1939). In 1869 Waagen fixed the term mutation in a definite technical sense, applying it to different forms of fossils of the same lineage, occurring in subsequent horizons (time levels). Waagen's mutations are what might be called subspecies in time. The term has had considerable popularity in the paleontological literature, in this original meaning. Completely ignoring this earlier usage, De Vries picked up the term again and introduced it into genetic literature with an entirely new meaning. He applied it to striking departures from the previous appearance of a species (on a genetic basis, of course). To him, as to Goldschmidt with his systemic mutations, each mutation "sharply and completely separates the new form, as an independent species, from the species from which it arose," while on the other hand "the usual [individual] variability cannot lead to a real overstepping of the species limits even with a most intense steady selection." As a matter of fact, very few of De Vries's mutations were gene mutations, most of them being cases of polyploidy or other kinds of cytological aberrations, as they so commonly are in the genus *Oenothera*, and the mutation concept of the modern geneticist resembles only vaguely De Vries's original concept. It is not surprising that the taxonomists and the paleontologists who examined De Vries's definition of mutation decided that it was not the kind of phenomenon that had anything to do with speciation. This opinion is typified by Osborn's (1927) often-quoted statement:

Speciation is a normal and continuous process; it governs the greater part of the origin of species; it is apparently always adaptive. Mutation [as defined by De Vries] is an abnormal and irregular mode of origin, which while not infrequently occurring in nature, is not essentially an adaptive process; it is, rather, a disturbance of the regular course of speciation.

This attitude toward mutations has by no means disappeared during the last fifteen years. One of the best North American bird taxonomists asked me in a letter, early in 1941: "Why do you think that the De Vriesian mutations explain species formation better than the ever present individual variation?" He said "De Vriesian mutations," not merely mutations, and this is really the crux of the matter. For a taxonomist, whose method is based on the acceptance of prior definitions, the meaning of a scientific name is that given it by the original describer. But the term mutation, as used by the modern geneticist, resembles De Vries's concept only vaguely. The term mutation itself has "mutated" repeatedly during the last forty years. Perfectly valid objections to De Vriesian mutations are not justified, if raised against mutation in its modern form. Mutation includes now (contrary to De Vries) all the small genetic changes of which individual variation is composed, as well as (contrary to Osborn) those changes which have potentially a selective value.

I have emphasized this shift in the mutation concept, because a realization of this change may help to overcome the objections of those who are still reluctant to admit the evolutionary significance of mutations. Since there seems to be no adequate definition of the term mutation in the modern genetic literature, the following may be suggested: *A mutation is a discontinuous chromosomal change with a genetic effect.* Such a definition would cover ordinary gene mutations, chromosome mutations (translocations, inversions, and so forth), and genome mutations (chromosome losses, polyploidy, and so forth). The majority, possibly the vast majority of mutations consist of gene mutations, but since there is no way of distinguishing phenotypically between gene mutations and other mutations, we must apply a broad definition. In fact, "what is described as gene mutations is merely the residuum left after the elimination of all classes of hereditary changes for which a mechanical basis is detected" (Dobzhansky 1941a, after Stadler).

Most of the mutations that were studied in the early days of genetics were gross aberrations, often of a pathological character. They are easy to work with and were therefore favored by the students of the laws of inheritance. This also strengthened the opinion of those who denied the evolutionary significance of mutations. However, Johannsen, as early as 1909, and several workers after him (Morgan, Baur, and others) found small mutants which fall well within the range of individual variation, and it is now agreed that the great majority of mutations produce small or even invisible changes. In fact, it is now assumed that all individual variation, outside of phenotypic changes, is due to recombination and mutation. It is therefore permissible, and in harmony with the above definition, to state that mutations and recombinations furnish the only known material of evolution. Even now we know very little about the nature of mutations, the term being merely a synonym for X, the unknown. There is, of course, much reason to believe that all mutations, even the "mechanical" ones, are, in the last analysis, due to biochemical processes. But nobody knows anything about the nature of these processes, nor has it been possible so far to design crucial experiments to solve this puzzle.

Speciation is explained by the geneticist on the assumption that through the gradual accumulation of mutational steps a threshold is finally crossed which signifies the evolution of a new species. The statement, of course, is little better than a tautological explanation to the effect that evolution proceeds by genetic changes. The "explanation" of evolution as being due to mutations would, indeed, mean very little if, biochemically speaking, many basically different kinds of mutations exist, which have Mendelian inheritance as their only common attribute. We have to keep this in mind when we discuss the nature of mutations and of the mutation process.

The opinion was formerly widespread among taxonomists (including even Darwin) that the germ plasm can react to the needs of the body. A change in the body would thus result in an appropriate reaction of the germ plasm. The extremists among the geneticists, on the other hand, insisted that the germ plasm lived a happy life of complete independence in the body, completely unaffected by the physiological processes and physical states of the body itself. Most modern geneticists are somewhat more cautious. They know that changes in the body may cause reactions in the germ plasm, that the mutation rate may be changed as a consequence of a change in temperature, and so forth. It is still believed, however, that a gene never mutates in response to a need. The connection between the gene and the body is, for most geneticists, strictly like a one-way street. This may be true, but if so it would be strangely different from most other biological processes, which are based on biological equilibria. A gene controls certain physiological processes, and it is therefore thinkable that the mutation rate might be raised at those loci which, owing to certain environmental conditions, have to be exceptionally active in the production of the particular chemical (enzyme?) which is produced by that gene (locus). I have mentioned this possibility merely to indicate that, in view of our present ignorance of the physiology of the gene and of the chemistry of the mutation process, it seems premature to assert with too much positiveness that all gene mutation is strictly random.

Another source of misunderstandings and misinterpretations is the tendency of workers to consider the actions of genes entirely as those of separate units. What my objections to this tendency are will be made clear by the subsequent discussion. If two animals that belong to the same natural or artificial population are crossed, it is theoretically always possible to work out a Mendelian segregation of their differences. If, however, two *species* are crossed, it is rare to find more than two or three characters displaying Mendelian inheritance due to a single gene, all other characters showing "blending" inheritance. The term blending inheritance is rather unfortunate because it suggests pre-Mendelian ideas of actual blending of the genetic basis of the parental characters. Such a supposition cannot be reconciled with chromosomal inheritance, and there is abundant proof against the validity of this pre-Mendelian concept. Authors who speak today of "blending" inheritance use this term descriptively to characterize the lack of clear segregation in the F_2, F_3, and following generations. Such "nonsegregating" is typical for species and subspecies crosses; it has been encountered by nearly every author working in this field. The geneticists interpret this by the action of multiple factors, respectively the so-called "modifiers." Harland goes so far as to say (quoted from Dobzhansky 1941a:84) that "the modifiers really constitute the species." It is by no means certain whether all these postulated modifiers really exist in the form of individual genes or whether other genetic factors, such as a chromosomal "ground substance" (Anderson 1939), exist, or whether there is in every species what might be termed by a neutral expression a specific gene environment. But even if the orthodox opinion should be proven— that "non-segregation" of species characters is due merely to the action of discrete modifying genes—it would be important to emphasize much more vigorously than has been done heretofore that such interaction of genes exists. Species differ in hundreds or even thousands of genes, and each mutation will result in a slight change of the genic environment of all the other genes. In a sense, therefore, Goldschmidt is right in insisting that every species is a different "reaction system," with the modification, however, that, as Hubbs (1941) states correctly, even every subspecies is, to a lesser degree, a different reaction system. It is dangerous, if not completely incorrect, in view of the interrelationship of the genes, to think of species merely as numerical aggregates of genes. Such a view underrates the important role which is played in speciation by the integration of the various gene effects. Speciation will not be fully understood until we have more information about the nature of this integration. Most of the past work on this and related problems has been based on the artificial production of mutations by the crude X-ray technique or has been restricted to the artificial piling up of such mutations in one individual. Such methods give valuable insight into the mechanisms of inheritance, but they produce nothing that resembles natural species. The opposite method, by which the workers attempt to break up into the genetic elements the differences between species and their natural subdivisions, is much more promising. The work of Harland, Hutchinson, and Silow on cotton species (*Gossypium*) has produced highly valuable results. The work of Sturtevant, Dobzhansky, Spencer, and Patterson, to mention only a few of the *Drosophila* workers, is also blazing a path in the right direction. Only after these population differences have been properly analyzed and evaluated will it be possible to study the integration of the individual components. It seems to me that intrapopulation work cannot give the complete answer to these questions.

I have tried, in the preceding discussion, to point out some of the reasons why taxonomists have been reluctant to accept all the conclusions drawn by geneticists. These mental reservations do not mean that an agreement between the two sciences is impossible. On the contrary, the disagreement concerns minor points, and it is possible to make a number of well-substantiated statements on the genetic basis of species formation without referring to these controversial problems. The following generalizations may be made, on the basis of the study of natural populations and of the analysis of the F_1 and F_2 hybrids of taxonomically well-established subspecies and species:

First, there is available in nature an almost unlimited supply of various kinds of mutations. Second, the variability within the smallest taxonomic units has the same genetic basis as the differences between the subspecies, species, and higher categories. And third, selection, random gene loss, and similar factors, together with isolation, make it possible to explain species formation on the basis of mutability, without any recourse to Lamarckian forces.

More detailed proof for the validity of these three statements was given in an admirable way by Dobzhansky, in his book *Genetics and the Origin of Species* (1941a). In order to avoid duplication, I have attempted to reduce to a minimum, in my own presentation, all references to genetic material.

CHAPTER IV

SOME ASPECTS OF GEOGRAPHIC VARIATION

THE TAXONOMIST looks at group variation with different eyes than does the geneticist. The latter is not concerned with such questions as to whether the differences between populations are slight or striking and whether or not they affect taxonomically important characters. No, the geneticist is concerned primarily with the analysis of the genetic nature of these differences, whether or not they are genotypical, whether they are due to different gene frequencies, and whether they are affected by hybridization or by the occurrence of new mutations. The taxonomist, on the other hand, with his more or less practical aims, is concerned first and foremost with the question of how this variation affects his taxonomic judgment. This criterion is clearly apparent in the conventional classification of group variation in (1) quantitative (degree of difference), (2) qualitative (presence or absence of characters), and (3) meristic (difference in numerical proportion) variation. If for example, in samples of two populations of a species of butterflies, one has a spot on the wing which the other population lacks, we speak of qualitative variation. In such a case there is a clear-cut difference between the two populations in regard to the quality of the color pattern of the wing. If the spot is larger in one of two populations and smaller in the other one, we speak of quantitative variation. Finally, if the individuals of one population have a greater number of spots on the wing than those of the other population, we speak of meristic variation (a difference in numbers).

In the case of qualitative and meristic variation the individuals can be grouped into clear-cut classes according to the presence or absence of certain characters, while all individuals are different by degree only in the case of quantitative variation. Some workers, therefore, prefer a different terminology and speak of "continuous" and "discontinuous" variability (Simpson and Roe 1939, Dobzhansky 1941a:65), a distinction which goes back to Bateson and Galton. At first glance this appears to be a completely superficial classification, but curiously enough it parallels a number of additional distinctions and is therefore, perhaps, of basic importance. The geneticist, who is interested in the mechanics of inheritance, finds that both types of variation seem to have the same genetic basis. The naturalist and perhaps also the physiologist, who are more interested in the manifestation of the genes, find a real difference. It seems as if the characters that are most frequently subject to continuous variation, such as pigmentation, size, proportions, and physiological constants, are almost invariably characters that indicate adaptive correlation. It may be useful, for these reasons, to classify variability into the two categories mentioned: continuous and discontinuous variation.

DISCONTINUOUS VARIATION

The opinion is widespread among taxonomists that the striking differences in general coloration or in special color patterns or structures, of which most discontinuous variation is composed, are mere incidental by-products of evolution, which tend to disappear in the phylogenies as quickly as they have appeared. This opinion is certainly justified in many cases, but there are several valid reasons for a more detailed treatment of discontinuous variation.

All the evidence indicates at the present time that the mode of inheritance (chromosomal-Mendelian) is exactly the same for continuous and discontinuous variation. In fact, there does not seem to be any sharp dividing line between the two kinds of variability; the difference seems to be primarily due to the number of genetic factors involved. We encounter discontinuous variation where only one or a few factors are involved, each producing a major effect, and we find continuous variation where many genetic factors, which produce small additive effects, unite in the shaping of a character. If this assumption is valid, it would be simplest to illustrate geographical variation with uncomplicated cases of discontinuous variation and to apply the conclusions to the more complicated situation of continuous variation. The study of discontinuous variation affords us, as the following section will show, a particularly graphic demonstration of the principle of geographic variation. A study of discontinuous variation also frequently permits us to indicate how the differences between individuals of one population are compounded into differences between populations and subspecies (races).

POLYMORPHISM[1]

Polymorphism, the occurrence of several distinct phases or types in

[1] Polychromatism is only a special case of polymorphism.

one population, is one of the most easily observed forms of discontinuous variability. Actually it is merely a pronounced type of individual variation, a form in which the variants can be classified into sharply delimited groups or classes. The genetic basis of intrapopulation polymorphism is, apparently, exactly the same as that of ordinary continuous individual variation. Nevertheless, polymorphism is of considerable importance to the taxonomist, not only because some of the particularly aberrant and striking forms of certain polymorphic species have been considered distinct species or even genera, but also because they are apt to illustrate, in a particularly simple manner, the behavior of Mendelian factors in natural populations. Nabours (1929) made a painstaking and interesting analysis of such a case. For these reasons, polymorphism has been treated in considerable detail by a number of recent workers, and those who are interested in polymorphism as such should turn to these treatises (Rensch, Robson and Richards, Dobzhansky, Goldschmidt, Timofeeff-Ressovsky, Ford, and others).

As far as the evolutionary significance of polymorphism is concerned, most taxonomists do not seem to think very highly of it. The rarer forms are generally called varieties or even "aberrations," particularly by the entomologists. Goldschmidt (1940) describes the situation rather correctly when he says (p. 12):

The taxonomists have never thought of these "varieties or aberrations" as being of importance for evolutionary problems, for they are very frequently of a type which occurs in the same way not only in different species but in different families and orders. Obviously, in these cases one rather generalized process of development is liable to be affected only in a few simple ways. Thus, albinism is found in innumerable mammals and birds, and also in mollusks and insects. Melanism, or partial melanism, or progressive, graduated melanism is a very frequent type of mutant in the same groups. Whenever red pigment occurs, yellow mutants are found, and white ones arise from yellow. . . . We agree with the taxonomists that these aberrations can not play any major role in evolution.

Goldschmidt and the taxonomists are probably justified in asserting that most of this variation is of minor significance in regard to speciation. The characters involved are usually not the characters which separate related species. However, Vavilov and his school have pointed out that this type of variation has some evolutionary significance, since similar mutations occurring in related species ("homologous series of mutations") give us certain clues as to the phylogeny of the germ plasm of the species involved (Rensch 1939a).

In the heron family (Ardeidae), for example, quite a number of species are polymorphic. Melanism and albinism are the two most common color deviations. Albinism, in particular, is of great interest, since it is the dominant phase or exclusive coloration in some of the species. Table 2 illustrates the occurrence of these color types in some species of the family Ardeidae (herons and bitterns):

TABLE 2

POLYMORPHISM AMONG HERONS

SPECIES	WILD COLOR	ALBINISM	MELANISM
Herons and Egrets			
Demigretta sacra	+	+	—
Egretta asha gularis	+	+	—
Egretta garzetta-euloph.	—	+	—
Cosmerodius albus	—	+	—
Florida caerulea	+ (ad.)	+ (juv.)	—
Ardea herodias	+	+	—
Bitterns			
Dupetor flavicollis	+	+	+
Ixobrychus exilis	+	—	+
Botaurus spec.	+	—	—

I have dwelt at length on this phenomenon of phylogenetically old (conservative) mutants, because taxonomists (and even some geneticists) have tended to base erroneous conclusions on it. In the West Indian sugar bird, *Coereba flaveola*, the populations (races) of certain islands are entirely melanistic, on other islands only some of the individuals are black, while all the individuals are normal on still other islands. A rapid spread of the black mutation (due to selective advantage) or a wave of recurrent mutations have been postulated on the basis of these distributional data. Phenomena such as the geographical variation of melanism in *Coereba* and *Charmosyna* (p. 79), as well as the color variation of herons, indicate that the germ plasm of related species and subspecies reveals its similarity by a corresponding similarity of unstable (or reversible) processes. Dobzhansky (1933) demonstrated the same phenomenon among the ladybird beetles (Coccinellidae). The basic potentialities of related species thus tend to be similar (*paripotency* of V. Haecker), and the mutational channels are more or less prescribed. A comparative analysis of the gene mutations of related species of *Drosophila* leads to the same conclusion (Sturtevant 1940, Sturtevant and Novitski 1941). It seems possible that many phenomena which look like introgressive hybridization (a theoretical process which in animals, at least, is not well supported by facts) can be explained on the basis of the great phylogenetic antiquity of certain alleles.

Polymorphism would be only of minor interest to the student of speciation, if it were always a static condition. However, the proportion of the alternate forms changes in many polymorphic species, both in time and space, leading in both instances to divergence within the species.

Ford distinguishes in a recent study (1940) (1) neutral polymorphism, (2) balanced polymorphism, and (3) transient polymorphism, relating to changes of polymorphism in time.

Neutral polymorphism is due to the action of alleles "approximately neutral as regards survival value." Ford (following Fisher) believes that this kind of polymorphism is relatively rare, because "the balance of advantage between a gene and its allelomorph must be extraordinarily exact in order to be effectively neutral." This reasoning may be correct in all the cases in which one of the alternative features has a definite survival value or at least is genetically linked with one. There is, however, considerable indirect evidence that most of the characters that are involved in polymorphism are completely neutral, as far as survival value is concerned. There is, for example, no reason to believe that the presence or absence of a band on a snail shell would be a noticeable selective advantage or disadvantage. Among the many species of birds which occur in several clear-cut color phases (Stresemann 1926 and later papers), there is, with one or two exceptions, no evidence for selective mating or any other advantage of any of the phases.

Even more convincing proof for the selective neutrality of the alternating characters is evidenced by the constancy of the proportions of the different variants in one population. The most striking case is that of the snails *Cepaea nemoralis* and *C. hortensis*, in which Diver (1929) found that the proportions of the various forms from Pleistocene deposits agree closely with those in colonies living today.

Gordon (unpublished work) also found a remarkable constancy of gene frequencies in wild populations of the Mexican fish *Platypoecilus maculatus*. Four collections have been made in the Rio Papaloapan. Sumicrast collected 13 specimens in 1869, Meek 68 fishes in 1902, and

TABLE 3

FREQUENCY OF FOUR COMMON GENES IN FOUR COLLECTIONS OF PLATYPOECILUS MACULATUS

YEAR OF COLLECTION	TOTAL NUMBER OF SPECIMENS	PERCENTAGE OF FOUR COLOR PHASES			
		Sp	p	P^o	P^{cc}
1869	13	7.7	30.8	0.0	15.4
1902	68	35.2	11.7	17.6	17.6
1932	101	21.8	14.7	18.9	14.9
1939	3,492	20.3	17.8	18.4	12.2

Dr. Myron Gordon 101 specimens in 1932 and more than 3,000 in 1939. The four most common color phases of the 1939 collection have been selected for Table 3.

The agreement is very close, if one considers the small size of the three earlier samples and the high number of possible variants. The symbols of the four variants are Sp (sex linked spots), p (absence of visible dominant autosomal gene), P^o (small spot), and P^cc (complete crescent). The autosomal spot genes (p, P^o, and P^cc) are allelic (Gordon and Fraser 1931).

Gerould (1941) found 16 percent white individuals in a collection of females of the yellow species *Colias philodice*, collected in 1911 in Hanover, New Hampshire. Among 161 females taken in the same locality twenty-nine years later (1940), again 11 percent were white. Neither is there in this species a seasonal fluctuation of this ratio. Kinsey (1941) states that within a period of ten years no change in the proportion of long-winged and short-winged individuals occurred in a population of gall wasps (*Biorrhiza eburnea*). Additional cases have been reported by Dobzhansky (1941a).

Balanced polymorphism is characterized by a stable optimum proportion of two or more forms, any departure from which in either direction constitutes a disadvantage. Ford (1940) discusses this at length. Timofeeff-Ressovsky (1940b) has reported on a highly interesting case of fluctuating balanced polymorphism in the lady bug *Adalia bipunctata*. The red phase prevails in spring populations of this beetle, while in fall populations the black phase is more common. More black than red beetles die during the winter. There is thus a balanced selection system in this species which works in favor of the red phase during winter and in favor of the black phase in summer.

Transient polymorphism is a temporary stage during the period of displacement of a gene by an allel usually of greater selective value. A period of transient polymorphism should be observable in any population in which an advantageous mutation has occurred which affects any of the visible characters. The rapid spread of industrial melanism in certain butterflies is usually explained on this basis. In birds, I know of three cases which might come under this heading.

The Pied Fantail (*Rhipidura flabellifera*) of New Zealand has a melanistic form (*fuliginosa*) which is fairly common on South Island. This black phase was unreported from North Island, N. Z., until 1864, but is believed to have since increased in numbers and range. Stresemann (1923) concludes, in view of the absence of migratory movements in this species, that black mutations have occurred and continue to occur spontaneously on North Island, with the result that the normal, pied phase is being replaced. Oliver (1930), however, considers the evidence as unsatisfactory, in view of the scarcity of the black phase on North Island. No better is the proof for transient polymorphism in the banana quit (*Coereba flaveola atrata*) of the West Indian island St. Vincent. Since 1903 the island has been visited by five or six collectors and bird students, all of whom found the normal (wild-colored) phase exceedingly rare or absent. However, the notes of an earlier collector (1878) seemed to indicate that he considered both phases about equally common. Lowe (1912), Stresemann (1926) and Meise (1928a) concluded from this evidence that the melanistic phase had largely replaced the normal phase between 1878 and 1903. The latest authorities (J. Bond *in litt.*) consider the early (1878) observations as very casual, and the case loses thereby most of its interest. It may be added that the black phase is also the common phase on the island of Grenada (although normal birds are fairly numerous at certain localities), "while only normal individuals are found on the Grenadines, even on Green Island, which is not much more than a stone's throw from Grenada" (J. Bond *in litt.*). Black races occur also on two other widely separated islands, Los Rogues and Los Testigos. More convincing is the case of an African Barbet (*Lybius torquatus*) (Salomonsen 1938). This species has a bright red head, which may become white with the loss of the red lipochrome. Such a white mutation has largely replaced the normal phase in southern Nyasaland. Among collections made between 1890 and 1900 in the Zomba district, about half the specimens belonged to the white-headed phase (*zombae*), while the others were of an intermediate, pinkish coloration. In 1932 J. Vincent failed to observe a single bird with red or pink head, among hundreds of birds that were encountered. There is little doubt that the white mutant (*zombae*) has, in this case, at least locally, completely replaced the original phase. Meise (1938:68) believes that this is due to the shifting of a hybrid zone.

GEOGRAPHICALLY VARIABLE POLYMORPHISM

Polymorphism can vary in space (geographically) as it can in time. Numerous cases have been described from most animal groups where a certain color phase occurs more frequently in one population of a species than in others. I shall content myself with treating, in more detail, cases that refer to birds, in particular those that have been encountered in my own work. As far as other animals are concerned, only such cases will be mentioned as have not yet been included in one of the above-cited collective treatments of the subject.

The term polymorphism may be applied, broadly speaking, whenever genetic factors break up a population into several classes, and it makes no difference whether the distinguishing characters concern visible morphological features or whether they relate to physiological, ecological, or other factors. The distribution of the gene arrangements in the third chromosome of race A of *Drosophila pseudoobscura* is a case of true polymorphism. The taxonomist, of course, studies, in general, only those cases that are accessible to him, that is, those which produce visible effects in structure or coloration.

The best-studied cases of polymorphism refer to color patterns. The European garden snails *Cepaea nemoralis* and *C. hortensis* may be without bands, or they may have five bands, or some of the five bands may be missing. The ground color of the shell may be whitish, yellowish, or pinkish. Four other variables in these species are: the order in which the bands appear in ontogeny, the width of the bands, the pigmentation of the bands, and the pigmentation of the lip. Each of these characters has a number of distinct expressions, and the number of possible phenotypes, due to the combinations of these factors, is almost unlimited. Some amateur collectors recognize and have named 208 varieties of *Cepaea nemoralis*. The interesting feature in this genus is (Rensch 1933) that there seems to be no significant geographic trend in this variation. Populations in Bohemia, in northern and in southern Germany may contain almost exactly the same proportions of the principal variant types, while populations that live only a few miles apart may have totally different compositions. In general, the geographical distribution of the forms in polymorphic populations and subspecies is not as irregular as in *Cepaea*. It is, in fact, the rule that in polymorphic species each geographic district is characterized by a different proportion of the various color phases.

In the reef heron *Demigretta sacra* three color phases are known to occur, which are irregularly distributed over the range of the species and the variation of which is independent of the size variation which also occurs in this species (Mayr and Amadon 1941). White birds comprise about 50 percent of the population of the Tuamotu Islands (Polynesia) and about 10-30 percent over most of the range of the species, but are absent or exceedingly rare on the Marquesas Islands, on New Caledonia, in South Australia, and on New Zealand. A third color form (mottled) is restricted to a continuous area from Micronesia to the Solomon Islands and Fiji, comprising about 15 percent of the individuals of these populations.

The hawk *Accipiter novaehollandiae* has a white phase in certain subspecies, which, however, is absent from all the twenty races which occur in the Lesser Sunda Islands, Moluccas, Biak, D'Entrecasteaux, the Louisiade and Bismarck Archipelagos, and the Solomon Islands. In New Guinea and in Australia both white and wild-type phases occur, while in Tasmania only the white phase is present. Not enough is known about the numerical proportion of the two phases in Australia and New Guinea to indicate whether or not a gradient in the proportions is involved.

The long-tailed New Guinea lory (*Charmosyna papou*) is divided into four subspecies three of which are very distinct, whereas one (*goliathina*) is slight. In three of these four geographic races a melanistic phase is known to occur (Stresemann 1926, with colored plate).

TABLE 4

DISTRIBUTION OF THE BLACK PHASE IN FOUR SUBSPECIES
OF CHARMOSYNA PAPOU

SUBSPECIES	LOCALITY	COLLECTORS	COLORED	BLACK	
				No.	%
papou	Arfak Mts.	Many	All	..	0.0
goliathina	Weyland Mts. (north)	Three	43	11	20.8
	Nassau Mts. (south)	Two	8	..	0.0
	Oranje Mts. (south)	Two	22	4	15.4
	Idenburg R. (north)	Rand	5	1	16.7
	L. Habbema (north)	Rand	2	20	90.9
	Schraderberg (north)	Bürgers	5	7	58.3
stellae	S.E. New Guinea	Many	55	3	5.2
	Herzog Mts.	Two	16	..	0.0
wahnesi	Huon Peninsula	Four	28	1	3.4

There are several interesting aspects of this variation. First of all, the black "gene" is apparently older than some of the races, since it occurs in three of the races, including the very distinct and isolated subspecies *wahnesi*. Furthermore, the black phase seems to be in the minority in all parts of New Guinea, except along the north slope of the central ranges, whence 83 percent of the known specimens come. The geographic variation of the two color phases is almost completely independent of the other subspecific characters of the species. Similar cases of geographically variable polymorphism have been described repeatedly in ornithological literature. Particularly interesting are the situations in the paradise flycatcher *Terpsiphone* (Stresemann 1924, Salomonsen 1933), and in the thrush *Copsychus* (Delacour 1931). M. Gordon (1941) found geographic variation in the proportion of different color patterns in the fish *Platypoecilus maculatus*.

Much more common and better studied is the geographical variation of polymorphism in insects. Dobzhansky (1933) has described the percentage occurrence of seven color variants in the Asiatic lady beetle *Harmonia axyridis*. All five of the major variants were present in apparently only three of thirteen examined populations, while in seven populations more than 80 percent of the individuals belonged to a single type. Ford (1940:503) quotes a considerable number of similar cases in butterflies, particularly in species in which the female is mimetic. Bovey (1941) has made a careful analysis of the color phases in *Zygaena ephialtes*. Some of the most interesting cases have been described from bumblebees (*Bombus*). We have an excellent recent review of their variation by Reinig (1939). The 3,000 described forms of *Bombus* belong to 300 species, 1,200 subspecies, and 1,500 individual variants. Some species have 30 and more described variants, of which as many as 7 or more may occur in a single locality. In other parts of the range of such species only a single variant is found.

Polymorphism is not restricted to coloration, but may also affect structure, as for example, the spiraling of snail shells. In many species of snails some individuals of a population are sinistrally spiraled, others dextrally (Crampton, Diver).

In birds we have some structural polymorphism in regard to the presence or absence of skin wattles and similar epidermal structures. In the honey-eater *Melidectes belfordi*, the race from southeastern New Guinea (*belfordi*) has only a cheek wattle, the race *rufocrissalis* from the Sepik Mountains has both a cheek and a throat wattle, while the subspecies *stresemanni* from the Herzog Mountains is polymorphic. Four specimens in a series of 8 birds have both wattles, while in 4 others the cheek wattle only is present. Structural polymorphism is common in insects, affecting the sculpture of the elytra, the wing venation, the number of teeth in the sex-comb, and so forth.

The point which must be emphasized is that in all these cases the proportion of the variants is different in various local populations. It occurs not infrequently that one of the several forms of a polymorphic species may become the dominant or even the exclusive variant in a particular section of the range of the species. From this phenomenon it is only a small step to the formation of clear-cut and well-segregated subspecies. For example, let us assume that a polymorphic species has the three forms n, w, and e. Let us also assume that N is the common form in the northern parts of the range, W in the western and southwest, and E in the eastern and southeastern. If eventually the unbalanced frequency of N, W, and E should reach the point where these forms occur in the three districts of the species to the exclusion of the other two forms, the taxonomist would consider this species to have three well defined sub-species: N, W, and E (Fig. 9).

The geneticist believes that most subspecific variation actually origi-nates in this manner. Such an origin is usually not obvious, since the genetic basis of the subspecific differences is, in most cases, more com-plex, involving multiple gene differences as well as chromosomal changes. Therefore, instead of finding clear-cut types, as in polymorphic species, we find complete intergradation. Only where subspecies differ by a simple alternative character can we hope to prove that they must have gone through a stage of transient polymorphism, which lasted from the time at which the "new" character made its first appearance in a population until the time when it completely replaced the "old" character.

Fig. 9. Diagram illustrating the probable role of transient poly-morphism in subspecies formation.

The hawk *Accipiter novaehollandiae* is now passing through this proc-ess. The white phase has completely replaced the normal one in the Tasmanian population, while in Australia and New Guinea the white phase is still restricted to a part of the population. Another interesting case is presented by the Solomon Islands flycatcher *Monarcha castaneo-ventris*. All of its races have a chestnut abdomen, except *ugiensis* from Ugi and St. Anna islands, which is entirely black. However, in a series of 28 specimens of *ugiensis* in the American Museum of Natural His-tory there is a single specimen with all the other racial characters of this form (large size, and so forth) but with a chestnut belly. On the other hand, among 33 specimens of the race *obscurior* from the Pavuvu Islands, there is a single all-black specimen which, at least in this re-spect, reveals the hidden potentialities of *ugiensis*.

In the Ugi and Pavuvu populations of *Monarcha castaneoventris* we can thus discover the last traces of a transient polymorphism. In the majority of the cases, however, in which geographic races differ by the kind of characters which might well be alternative features in poly-morphic populations, the difference is absolute and not merely meristic. Each character is associated with and restricted to one particular geographic area. There can be no intermediates, and this is why we find such typical cases only in species with well-isolated, that is insular populations.

Several of the other races of *Monarcha castaneoventris* are characterized by this type of variation (Fig. 10). All the males from the Central

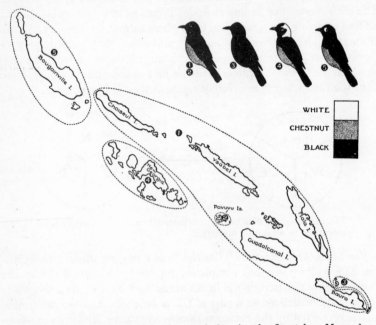

Fig. 10. Discontinuous geographic variation in the flycatcher *Monarcha castaneoventris* from the Solomon Islands. Four principal color patterns are represented among the six recognized subspecies: 1 = *castaneoventris* and *megarhyncha*; 2 = *obscurior*; 3 = *ugiensis*; 4 = *richardsii*; 5 = *erythrosticta*. An initial and a final stage of transient polymorphism occur in the subspecies *obscurior* and *ugiensis*.

Solomon Islands (New Georgia group, and others) are of the *richardsi* (4) type of coloration, which is characterized by a white collar; and all of the birds from the Bougainville group are of the *erythrophthalmus* (5) type, in which males have a white, females a tawny spot in front of the eye. A similar distribution of color patterns is very common among island birds. It has been described from the genera *Pachycephala*, *Myzomela*, *Rhipidura*, and others (Mayr *et al.* 1931ff.) and is also well illustrated in the *Turdus poliocephalus* group (Fig. 8).

This mode of strictly discontinuous geographic variation of alternative characters is much rarer in continental regions and also restricted more or less to species with well-isolated subspecies, such as are particularly common in mountain animals. The New Guinea birds of paradise and the Andean hummingbirds offer many splendid illustrations. A particularly diagrammatic case is presented by the Asiatic bulbul *Microscelis leucocephalus*. Since all the races of this species are very much alike as to size, proportions, and general structure, most of the variation is caused by a varying combination of only three colors (white, gray, black). According to the distribution of these colors in the various parts of the body, six very distinct combinations are produced (Fig. 11).

TABLE 5

RACES OF *Microscelis leucocephalus*

TYPE	RACE	RANGE	HEAD THROAT	BREAST	BACK BELLY	WING
1	*psaroides*, and relatives	India Ceylon Burma	gray	gray	gray	gray
2	*stresemanni*	Yunnan	white	white	gray	gray
3	*leucothorax*	Szechuan	white	white	*black*	*gray-black*
4	*leucocephalus*	S. China	white	*black*	*black*	*black*
5	*nigerrimus*	Formosa	*black*	*black*	*black*	gray
6	*perniger*	Hainan	*black*	*black*	*black*	*black*

FIG. 11. Geographic variation in *Microscelis leucocephalus*.

These forms show little variation whenever they are isolated on is-lands (Hainan, Formosa) or on the mountain ranges that radiate from the Himalayas into southeastern Asia. But we find populations that are composed of a medley of hybrid forms where several of these forms come in contact with one another, which occurs in a broad belt stretching from eastern Burma to central China south of the Yangtse River. It is possible to find types 1, 3, 4, and 6, as illustrated, as well as all inter mediate stages, in a single local interbreeding population.

CONTINUOUS VARIATION

In cases of polymorphism and discontinuous variation we can dis-tinguish a number of clear-cut variants within each species. There are, however, numerous other species without such striking differences. They show, instead, gliding intergradation between the characters of the in-dividuals of one population as well as between neighboring populations and subspecies. This so-called continuous variation affects most fre-quently the total size of the animal, or the relative and absolute size of parts, or various degrees and shades of coloration, characters which are particularly prone to vary geographically. Continuous variation is a typical mode of geographic variation in most animals with continuous ranges in continental areas. In contradistinction, we might expect, and we actually find that continuous geographic variation is rare or ab-sent in those species whose range is broken up into well-isolated popula-tions, as for example in tropical archipelagos or on mountain peaks.

Continuous variation belongs to the class of quantitative variation and can therefore best be studied in characters that can be measured, counted, or otherwise expressed in figures. Any such study requires the collecting of reasonably large numbers of specimens throughout the range of the species, the measuring of the variables in these specimens, and finally the statistical analysis of such measurements. There is the additional difficulty that completely reliable measurements can be made only in animals with rigid exoskeletons. These methodological difficul-ties are the reason that so few good studies have so far been made in this field, quite aside from the fact that most taxonomists are over-burdened with other, more pressing tasks. Blair (1941) took four meas-urements (length of body, foot, parotoid gland, and so forth) on about 5,000 specimens of several species of North American toads, of which 1,553 were adult *Bufo fowleri* from twenty-five localities. He found that each local population was characterized by a different set of constants, that the measurements for body size, absolute foot size, parotoid gland length, and parotoid gland width varied irregularly within the range of the species, and that the relative foot length and the amount of dorsal spotting tended to increase from the southwestern to the northeastern portion of the range. No pronounced breaks in the character combinations were noticeable anywhere, that is, there were no striking discontinuities. This is probably the reason why no subspecies are recognized in *Bufo fowleri*, in spite of the distinct geographic variation. Intergradation between the subspecies of a species is frequently of the same continuous (gliding) character as between the populations of *Bufo*. This has been described by numerous authors, and I shall limit myself to quoting one particularly well-analyzed case (Dice 1940c):

There is a broad area of intergradation across North Dakota between the small, dark-colored, eastern subspecies, *Peromyscus maniculatus bairdii*, and the larger, paler-colored, western subspecies *osgoodi*. The transformation of the characters of *bairdii* to those of *osgoodi* is correlated with the increase in elevation, with the decrease in the amount of precipitation, with the more arid character of the vegetation, and with the increasing paleness of the surface soil from east to west in North Dakota. The intergradation between *bairdii* and *osgoodi* which occurs in North Dakota is, however, not a gradual, progressive change from one form to the other. On the contrary, the transition between the two forms often is obscured or locally reversed by the general occurrence of local races which depart more or less from the expected gradient of change.

In birds only few good studies have been made on population differences within subspecies and on the variation in the zone of contact between two subspecies. A. H. Miller's study of *Junco* populations (1941) is, perhaps, the finest study of this sort in ornithological literature, although many of the populations of this species group are isolated and the variation discontinuous.

ADAPTIVE VARIATION

Students of Holarctic birds and mammals observed, as much as one hundred years ago, that many of these small differences between local populations were obviously correlated with environmental conditions and they concluded, therefore, that they were "adaptations." The word adaptation has, unfortunately, somewhat of a double meaning, according to whether one sees in adaptation a process or the result of a process, in other words, whether one considers adaptation as something active or passive. Whenever the words adaptive or adaptation occur in the following discussion, they are used in a descriptive sense to indicate the result of a selective process.

However, it should not be assumed that all the differences between populations and species are purely adaptational and that they owe their existence to their superior selective qualities. We have already pointed out the fallacy of such a point of view in the discussion of neutral polymorphism. Many combinations of color patterns, spots, and bands, as well as extra bristles and wing veins, are probably largely accidental. This is particularly true in regions with many stationary, small, and well-isolated populations, such as we find commonly in tropical and insular species. We shall not enter, at this point, into a discussion of the problem of the evolutionary prosperity of characters that either have no selective value or that seem to cause selective disadvantages (Ludwig 1940), but we must stress the point that not all geographic variation is adaptive.

Directly selective characters.—If the color of an animal agrees with the background on which it lives, the survival value of this adaptation is obvious. Most smaller animals, such as insects, that show such adaptations agree in color and live on a specific part of a plant (leaves, bark, and so forth), and these color variants are therefore not geographically restricted. Geographic races can develop on the basis of the background adaptation in all those cases in which regionally restricted soil coloration is involved.

The Palearctic larks (Alaudidae) were the first birds in which this correlation between soil and coloration was discovered. These larks live on steppes and other regions with scanty vegetation and are obviously very vulnerable to predation in this exposed habitat. Hartert, Kleinschmidt, and others have called attention repeatedly to the minute agreement in color between some of the races, particularly in the genus *Galerita*, and the soil on which they live. Meinertzhagen (1924) discovered on a lava flow in eastern Syria a blackish lark (*Ammomanes deserti annae*), which was sandwiched in between two pale sand-colored subspecies that live in the sandy desert. "On these dark flint stones [of the lava flow] the *Ammomanes* were scarcely visible, so exactly did the plumage of their back resemble the color of the flint, but the pale sandy-colored *Eremophila* [migratory Horned Lark] could be spotted at many hundred yards distance."

Niethammer (1940) reviews the literature on cryptically colored larks, and his paper should be consulted for further details. In a series of colored plates, he illustrates the close correlation between soil and coloration of southwest African larks. The most remarkable part of this adaptation is that not only the general tone of color is reproduced accurately in the bird, but also its physical quality. The birds will have a smooth, even coloration, if they live on a fine-grained, dusty, or sandy soil. If, on the other hand, they live on a pebble desert, they will have a coarse disruptive pattern of coloration. Even more remarkable is the fact that the birds become very much attached to the soil to which they are adapted (see p. 247).

Most mammals are nocturnal and are therefore not as continuously exposed to predation as desert birds. It seems as if they were not quite as well adapted to their backgrounds as some of the larks. On the other hand, it is much easier to obtain them in quantities, and the background adaptation of mammals has therefore been even better analyzed than that of birds. Following the pioneer work of Sumner (1932) on desert races of *Peromyscus* and Benson's (1933) studies of melanistic rodents on lava flows, Dice and his coworkers have devoted themselves recently to a detailed analysis of these adaptations (Dice and Blossom 1937).

The most important conclusion of these studies, as already maintained by Kleinschmidt and other ornithologists more than thirty years ago, is that this adaptive coloration cannot be due to climatic influences (or only to a negligible degree), since the blackest races (on lava flows) occur sometimes in the immediate vicinity of the palest races (in sand-dune areas). It is obvious that selection by predators must have played an important role in the evolution of these localized color races. The selective value of the white arctic coloration is obvious in animals that are subject to predation, but it seems likely that the white color of arctic predators was developed in a more indirect manner. Direct background selection of microgeographic races has also been demonstrated for a number of insects, particularly grasshoppers. Hovanitz (1940) has analyzed a case in a Californian butterfly.

Complex (indirect) selective factors.—In cases of background adaptation of desert rodents or larks, there can be little argument as to the nature of the selective factors or the survival value of the adapted animals. Dice and Blossom (1937) extend this conclusion to the color differences found between animals of arid and humid regions. They note that the soil in humid regions is darker, owing to its high humus content, and claim, therefore, that this favors the selection of dark-colored races, exactly like lava flows. The darkening of the soil in humid regions may or it may not be responsible for the parallel darkening of local populations of ground mammals, but this factor can certainly not be held responsible for the darkening of bats, and of bush and tree birds. These animals do not show the close correlation between their color and that of the soil, as shown by larks or rodents; still, they tend to be much less pigmented in arid areas.

The fact that this change in pigmentation parallels a number of other changes is very suggestive of a more generalized effect of climate, rather than of the specific selective action of predators. If we find, for example, that nearly all endemic races of British birds (and also most of the Japanese) are smaller and darker than the corresponding mainland races, we are tempted to correlate this with the humid and uniform insular climate. If we find that desert hawks are much paler than the races from more humid districts, we are forced to the conclusion that it cannot be background selection by predators that caused this trend. A direct selective or adaptational value is not particularly obvious for most of the characters that are subject to such climatic adaptation. We must rather assume that the inheritance of general size or of the degree and kind of pigmentation is correlated with some organ (let us say the thyroid or pituitary) the variation of which is of selective value. It is therefore possible and probable that many of these characters are due to the effects of pleiotropic genes.

The following example will illustrate their importance:

When the genes underlying various coat color and hair form varieties of the Norway rat are displayed upon a fairly uniform residual hereditary background, they are found not only to affect bodily weight but also the dimensions of body and skull, size of the various glands, weight of the brain and its parts, degree of wildness, degree of savageness, amount of voluntary exercise taken, and those complex characteristics of behavior that may be termed "personality."

Reduction of the size of olfactory bulbs (with probable loss of acuity of smell), reduction in brain size, reduction in the amount of exercise taken, tameness and docility found in the King inbred albino rat and formerly thought to be the "marks of domestication" impressed upon it by many generatîons in captivity, are shown to be due principally to the multiple effects of three coat color genes determining hooded, black, and albinism, respectively, for which three genes King inbred albino rat is purebred. (Keeler and King 1941).

ECOLOGICAL RULES

The modern taxonomist compares samples of local populations (series) of a species with each other, in order to determine the geographic variation. One of the most important generalizations to be derived from this work is the establishment of so-called ecological rules. It was found, as was to be expected if we believe in the influence of natural selection, that many species show parallel variation under parallel conditions. We have already mentioned that animals tend to become dark in humid climates and pale in arid climates. In warm-blooded species the populations that live in a cooler climate tend to be larger than those that live in a warm district. The subject is by no means new, since Gloger devoted to it, as early as 1833, an entire book of 159 pages: *The Variation of Birds under the Influence of Climate*. Bergmann, J. A. Allen, and others made notable contributions during the nineteenth century, but it was Rensch (1929, 1933, 1936, 1938a, 1938c, 1939b) who gathered all this scattered information and formulated a series of "ecological rules." Unfortunately, he quoted these rules in his earlier writings (1929–1933) as evidence for a direct (Lamarckian) influence of climate on geographic variation, and this has caused some of his adversaries to reject the rules as invalid or meaningless. A healthy compromise has since been reached concerning the existence and the causes of the regularities on which these rules are based, and nearly every student of natural variation now admits their importance. They deserve detailed discussion.

Widespread species live in many different environments. The extreme case in birds is probably that of the raven, *Corvus corax*, which is found from the icy wastes of Greenland to the heart of the Sahara and the Arabian desert. It must be adapted in each region to its specific environment. However, the raven is not a "plastic" bird, and the populations from all these regions are not very different. The desert birds are more brownish, and the birds in the Far North are larger, with a relatively smaller bill. Geographic variation and the correlation between environment and taxonomic characters is much more striking in many other birds and animals.

The correlation between environmental factors and the geographic variation of an animal may not become apparent until a detailed analysis is made. The size variation of *Cacatua galerita triton* (Fig. 2) seems exceedingly haphazard and irregular, but close study shows that (with the exception of the Biak population) all the populations that are found on small and flat islands in the hot tropical sea, or near the seacoast, or on large hot lowland plains are of small size, while the populations that live on large mountainous islands or in mountainous districts of the mainland are of large size. It is therefore obvious that even the seemingly irregular variation of *Cacatua* follows the general temperature rule that in warm-blooded land animals the populations in the cooler districts are of larger size than populations of the same species in warmer districts.

A careful study of the geographic variation of the characters of animals of various taxonomic groups has led to the establishment of a number of rules. We shall refrain from more detailed treatment, since there are a number of admirable recent summaries (Rensch 1936, 1938a, 1939b).

RULES APPLYING TO WARM-BLOODED VERTEBRATES

Bergmann's rule.—The smaller-sized geographic races of a species are found in the warmer parts of the range, the larger-sized races in the cooler districts. The reasons for exceptions to this rule are but rarely apparent. The depth of the soil was found to be the decisive factor in the case of a burrowing mammal. High-altitude populations of a species of pocket gophers (*Thomomys*) from Idaho, Nevada, and other western states are of smaller size than the populations from lower altitudes and particularly from the fertile valleys. The selective force of the shallow soils and the short growing season at the higher altitude was thus stronger than the temperature factor. The various dwarf mountain races are not closely related because the geological history indicates that each of the mountains was settled from the neighboring valley (Davis 1938). The size variation of meadow mice (*Microtus*) also seems to be largely independent of local temperature factors (Dale 1940). The number of exceptions in Palearctic Passerine birds is about 16 percent (Rensch 1939b).

Allen's rule.—Protruding body parts, such as tails, ears, bills, extremities, and so forth, are relatively shorter in the cooler parts of the range of the species than in the warmer parts.

Gloger's rule.—The melanins increase in the warm and humid parts of the range. Reddish or yellowish-brown phaeomelanins prevail in arid climates where the blackish eumelanins are reduced. The phaeomelanins are subject to reduction in cold climate, and in extreme cases also the eumelanin (polar white).

Frank (1938) has demonstrated the validity of this rule very neatly by a microscopic analysis of the feather pigments of *Parus atricapillus* (Fig. 12). Mayr and Serventy (1938) illustrated its effect on the subspecies of Australian warblers (*Acanthiza*). A similar correlation between climate and pigment holds in many insect groups, as demonstrated for *Polistes* by Zimmermann (1931), for Bembidiinae by Netolitzky (1931), for Coccinellids by Dobzhansky (1933), and for California butterflies by Hovanitz (1941a).

RULES APPLYING TO BIRDS ONLY

1. The races of a species which live in the cooler parts of the range of that species lay more eggs per clutch than the races in the warmer parts of the range (Rensch 1938c).

2. Stomach, intestines, and caeca of birds that live on a mixed diet are relatively smaller in the tropical than in the temperate-zone races (Rensch 1931).

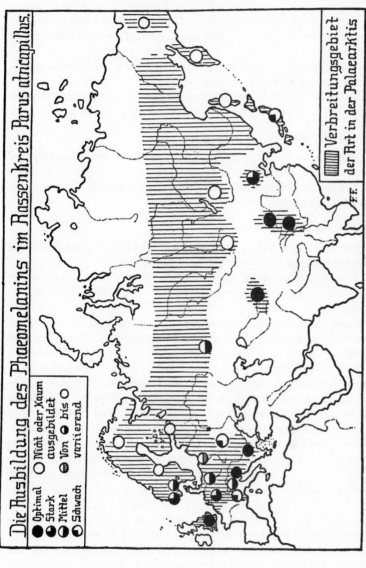

Die Ausbildung des Phaeomelanins im Rassenkreis Parus atricapillus.

Optimal ● Nicht oder kaum ausgebildet ○
Stark ◐
Mittel ◑ Von ● bis ○
Schwach ◔ variierend

Verbreitungsgebiet der Art in der Palaearktis

F.F.

FIG. 12. The geographic variation of phaeomelanin pigmentation in the titmouse *Parus atricapillus*. The range of species is indicated by shading. The amount of phaeomelanin decreases from south to north. (From Frank 1938.)

3. The wings of races that live in a cold climate or in the high mountains are relatively longer than those of the races which live in the lowlands or in a warm climate (Rensch 1936, 1938c, Meise 1938, Stresemann 1941, Rand 1936).

4. Races in the cooler climates are more often and more strongly migratory than the more southerly races.

5. Island birds have longer bills than related mainland races (Murphy 1938:538). This is possibly only a special case of Allen's rule.

Rules Applying to Mammals Only

1. The races in the warmer climates have less under fur and shorter contour hairs (Rensch 1936).

2. The number of young in a litter averages higher in the cooler climates (Rensch 1936).

Rules Applying to Snails

1. Land snails reach their greatest size in the area of optimum climate within the range of the species (Rensch 1932).

2. The relative weight of the shell is highest in the forms exposed to the highest radiation of the sun (insolation) or to the greatest aridity (Rensch 1932).

3. Land snails tend to have smooth glassy brown shells in cold climates, to have white or strongly sculptured shells in hot dry climates (Rensch 1932).

Klemm (1939), in a study of the species of the genus *Pagodulina*, finds, in accordance with the above rule (3), that the ribs on the outer surface of the shells are broader at the more southerly localities and narrower at higher altitudes. It is obvious that temperature (or speed of growth in connection with temperature) is the decisive factor in this variation, and not direct sun radiation or moisture, since these snails always live in the shade and in moist places. In some instances collections from the same localities, made one hundred years apart, were compared and showed no tangible differences. Knipper (1939) tested the rules established by Rensch on the Helicidae of southeastern Europe and found them confirmed. In regard to size variation he finds that each species seems to have, in its range, an "optimal" district, in which the species reaches its maximum dimensions. These optimum districts are different for every species, because no two species are adapted to an identical set of conditions, some being xerophilous, others hygrophilous, some warm-, and some cold-adapted. Many alpine species reach their smallest dimensions near the upper altitudinal limit of their range. The lower limit of distribution of such species is often determined by lack of humidity rather than by high temperature. Hence the maximum size is reached in such species near the lower limit of the range. The southern forms are generally larger in moisture-loving species than the northern forms, provided there is enough moisture available. Exceptions are not rare, particularly on islands where large-sized and small-sized races are found on neighboring islands. Knipper also tries to correlate climate with the following other characters of shells (*op. cit.*, p. 510): the size of the shell mouth, the presence or absence of teeth and hair, the form of the shell (proportion of length and width), the number of whorls, and so forth. Many of these correlations are but poorly established, particularly since the ecological background against which the races have developed is insufficiently known, and since it is probable that some of these variations are phenotypical. Kaltenbach (1936) examined the snails of post-glacial marl deposits covering the period from 20,000 B.C. to modern times. In many species there is a definite correlation between the size of the shells of a certain stratum and the climate of that period. Welch (1938) finds a definite correlation between altitude and both pigmentation and size in the Hawaiian snail *Achatinella mustelina*.

Most species of animals have not yet been studied intensively enough to enable us to formulate definite ecological rules, even though certain adaptational correlations are obvious. Hubbs (1940a) points out that a very close correlation exists in fresh-water fish between environment and body form. Populations of the same species that live in swift waters have different shapes and growth forms than those of slow waters. It may be mentioned, however, that in fish some of these differences seem to be purely phenotypical. *Ambystoma tigrinum* in Colorado are darker in higher altitudes (Myers 1939). Krumbiegel (1932, 1936a,b,c) shows the rather close correlation between environment and characters in many species of *Carabus*. It has not yet been possible to formulate definite rules on the basis of regularities in the size variation of cold-blooded marine animals (Rensch 1939b, Wimpenny 1941).

The existence of additional ecological rules has been suspected, but it is not certain that the evidence is not merely the expression of phenotypical modifications. It concerns the decrease of size with the decrease of salinity in certain marine animals, the reduction of the number of fin rays in warmer oceans, the numbers of caudals and ventrals in snakes, and so forth. The study of these ecological correlations and the establishment of definite rules is such a new field that we may consider ourselves merely at the beginning of the work.

All these ecological rules have exceptions, a point Rensch has emphasized again and again. While most birds and mammals grow larger in the more northerly parts of the range, there are some species which get smaller. If birds of higher altitudes differ in size from lowland populations, they are generally larger. Rand (1936) found only one exception (*Pitohui dichrous*) to this rule among New Guinea birds. Rensch has worked out the number of exceptions statistically and has shown that they are under 25 percent for most of the ecological rules.

In addition to the exceptions, in which the variation runs in the opposite direction to that expected on the basis of the rules, we also have numerous cases in which there is no variation at all, at least none that is connected with the rules. Dice (1939b), on the basis of careful measurements of a number of populations of *Peromyscus maniculatus*, found no consistent difference in size "between the stocks from the mountain forest, and those from the bunch-grass and sage brush of lower elevation. Long skulls or long tails seem as likely to occur in stocks from arid habitats as in those from the mountain forest." It may be mentioned, however, that in this case all the localities were within a radius of about one hundred miles and that even the forest was rather arid.

There are not enough of these exceptions to invalidate the important ecological rules, which are of twofold value to the taxonomist. They help him in organizing his material and also prove the intimate correlation between environment and the characters of animals—in other words, they prove the existence of adaptation.

It should be mentioned, to avoid misunderstandings, that these rules apply only to *intraspecific* variation. The larger individuals are favored in the colder parts of the range, according to Bergmann's rule. This does not mean, however, that the largest-sized species will be concentrated in the arctic and the pigmies in the tropics. There are some definite ecological regularities which reach beyond the species level (white arctic species, metallic-colored tropical birds, and so forth), but nobody seems to have had the courage as yet to establish definite rules and to test their validity statistically.

CLINES

Each population is more or less adapted, as we have seen, to the particular environment in which it lives. Neighboring environments are similar, and we might therefore expect that neighboring populations would be similar in their external and internal characters. This has been found to be true in areas in which there are no striking environmental changes. In such areas, as for example in neighboring continental districts or on chains of islands, each local climate intergrades with the neighboring ones to form one continuous gradient. It has also been found, as we would expect from these premises, that such morphological characters as tend to be correlated with climatic factors—as, for example, size, proportions, and pigmentation—show a similar and parallel gradient. Huxley (1939) has introduced the term "cline" for such character gradients. The existence of clines, which has been known to the naturalist for more than one hundred years, is a necessity, if we believe in the adaptive power of natural selection by the environment. Huxley has given a detailed and rather complete summary of the field, and it seems superfluous to cover the same ground. Clines have been studied in a number of additional recent works. Blair (1941) found that in the two species of North American toads, *Bufo fowleri* and *B. americanus,* a parallel cline exists for two characters, relative length of foot and amount of dorsal spotting. Five other measurable characters in these species show no indication of cline formation. Ticehurst (1938a) found clines affecting the shape of the wing in two eastern Asiatic species of warblers. In both cases the northernmost race has the most pointed wing (Rensch's wing rule). In *Phylloscopus proregulus* the southernmost race (*chloronotus*) has the second primary longer than the ninth in 9 percent of the individuals, in the intermediate race *kansuensis* in 37 percent, and in the northernmost race (*proregulus*) in 97 percent. In the species *Phylloscopus trochiloides* the respective figures for the equivalent three races are 12 percent, 68 percent, and 100 percent.

The percentage of certain color phases in neighboring populations may also change in clinal progression. Southern (1939) showed this for the bridled form of the Atlantic murre. Cowan (1938) analyzed fur-trade data and found that the percentage of the dark forms in the black bear and red fox decreased from the humid and cold north (British Columbia) to the drier and warmer south. The data of seven stations are included in Table 6.

TABLE 6

CLINAL VARIATION OF POLYMORPHISM

SPECIES	PHASE	PERCENTAGE, BY STATIONS							CHANGE FROM NORTH TO SOUTH
		1	2	3	4	5	6	7	
Black bear	Brown phase	7	7	7	21	40	58	63	Increase
Red fox	Black phase	19	25	14	6	8	3	1	Decrease
	Cross phase	46	45	34	34	25	17	16	Decrease
	Red phase	35	30	52	60	67	80	83	Increase

Very few clines have been studied in detail. Dice (1940c, 1941) examined the clines which exist between two races of the deermouse (*Peromyscus maniculatus*) (Dakota, Nebraska). He found that there was no question about the general trend of the cline, but that this trend was often locally reversed. Krumbiegel (1936a,b) found the same to be true for several character gradients in *Carabus*. It is probable that clines represent only the averages of a fluctuating trend.

Frequently the clinal character seems to be quite independent of environmental gradients; it seems, rather, to indicate the gradual declinin the frequency of one of two alternative characters from the center of its distribution. A striking illustration of this kind of cline was given by Zimmermann (1935) for a certain tooth structure of a German mouse. Likewise it is difficult to see why the gradual decrease from the north to the south in the number of the bridled individuals (*ringvia*) in populations of the Atlantic murre (*Uria aalge*) should have an adaptational significance (Southern 1939). In some of these cases it is not the proportion of several characters which changes in a regular manner, but one entire character.

A particularly good case of this type of variation is presented by the Bird of Paradise of eastern New Guinea, where in the races of *salvadorii-raggiana-intermedia-granti-augustaevictoriae* the amount of yellow on the back increases and the intensity of red in the plumes decreases as we proceed along this series of races (Fig. 13). Since the entire change of the back color occurs in the red-plumed birds, and the entire change of the plumes in the yellow-backed birds, it is probable that the two processes are largely independent of each other. The convergent development in several species of *Draco* also seems to belong to the category of nonadaptive clines (Hennig 1936b).

Similar character gradients, seemingly largely independent of environmental gradients, are known to me in a number of tropical species. The interpretation of such cases would have to be based on the instability of certain genes and on the loss of alleles in the border populations of an expanding species. It is probable, however, that selective factors are involved to some extent, even in these cases.

There has been some doubt concerning the evolutionary significance of clines. Goldschmidt seems to believe that geographic speciation is plausible only if species formation is correlated with clines. He says (1940: 141): "The Darwinian incipient species makes sense, therefore, only if the track leading to specific differences is a continuation of the subspecific clines. Otherwise any isolated population would potentially be an incipient species." The possibility expressed in the last sentence is, of course, a fact, and this invalidates Goldschmidt's argument. Indeed we might even go further than that. Clines occur most commonly and most typically where continuous series of populations are found, such as in unbroken continental areas. However, as soon as isolating factors appear, we encounter discontinuities, and the greater the distributional

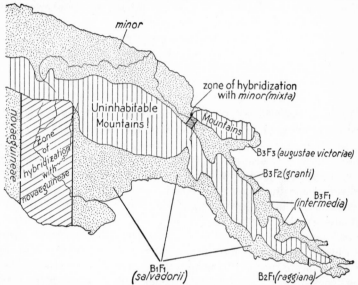

FIG. 13. Independent variation of two characters in *Paradisaea apoda* in New Guinea. A cline that is independent of environmental gradients. B = coloration of back. B_1 = entire back brown, B_2 = upper back yellow, lower back brown, B_3 = entire back yellow. F = coloration of the plumes (flank feathers). F_1 = plumes red, F_2 = plumes orange-red, F_3 = plumes orange. Diagonal hatching indicates hybrid zones. (From Mayr 1940a.)

discontinuities are, the more pronounced are also the irregularities in the character patterns. Clines indicate continuities, but, since species formation requires discontinuities, we might formulate a rule which, in a way, is just the opposite to Goldschmidt's statement quoted above: *The more clines found in a region, the less active is species formation.* We can prove this if we compare regions in which clines are frequent with areas in which they are rare (Mayr 1940a). In continuous areas of temperate-zone continents, with numerous clines, there are far fewer signs of active species formation than in tropical archipelagos or other areas with insular species ranges.

The significance of clines lies in a different field. The fact that neighboring populations respond accurately to the small climatic differences that exist between their respective habitats indicates the extreme sensitivity of the process of natural selection. Moreover, the exact knowledge of clines in one species will often give the taxonomist valuable clues as to the kind of geographic variation he may expect in other species with similar ranges.

Clines exist also in plants, as has been proven in a number of recent studies. The study of these gradients is, however, impeded by the fact that plants are of course strictly sedentary, and local conditions therefore tend to obscure the more general trends.

POPULATION STRUCTURE AND VARIATION

The practical aims of taxonomy demand that the subdivisions of the species, where such exist, be well-limited and well-defined units. The picture of the species, as presented by the taxonomist, is, however, not necessarily a very accurate rendering of the situation as it exists in nature. It is merely due to the need of the museum worker to identify every individual and to place it in a definite pigeonhole. The species of the taxonomist, is like a jigsaw puzzle, consisting of a certain number of definite, clearly delimited, individual pieces. The species of nature is usually much more complicated, and all the work that we have reviewed indicates that even the infraspecific categories, such as the subspecies, are by no means the final "atoms" of the species. They are still composite units consisting of small local populations, each of which differs noticeably or statistically from other local populations. The taxonomist may be content with resolving the species into subspecies, but the student of speciation wants to go to the bottom of things, and this means a study of these basic populations.

The most fundamental questions that present themselves during such an investigation are: What rules can be formulated relating to the changes from population to population? Are these changes gradual, or are there areas consisting of rather similar and uniform populations, bordered sharply by another region inhabited by populations with a different character combination? It would lead too far to review the entire pertinent literature, but it is clear that it is necessary to study individual traits in order to obtain a reliable answer to these questions. Such studies reveal that the character gradients are nearly always sloping (widespread uniform populations seem to be rare), but that these slopes tend to be considerably steeper along certain zones. The taxonomist is likely to simplify such a situation and call an area of steepened slope a zone of intergradation between two uniform subspecies. Such simplification may be justified in a purely taxonomic study, but it may lead to erroneous conclusions in a study of speciation. To begin with, the term intergradation is purely descriptive, meaning that two reasonably distinct units come into contact and gradually merge in the area under consideration. The term intergradation reveals nothing as to the character of the intermediate populations or the history of the factors that caused the two units to diverge originally. This is the reason two different kinds of phenomena are consistently confused, in taxonomic literature, under the name intergradation, two phenomena which may be exceedingly similar in appearance, but which are the result of two entirely different biological processes. I call these two phenomena "primary" and "secondary" intergradation. The time has not yet come when we can analyze every situation of intermediacy and label it as primary or secondary; in fact, even the definition of these terms must be considered as entirely tentative, but we cannot hope to make any headway in this field unless we at least attempt a classification.

Primary intergradation exists if the steepening of the slope developed gradually and took place while all the populations involved were in continuous contact.

Secondary intergradation refers to cases in which the two units, now connected by a steeply sloping character gradient, were separated completely at one time and have now come into contact again after a number of differences have evolved.

Primary intergradation in a mild form occurs, of course, almost anywhere in the range of a species, since no two local populations are exactly identical in their genetic and taxonomic attributes. A taxonomist speaks, in general, of a zone of intergradation only if he encounters regions with a noticeable change in the populations. Such zones of fairly abrupt primary intergradation are quite frequent; they occur repeatedly in nearly every species, but little is known about their origin. It is possible that such a steepening of the slope can develop in a zone in which a particularly abrupt change of environmental factors occurs. It is also possible that certain gene combinations (the "adaptive peaks" of Sewall Wright) have a much greater survival value than others and that an abrupt steepening of the character gradient may develop in the zone in which one balanced and successful gene combination changes into the next one. The existence of zones of primary intergradation due to inferior gene combinations is, at present, entirely hypothetical. It is not known whether the slope in a zone of primary intergradation can become continuously steeper, up to the point where one species breaks into two. It seems unlikely, on the basis of our knowledge of gene dispersal, that this would happen without other isolating mechanisms becoming involved.

Zones of secondary intergradation, or zones of hybridization, as the taxonomist prefers to call them, are also of frequent occurrence. They are generally recognizable by a high degree of individual variation. A more detailed discussion of these zones of secondary intergradation, which are caused by the elimination of a former isolating factor, will be presented in a later chapter (p. 263).

The above picture applies only to continuous populations in continental areas. Populations that are more or less strictly isolated from neighboring populations, as on islands or mountains, generally exhibit the following phenomena:

1. The appearance of marked discontinuities in taxonomic characters, as compared to neighboring geographically representative populations.

2. The development of aberrant traits, often of a nonadaptive character, rare or absent in other parts of the range of the species.

3. Increasing divergence of the isolated form, with increasing effectiveness fo isolation and decreasing population size.

Numerous illustrations for these trends have already been quoted, in our discussion of geographic variation. A fuller discussion of the effects of geographic isolation on speciation will be given in a later chapter (p. 154ff.).

Some additional phenomena of variation in relation to population structure may be summarized as follows:

1. Populations are characterized by mean, maximum, and minimum values in the characters subject to gliding (intergrading) changes (size) and by percentage values of the proportions present of dimorphic or polymorphic characters.

2. The various characters may vary independently from each other, that is, size may increase from one population to the next, while the pigmentation may remain constant, or the size may increase while the pigmentation decreases. Therefore:

3. Neighboring populations agree in some characters and differ in others.

4. Each population is composed of genetically different individuals (biotypes), and we therefore find, as we should expect from these premises, that even the smallest subpopulations show slight statistical differences.

5. Neighboring populations intergrade, unless separated by definite barriers which cause gaps in the distribution.

6. Intergradation, as manifested by a change of characters from one

population to the next, may be exceedingly gradual or it may be characterized by a sudden step, even where natural barriers are absent.

7. Character changes frequently continue in the same direction over a series of populations; for example, each successive population of the same series may become darker or larger, or whatever the trend is.

8. Many characters of local populations have clearly an adaptive value; others seem to be due to accidents of sampling.

9. Some characters behave independently of such trends, showing a checkerboard type of variation.

10. The characters of a population tend to be rather constant over considerable periods of time. This is valid for the statistical properties of quantitative characters, as well as for the proportions of meristic characters.

CHAPTER V

THE SYSTEMATIC CATEGORIES AND THE NEW SPECIES CONCEPT

LINNÆUS did a great service to taxonomy when he invented a definite terminology for the systematic categories and showed that they could be arranged in a graded hierarchy: species, genus, order, and class. Even though Linnæus recognized the variety as an infraspecific category, in exceptional cases, nevertheless the species was, for him, the basic category. His early species concept (1758) is typified by the well-known sentence: "*Species tot sunt quot diversas formas ab initio produxit infinitum Ens.*" Linnæus himself somewhat modified his views in his later writings (Ramsbottom 1938); still he adhered always to an essentially static and morphological species concept. The acceptance of the theory of evolution (1859) and the discovery of the wide occurrence of geographic variation was bound to produce, sooner or later, a revolutionary change in the concepts of the taxonomist. The present chapter will be devoted to an investigation of this change and to an exposition of current ideas on the lower taxonomic categories.

Before we can begin to define them, we must emphasize that, to some extent, all taxonomic categories are collective units. Even the subspecies is generally composed of a number of slightly distinct populations, some of which connect it with neighboring subspecies. Variability and composite character are true for the species also, excepting only those with very small range. The genus is based on a group of more or less widely differing species, the family on genera, and so forth. The subgroups within one of these categories are not entirely equivalent and uniform. Nature is not as simple as that. Some of the subspecies of a species are more similar to each other than others, some species of a genus may be very similar, other species may be somewhat aberrant. The terminology of the taxonomist, designed for practical purposes, is always an idealization and represents the facts as simpler than they are. The nontaxonomist and the beginner among taxonomists will save themselves much trouble if they realize this situation fully. Not even the most extreme splitting will ever lead to completely homogeneous categories.

Up to this point we have refrained from defining the term species or from saying what units the taxonomist distinguishes within the species. The reason for this delay is that no fruitful discussion of the species problem is possible without a full understanding of the problems of geographic variation. The facts presented in the preceding two chapters make it apparent that it is wrong to conceive of the systematic units as something static. The words variation and evolution imply change, and only through a dynamic concept of the species and the other systematic categories can we hope to present the situation adequately. It is a curious paradox that so many taxonomists still adhere to a strictly static species concept, even though they admit freely the existence of evolution.

Before we begin an analysis of the species criteria, we shall attempt to give a short survey of the terminology of the taxonomic categories. Such a survey is rather necessary, since in the course of years a vast and rather confusing terminology of systematic categories has developed. It seems as if every author who encountered some particularly difficult situation has tried to solve it by the introduction of a new term. These authors did not realize that *no system of nomenclature and no hierarchy of systematic categories* is able to represent adequately the complicated set of interrelationships and divergences found in nature. The fact that students of nearly every major systematic group (from bacteria to mammals) have developed their own set of terms has added to the confusion.

There are a number of recent books and papers available which trace the history of the various taxonomic concepts, and it would be mere repetition if I were to go over this field again. (See Du Rietz 1930, Cuénot 1936, Rensch 1929, 1934, Robson and Richards 1936, Semenov-Tian-Shansky 1910, and Uhlmann 1923.) My own treatment will be rather selective and will consist in a discussion of only those concepts that are likely to have a continued importance in the field of zoölogical taxonomy.

Let us begin with the infraspecific categories.

INFRASPECIFIC CATEGORIES

The species was the lowest category for Linnæus. He used the term variety only very rarely, to signify some situation not fully understood. This term had no well-defined meaning and covered a multitude of sins. The use of the term variety was also correlated with the idea that only the type of the species was "typical." Anything that differed from this typical specimen was a "variety." As our knowledge of the variation of animals grew during the nineteenth century, it became obvious that a number of unrelated phenomena had been thrown together under the single heading variety, and an effort was made by various authors to segregate them into their proper categories. The result of such efforts depended largely on the species concept of the respective authors. Those who cling even today to a strictly Linnæan concept of morphologically defined species consider every morphologically well-characterized population a distinct species and apply the term variety either to those populations which are poorly characterized or to aberrant individuals or to phenotypical variants. The term variety is rapidly going out of use in all those taxonomic groups (such as birds, mammals, snails, certain insects, and so forth) in which a biological species concept prevails. In fact, most modern authors refuse altogether to employ the term, at least as a taxonomic category. If it is used at all, it is definitely applied to individuals and not to populations. It is, in other words, a term used for individual variants, such, for example, as a red-haired person in a brown-haired population, or an unspotted butterfly (var. *immaculata*) in a spotted species.

Individual variants.—Some specialists of butterflies and other variable groups of insects, as well as of mollusks, seem to feel that the extraordinary variability of their material calls for a special nomenclatorial treatment. They therefore segregate the conspicuous variants within an investigated population into definite groups and give a special variety name to each of these groups. To illustrate this procedure, I might apply it to human systematics. It would correspond to the procedure of an anthropologist who gave names not only to the conventionally recognized human races, such as to Mongolians, Australian aboriginals, Pygmies, Negroes, and so forth, but also to red-haired, black-haired, brown-haired, blond-haired individuals, also to those with blue eyes or brown eyes, with straight, wavy, curled hair, of small or large stature, and so forth. In addition he would give special names to aberrations, that is to individuals which showed rarer deviations from the normal, such as harelip, clubfoot, birthmarks, and so forth. By applying this procedure to the species *Homo sapiens*, it becomes obvious how absurd it is, and this is equally true for animals. The nomenclature of some genera of beetles, lepidoptera, and snails has become so top-heavy with names given to "varieties" and "aberrations" (individual variants), that the picture of the significant intraspecific variation and population structure has become completely obscured.

To what degree the elimination of such variety names clarifies the system may be illustrated by a few simple examples. The only subdivisions which Davenport (1941) recognizes in the latest revision of the species *Coenonympha pamphilus* are 5 geographically well-defined subspecies. Forty-six variety names, of which 35 had been coined by a single author, had to be put into the synonymy. An additional number of 23 different aberration names had been applied to specimens of the same species. A sane, progressive taxonomist was thus able to reduce a chaos of 69 names to 5 subspecies. Davenport presents a well-reasoned statement as to why it is useless, if not misleading, to give names to all aberrations and hypothetical or real seasonal forms. Similar chaotic conditions exist in certain species of snails.

A painstaking study of the banded snail *Cepaea nemoralis* led, in the course of time, to the establishment of 28 varieties and 180 subvarieties. . . . Even with this wealth of names available, the actual variability of the species was by no means exhausted by the 208 classes of varieties, since within every one of these band and color varieties there are individuals with shells that are relatively high or rather flat, that are large or small, that are smoother or rougher; there is also considerable variability in the color of the soft parts, in the anatomical structures, and so forth. [Rensch 1934: 289 f.]

If somebody were to name consistently everything that is different, he would have to give a name eventually to nearly every single individual. This is, of course, exactly what some extreme authors have done.

There are among birds a number of species with an individual variability which is almost of the same extent as that found in insects. The common European buzzard (*Buteo buteo*), for example, has individuals which are almost uniformly brownish-black, others are of a uniform whitish or rufous underneath; some are heavily spotted underneath, others hardly at all; the tail is sometimes with, sometimes without conspicuous bars; these bars may be dark brown on a light brown background, or dark brown on a rufous ground, or rufous on a whitish ground, and so on. An author with sufficient imagination could easily coin fifty names to take care of the various combinations of characters just mentioned. However, it is known to the ornithologist that any two of these types may breed together and that they may occur among brothers and sisters in the same nest. A convention was therefore silently and wisely adopted among bird taxonomists not to name any of these variants, but, if necessary, to refer to them only in a descriptive way: "the blackish, the whitish, the rufous-banded one, and so forth."

Individual variants should be given vernacular names, not Latin names, which are to be reserved for the systematic categories. The *Drosophila* geneticists have fortunately adopted this procedure for their mutants (*white, cut, bar, forked,* and the like) and Gordon and Fraser (1931), in their terminology of individual variants of the fish *Platypoecilus,* have also chosen vernacular names (*twin-spot, moon, crescent, comet,* and so forth). Vernacular names are as clear as the Latin terms, and their use prevents confusion with subspecific names.

The Subspecies.—The subspecies, or geographic race, is a geographically localized subdivision of the species, which differs genetically and taxonomically from other subdivisions of the species. Every subspecies that was ever carefully analyzed was found to be composed of a number of genetically distinct populations. It is, in many cases, entirely dependent upon the judgment of the individual taxonomist how many of these populations are to be included in one subspecies. The limits of most subspecies are therefore subjective, and we can give only an empirical definition for this taxonomic category. For the sake of completeness, I shall add Rensch's definition (1934):

A geographical race is a complex of interbreeding and completely fertile individuals which are morphologically identical or vary only within the limits of individual, ecological and seasonal variability. The typical characters of this group of individuals are genetically fixed and no other geographical race of the same species occurs within the same range.

The taxonomist is an orderly person whose task it is to assign every specimen to a definite category (or museum drawer!). This necessary process of pigeonholing has led to the erroneous belief among nontaxonomists that subspecies are clear-cut units which can easily be separated from one another. Such situations exist occasionally, in regions where the range of the species is broken up into definite, isolated sections. But subspecies intergrade almost unnoticeably in nearly all the cases in which there is distributional continuity. In a long chain of populations we often find that every population is intermediate between the two neighboring ones, thereby connecting the two extremes. An additional complication is provided by the fact, mentioned in the last chapter, that the various characters of a subspecies tend to vary independently of one another. These practical difficulties are encountered in every conscientious taxonomic study of geographic variation. A good description of it is given by Dice (1941) in regard to the intergradation among the subspecies *bairdii, nebrascensis,* and *osgoodi* of the deermouse *Peromyscus maniculatus* in western Nebraska, where the dividing lines among these three races are purely arbitrary.

Subspecies are generally ignored in the lesser-known taxonomic groups, that is in orders and families in which the greater proportion of the species is still undescribed. Well-defined subspecies are given specific rank in these same taxonomic groups. On the other hand, most of the taxonomic work of the specialist of better-known groups (such as birds, mammals, butterflies and snails) is devoted to the elucidation of the subspecies. In some of these groups, as for example Palearctic and Nearctic birds, even most of the "good" subspecies are already described, and a phase of excessive splitting has been reached. New subspecies are described because the means of the measurements differ by a few percent or because there is a very slight difference in the tone of general coloration. The populations on which such "subspecies" are based are admittedly genetically different from others of the species, but to name them is impractical since it obscures rather than facilitates the presentation of the facts of intraspecific variation. A convention has therefore been rather generally adopted among ornithologists that a group of populations may be described as a separate subspecies only if at least 75 percent of the individuals can be determined accurately (as differing from previously described subspecies of the species). Irregular distribution patterns force the adoption of large collective subspecies (see *Cacatua*, Fig. 2). Some obviously distinct insect populations seem to be restricted to a single cliff or to a single field or to some other locality only a few hundred square feet in extent. It is not customary to provide scientific names for microsubspecies based on such small populations. Considerably more material must be examined, in order to recognize subspecies, than is needed for the description of good species. A single specimen or even part of one may prove the distinctness of a new species. The distinctness of a subspecies can often be proven only by the careful comparison or biometric analysis of large series from various parts of the range of the species.

After having considered these practical aspects of the subspecies, we are faced with some questions of a more general nature concerning the properties of subspecies. The first question is: What is the criterion by which the subspecies can be distinguished from the species? We shall postpone a discussion of this question until after we have defined what we consider a species. The other question is: Is there only one kind of subspecies, the geographic race, or is there a second kind, the ecological race? The answer to this question likewise will be postponed, so that it may be treated in its proper place (Chapter VIII). The terms subspecies and geographic race will be considered, in the meantime, as synonymous.

The higher categories.—The classifying taxonomist is not satisfied with an endless aggregation of equivalent species. He finds that some species are more similar to one another than others and that it is possible to arrange all species in groups. Such groups, which include similar species of supposedly common descent, are called genera. The genera can be further rearranged into similar groups. In short, it is possible to establish a whole hierarchy of higher systematic categories. Linnæus recognized only four categories—species, genus, order, and class, while the modern taxonomist has an almost unlimited number of such categories available—subgenus, genus, supergenus, tribe, section, subfamily, and so forth. We shall discuss the biological significance of these higher categories in one of the later chapters (Chapter X).

The neutral terms.—Rensch (1934) has emphasized with good reason that some terms must be reserved in systematic work, to be used in incompletely analyzed cases. The neutral terms which, in zoölogy, are used most frequently are: *form*, for a single unit, and *group* or *complex*, for a number of units. We often speak of a *form* when we do not know whether the systematic unit in question is, for example, a full species or merely a subspecies of a larger species, or whether it is a subspecies or an individual variant, or whether it is a subspecies or a phenotypical modification. We also use the term (in the plural) when we combine two unequal units; for example, in order to characterize the joint attributes of a species and a subspecies, we say "these two forms."

The term *group* is most commonly applied to an assembly of closely related species of a genus. But it is also applied to subspecies in species with many subspecies. The common Palearctic jay, *Garrulus glandarius*, has a total of 41 subspecies, but they can be arranged in 8 groups, the *garrulus* group, the *bispecularis* group, and others (Stresemann 1940b). The term group is also used, although more rarely, to denote a number of closely related units in the higher categories, genera, for example. The word *complex* is frequently used synonymously with the term group.

We are now ready, after having treated all the other categories, to discuss the most important one of all, the species.

THE CHANGING SPECIES CONCEPT

The methods and techniques of a field of science are often like the rules of a game. It was Linnæus's principal service to biology that he established a set of rules by which to play the taxonomic game. Every species was, according to him, the product of a separate act of creation and therefore clearly separated from all other species. Groups of similar species were united in genera, and consequently each species was given two names, one to designate the species and one the genus. This is what we understand by binary and binomial nomenclature. It is a system which is intimately connected with a static and strictly morphological species concept. The taxonomist who follows this concept sets up a number of standards ("types") to which he applies his species names. As he receives additional specimens from new localities, he compares them with his standards. If they are different, he describes them as new species, if they agree more or less, he unites them with the known species. A frank description of this "type method" was given by Bernard (1896:20):

> Certain striking and conspicuous specimens (or single specimens which have already been described by previous workers) are selected as types, and the remainder are divided, according as, in the opinion of the individual worker, they approach one or the other of these favored specimens. The types are thus in the highest degree arbitrary and accidental, as is also, it must be confessed (though in a less degree), the selection of other specimens to be associated with them.

This method of handling taxonomic material and of pigeonholing it in collections works well as long as only a few specimens are known in every species. It is therefore, with minor modifications, even today the dominant practice in all poorly known taxonomic groups (including many branches of paleontology).

However, in the better-known groups, particularly in birds and butterflies, certain troubles began to develop, in the course of the nineteenth century, which shook the taxonomist out of his self-satisfied complacency and forced him to revolutionize his methods as well as his species concept. This "revolution" has reached its final stages in certain groups, such as birds, while in other groups it has not yet even started. The reason for this change of the species concept was twofold: the discovery of variation and the drowning of the system in minute "species." Let us look a little more closely at both of these phenomena.

The existence of a certain degree of variation was already known to Linnæus, who commented on it repeatedly, particularly in his later writings. As the number of zoölogical collections increased during the nineteenth century and as ever-growing numbers of new localities were visited, more and more phenomena were discovered which could not be reconciled with a static species concept. Darwin, for example, was confronted by such an observation when he studied the finches (Geospizidae) of the Galápagos Islands, and it made such a deep impression on him that, as he himself declared, it became one of the primary motifs for his studies embodied in *The Origin of Species*. Wallace, who, at the same period, pursued his studies on the geographic variations of the mammals, birds, and insects of the Malay Archipelago, came to almost the same conclusions as Darwin. The number of cases increased daily in which "good" species were found to be connected by intermediates or in which one species had slightly different attributes in different parts of its range. In other words, the study of the phenomena of geographic variation, such as were presented in Chapters III and IV, showed clearly that a static species concept was no longer tenable and that it had to be replaced by a dynamic one. This change was hastened by the confusion caused by the species splitters. These authors took the morphological species definition as an excuse to describe as new species every population that was characterized by some morphological characters peculiar to itself. In fact, some authors carried this tendency to such an extreme that they named not only clearly characterized populations, but also those that differed merely in their means or extremes. This tendency eventually led to a vast accumulation of similar species in all the more common genera. Some of these "species" were closely related to one another, others seemed to be rather isolated. Some species seemed to be rather uniform throughout their range, others seemed to include dissimilar populations. Specimens were found with increasing frequency which had to be placed in "species" *a* on the basis of one character and in "species" *b* on the basis of another character. It gradually became obvious that the set of rules which Linnæus had given to the game of taxonomy had to be revised, or else the whole procedure of taxonomy would turn into a farce.

By the middle of the nineteenth century the ornithologists were ready to consider such revision. The remedy for the shortcomings of the taxonomic species was, at first, a purely technical one and consisted in the introduction of the ternary nomenclature. H. Schlegel was apparently the first author (from 1844 on) to use trinomials consistently (even though hesitatingly) for geographic subdivisions of the species. This procedure found, at first, little approval among the ornithologists of Europe, but it was eventually adopted under the leadership of the American ornithologists. Toward the end of the century it was quite customary to describe less distinct forms as subspecies, and particularly to reduce to the rank of subspecies all those "species" which were geographic representatives of other species with which they were broadly intergrading.

The consistent employment of trinomials for such intergrading "species" had a very wholesome effect on the practical classification within the genera. It did away with a great many poorly characterized species and thus led to simplification and clarification. However, these practical advantages were more than counterbalanced by a theoretical difficulty. The Linnæan species was the lowest category, it was monotypic, it was static, it was defined on a strictly morphological basis. None of these attributes was any longer entirely valid for the new polytypic species concept, as developed by the progressive students of birds, mammals, butterflies, and snails. We shall analyze this change in the species criteria in a later section of this chapter, and show how it affected the species definition. For the present, we shall merely consider how this change of ideas affected the species as a systematic category.

Additional collecting and the study of geographic variation and distribution led again and again to the discovery that geographically isolated species might be connected by intergrades with some other species. This necessitated the uniting of the two (or more) separate species into one polytypic species. There was, however, another group of "species" which were morphologically as close to some other species as the intergrading ones, but which did not and could not intergrade because they were prevented by some geographic barrier from coming into contact with this neighboring species. Logical and consistent authors contended that such isolated (insular or mountain) species should also be included with the polytypic species to which they belonged, because the smallness of the morphological gap indicated clearly that they would interbreed with the geographic representative if they were not prevented from doing so by an entirely extrinsic factor, physical separation. This entirely logical reasoning led to the most useful of all the working hypotheses in taxonomy, that of geographic representation (Kleinschmidt, K. Jordan). The basic idea is that the next relative of any species occurs usually in a more or less disguised form, in a geographically adjacent area. Such geographically representative forms are to be united into groups, the polytypic species or *Rassenkreise* of the modern workers.

The change from the orthodox Linnæan species to the latest model of the polytypic species signifies a very striking evolution of the species concept of the taxonomist. The end members of this evolutionary series are just as different as those of an equivalent evolutionary series of an animal group. This poses a very serious problem for the taxonomist. There are now two entirely different kinds of species in practical use, the old-fashioned Linnæan one and the new synthetic polytypic species of the modern taxonomist. In spite of the common name "species," the two concepts are at least as different as the De Vriesian mutation is from that of the modern geneticist.

Kleinschmidt (1900) was perhaps the first taxonomist to realize the full implications of this situation. He recognized that the new concept was something quite different from the species of Linnæus and the post-Linnæan authors and therefore proposed to give a new term, *Formen-*

kreis, to the new concept. He hoped to accomplish two things by the introduction of this new term: first, to emphasize the distinction between the new concept and the Linnæan species; and, second, to overcome the opposition to the new technique by those who refused to give up the species with its Linnæan connotation. Even an adherent of the Linnæan species could group these species into *Formenkreise*. Kleinschmidt himself was the first taxonomist to make a consistent effort to establish such *Formenkreise* and to search the corners of the earth for possible geographic representatives of every species with which he was working. It was his motto that of every species a "representative in disguise" might be found almost anywhere. His papers on the peregrine falcons and gyrfalcons are instructive examples of this method. He would, for example, study the gyrfalcons of the Arctic region and then ask himself which falcon of central Asia, of the Mediterranean countries, of Africa, of North America was the "gyrfalcon in disguise" of such countries. Again and again he was successful in singling out one of the many species of *Falco* of the regions mentioned as the unquestionable relative and geographic representative of the gyrfalcon. It is, of course, not always possible or even desirable to call such representative species subspecies; the important fact is that most "species" (in the widest sense of the word) have a much more extensive range than is generally realized. Kleinschmidt's method is unquestionably one of the most productive working hypotheses of taxonomy.

To make a distinction between the terms species and *Formenkreis* was quite useful in the period during which the geographic species concept was struggling for recognition. The term *Formenkreis* itself had many weaknesses, to which Rensch (1929) called attention, the most serious of which was Kleinschmidt's singular ideas on evolution (1930). He admitted ordinary organic evolution within each *Formenkreis*, but insisted on the special creation of each of these major units. There is a curious parallelism between these ideas and Goldschmidt's more recent ones (1940). Rensch therefore suggested replacing the term *Formenkreis* by *Rassenkreis*, a term which has gained considerable popularity among recent writers. Rensch makes a terminological distinction between species which break up into geographic races (*Rassenkreis*) and those which do not (*Art*), but this terminology has not found many adherents.

Another group of workers, led by Hartert and K. Jordan of the Rothschild Museum in Tring, declined to accept any new terms. They insisted that the species of Linnæus was an empirical (practical) concept and that the term could be retained, even if the concept was modified. In fact, both of these authors and their followers gave the species as broad an application as Kleinschmidt his *Formenkreis* or Rensch the *Rassenkreis*. In the meantime, it was found, in well-worked groups of animals, that there are actually fewer species which do *not* break up into local races and subspecies than which do, and it was realized that *Rassenkreise* were not a special and rare kind of species, but rather that the majority of species were polytypic. The workers in ornithology have become so used to the fact that the species is a group concept that most of them have now given up the term *Rassenkreis*, since this is really merely another word for the species in its modern, revised meaning. Huxley (1940) has suggested that taxonomists make a distinction between monotypic species, that is, those which do not break up into races, and polytypic species, those which are composed of geographic races. Ökland (1937) calls them uniform and multiform species. This distinction may help to appease those workers who believe that the word species without qualification can apply only to the lowest taxonomic unit.

SPECIES CRITERIA AND SPECIES DEFINITIONS

The species has a different significance to the systematist and to the student of evolution. To the systematist it is a practical device designed to reduce the almost endless variety of living beings to a comprehensible system. The species is, to him, merely one member of a hierarchy of systematic categories. In his discussion of the species the systematist concentrates on methods of distinguishing species from subspecies and from other species. A change in the species concept will have certain practical consequences, but it will not vitally affect his work. It is different with the student of the problems of evolution or, more exactly, with the student of speciation. To him the species is a passing stage in the stream of evolution. He studies the evolutionary level which is exemplified by the species; he wants to know whether the characters of the categories below and above the species differ in kind or in degree; he wants to know by what processes (genetic and ecological) a species becomes separated from others. In short, he is primarily interested in the dynamic qualities of species. A concise definition of the species is, for him, a necessity, because his interpretation of the speciation process depends largely on what he considers to be the final stage of this process, the species.

Many of Darwin's followers, including most of the taxonomists of the old school, thought that the problem of species formation was solved when they found that intermediate forms connect what were formerly considered two perfectly distinct species. They concluded that species are transformed into new species as they spread into new areas. This complacent attitude was distinctly associated with the old morphological species concept and it reigned supreme until the new biological species concept began to replace it. Then it was suddenly realized by the more progressive systematists that those species between which they found intergradation were their own creations, and not biological units. As the new polytypic species concept began to assert itself, a certain pessimism seemed to be associated with it. It seemed as if each of the polytypic species (*Rassenkreise*) was as clearcut and as separated from other species by bridgeless gaps as if it had come into being by a separate act of creation. And this is exactly the conclusion drawn by men like Kleinschmidt and Goldschmidt. They claim that all the evidence for intergradation between species which was quoted in the past was actually based on cases of infraspecific variation, and, in all honesty, it must be admitted that this claim is largely justified. But there is one serious flaw in the arguments of Kleinschmidt and Goldschmidt: they fail to define what *they* consider a species.

If we do not want to fall into the same error, we must make an attempt at a species definition. In doing this we are confronted by the paradoxical incongruity of trying to establish a fixed stage in the evolutionary stream. If there is evolution in the true sense of the word, as against catastrophism or creation, we should find all kinds of species— incipient species, mature species, and incipient genera, as well as all intermediate conditions. To define the middle stage of this series perfectly, so that every taxonomic unit can be certified with confidence as to whether or not it is a species, is just as impossible as to define the middle stage in the life of man, mature man, so well that every single human male can be identified as boy, mature man, or old man. It is therefore obvious that every species definition can be only an approach and should be considered with some tolerance. On the other hand, the question: "How do species originate?" cannot be discussed until we have formed some idea as to what a species is.

A second difficulty which confronts us in our attempt at a species definition is that there is, in nature, a great diversity of different kinds of species. Even if we do not consider such aberrant phenomena as the apomictic species in plants and the strains of bacteria, there is, even among animals, a great variety of different taxonomic situations which are generally classified as species. The question as to whether the species of birds, of corals, of protozoa, and of intestinal worms are the same kind of evolutionary phenomenon is entirely justified. Actually no answer can yet be given to this question, since most taxonomic groups are not yet sufficiently well known to have reached a stable species concept. The species concept that prevails at the present time in any given taxonomic group depends more on the degree to which this group is known taxonomically than on any other factor (Doederlein 1902). It may not be exaggeration if I say that there are probably as many species concepts as there are thinking systematists and students of speciation. Dobzhansky (1941a:372–374) has listed a good many of the recent concepts, and I have discussed some of them in a recent paper (Mayr 1940a). However, all these concepts, and the definitions that go with them, may be classified into four or five groups, of which I shall try to give a short characterization.

The practical species concept.—Darwin said in 1859: "In determining whether a form should be ranked as a species or a variety, the opinion of naturalists having sound judgment and wide experience seems the only guide to follow." This is a species definition which would still find favor, in a slightly modified form, among a good proportion of the working systematists of today. In its modern form this definition would read about as follows: "A species is a systematic unit which is considered a species by a competent systematist (preferably a specialist of the group)."

Such a definition is eminently practical for taxonomic routine work and the element of judgment which it implies cannot be entirely ruled out of any species definition. On the other hand, it cuts the Gordian knot and is therefore quite unsuitable in a more theoretical discussion of the origin of species. Furthermore, it suggests that the species is an entirely subjective unit, which is not true, as we shall shortly see.

The morphological species concept.—A concept based on the degree of morphological distinction is the typical species concept of the old systematics and is even today the only practical one in all those systematic groups which are still in the descriptive or cataloguing stage. It is the species concept with which Linnæus started the science of systematics in his *Systema Naturae*. It is, by necessity, the prevailing species concept of the paleontologist. The characters which the taxonomist enumerates in his species diagnosis, such as structure, proportions, color patterns, and the like, are the conventional criteria used in the old systematics to define a species. "A species is a group of individuals or populations with the same or similar morphological characters." The trouble with such a definition is that it does not delimit true species from subspecies below or genera above. The species, as such, has no morphological or structural attributes by which it can be distinguished from the next lower or next higher categories. Exactly the same features are used to characterize subspecies, species, and genera. What is used as a generic or even family criterion in one group is only a subspecific criterion in another group or else it is of no systematic value at all, because it indicates merely an age or a sex difference (see Chapter II, p. 22). Furthermore, as we have seen, every "species character" is subject to geographic variation.

The objection may be raised that it is not the kind of characters that separate subspecies, species, and genera, but the degree of difference. This actually is the criterion of a great many systematists: "A species is what can be separated on the basis of clear-cut, qualitative key-characters, a subspecies is characterized by quantitative differences and can be identified only by the actual comparison of material of the two studied forms." The practical consequence of such a viewpoint is that some unquestionably good species (sibling species) have to be called subspecies on account of their great similarity, while in other cases obvious subspecies have to be called species. There are many genera of birds, and the same is true for all groups of animals, in which it is impossible to identify perfectly good species with the help of a key. The distinguishing characters cannot be adequately expressed in words, even though they are quite obvious as soon as actual specimens are compared. The Indonesian cave swiftlets (*Collocalia*), New Guinea honey-eaters (*Meliphaga analoga*-group), American flycatchers (*Empidonax*), and the white-eyes (*Zosterops*) may be mentioned in this connection. Additional cases will be quoted in the discussion of sibling species (p. 200).

The exact opposite of this condition exists in certain families (for example Phasianidae, Paradisaeidae, Trochilidae) in which geographic races normally differ much more conspicuously than the good species in the previously mentioned families. Furthermore, in most polytypic species there is very little difference between neighboring races, but the peripheral forms are very distinct. Where should the line be drawn between the quantitative and the qualitative differences?

The most serious objection to a purely morphological species definition lies, however, in the fact that fertility and crossability vary to some extent independently of morphological characters, and the latter are thus of no use in the all-important border-line cases. A morphological species definition ("degree of difference") should therefore be applied only as a temporary and provisional expedient as long as no additional information is available (see below, p. 121).

The artificiality of the morphological species concept becomes most apparent when we study isolated populations, such as are found on islands, mountains, or other segregated parts of the range of the species. Such populations may be, biologically speaking, inseparable from the main body of the species, and they may be completely fertile and without any reproductive isolating mechanisms, but they may show some peculiar morphological (and thus taxonomic) characteristics without intergrading (by individual variation) with the equivalent characters of the mainland population. Chapman (1924) has expressed admirably the biologists' opinion on the treatment of such geographically isolated and morphologically distinct populations. On the question of how to classify them,

the systematist to whom the fact of non-intergradation is a sufficient test replies "as species," but I am convinced that it is often biologically incorrect and misleading to follow this course.

Is the Towhee of Guadeloupe Island any less a race of *Pipilo maculatus* because its range is insular and hence isolated? Is the Horned Lark of the Bogotá, Colombia savanna any less a race of *Otocoris alpestris* because its range is separated from its nearest relative by all Central America?

To rank these birds as species is, to my mind, not only biologically false, but it results in the adoption of a nomenclature which to an extent conceals their origin and relationships.

Extremes of an intergrading series of subspecies are often much more different than these isolated populations. There is no reason to call the latter species if the former are considered subspecies.

Some recent authors have attempted to refine the morphological criteria, in the belief that they had thereby evolved a superior type of species definition. The following definition of Wilhelmi (1940) may serve as a sample: " 'Species' of helminths may be defined tentatively as a group of organisms the lipid free antigen of which, when diluted to 1:4000 or more, yields a positive precipitin test within one hour with a rabbit antiserum produced by injecting 40 mg. of dry-weight, lipid-free antigenic material and withdrawn ten to twelve days after the last of four intravenous injections administered every third day." In spite of its modern ring, this is basically a thoroughly old-fashioned morphological species definition, based on the degree of difference.

The species and not the subspecies was to Linnæus the lowest systematic unit, as we have seen in the historical survey. Some of the adherents of the morphological species concept are consistent in their discipleship of Linnæus and follow him also in this respect. Kinsey (1937a), a well-known advocate of this concept, expresses it in the following words:

Confusion will be avoided, if we call the basic taxonomic unit the species. It is the unit beneath which there are in nature no subdivisions, which maintain themselves for any length of time or over any large area. The unit is variously known among taxonomists as the species, subspecies, variety,

Rasse or geographic race. It is the unit directly involved in the question of the origin of species, and the entity most often indicated by non-taxonomists when they refer to species. Systematists often introduce confusion into evolutionary discussions by applying the term to some category above the basic unit.

Goldschmidt (1937) has already disputed some of these statements, in particular the claim that this lowest unit is the one which is "directly involved in the question of the origin of species." In a recent paper I have discussed some of the other points (Mayr 1940a:252):

It is not true that "there are in nature no subdivisions" below the species [of Kinsey], "which maintain themselves for any length of time." Actually every intermediate condition exists between "the effective breeding population" within a continuous array of populations and the subspecies which is completely isolated by geographical barriers. Recent genetic work (Dobzhansky, *et al.*) as well as Kinsey's own taxonomic work shows this quite clearly. Furthermore, the lowest category is not "the entity most often indicated by non-taxonomists when they refer to species." When the layman or non-taxonomic biologist speaks of "the song sparrow," he is not concerned with the numerous subspecies of this species, as for example the Atlantic, the Eastern or the Mississippian race. He means the total sum of all these races, or else, the particular local race wherever he meets it. Neither do we call the human races species, although they are the basic taxonomic units of *Homo sapiens.*

Genetic species concept.—Lotsy (1918) and some other geneticists in the earlier parts of the century tried to establish a species concept on a purely genetic basis, with approximately the following definition: "A species is a group of genetically identical individuals." ("Chez les organismes à reproduction sexuelle, l'éspèce peut donc être definie comme l'ensemble de tous les individues homozygotes qui ont la même constitution héréditaire"). We now know that not only all the subspecies are genetically different, but also the populations within the subspecies (Dobzhansky for *Drosophila pseudoobscura,* Sumner and Dice for *Peromyscus,* Goldschmidt for *Lymantria dispar,* and so forth). In fact, except for identical twins, every individual in bisexually reproducing species is a different biotype. We take this for granted in regard to man, domestic animals, and cultivated plants, but it is, of course, equally true for all wild animals. Genetic distinction is not a species criterion, since it is a *sine qua non* condition. It is therefore an unnecessary embellishment in a species definition, unless some day natural populations are found that are genetically identical with others. The logical consequence of Lotsy's definition is to consider as hybrids all individuals of sexually reproducing animals. Speciation is, then, by necessity associated with hybridization. Lotsy's species concept is thus the reason for some of his curious theories on speciation.

Species concept based on sterility.—If two animals produce fertile offspring, they usually belong to the same species, and, vice versa, if such matings are sterile, they generally belong to different species. It is not surprising, therefore, that the criterion of fertility is part of many modern species definitions. "All forms belong to one species which can produce fertile hybrids." Unfortunately, this statement is not at all true, there being numerous cases known in which good species have freely produced completely fertile hybrids, while on the other hand a number of cases are known in which geographic races of one species exhibit reduced fertility or are completely sterile. A species definition in which sterility is the principal criterion is therefore not acceptable, at least not for most groups of animals. It may be stated here, in all fairness, that some of the authors who speak of fertility and sterility have something else in mind: crossability. Two animals (of different sexes) may meet in nature and never cross. The same animals, if given no other choice, may mate freely in captivity and produce completely fertile offspring. Such animals are fertile, but not crossable. They are reproductively isolated, but not sterile. This difference is of the utmost biological importance, but its significance has not been realized by many recent authors.

The biological species definition.—Most of the species definitions up to 1935 were based on static taxonomic units, without reference to their phylogenetic history. Dobzhansky (1937) felt that a more adequate definition of the species would be possible by emphasizing the dynamic aspects of the species. He therefore defined the species as "that stage of the evolutionary process at which the once actually or potentially interbreeding array of forms becomes segregated into two or more separate arrays which are physiologically incapable of interbreeding." This is an excellent description of the process of speciation, but not a species definition. A species is not a stage of a process, but the result of a process. Dobzhansky's definition has, nevertheless, influenced subsequent species definitions, because it stresses the two basic elements of a biological species definition, the interbreeding of the populations that belong to the species, and the "reproductive isolation" (A. Emerson) against the populations, which do not belong to the species. Stresemann (1919:64) stated it in these words: "Forms which have reached the species level have diverged physiologically to the extent that, as proven in nature, they can come together again without interbreeding." The most important aspect of the biological species definition is that it uses no artificial criteria, but decides each case on the basis of whether certain organisms behave as if they were conspecific or not. A straight biological species definition would be ideal, (1) if sufficient information were available about all species and (2) if all species were in spatial contact with the next related ones during their breeding season. All the difficulties of the taxonomist would disappear if these two conditions were fulfilled, but it is an impossible demand, since "continuous spatial contact" is incompatible with isolation and, as Romanes said (with some exaggeration), "without isolation or the prevention of interbreeding, organic evolution is in no case possible."

A biological species definition, based on the criterion of crossability or reproductive isolation, has theoretically fewer flaws than any other. In practice, however, it breaks down just as quickly. Like them, it is not applicable to the isolated forms, and these are the really important ones. As long as populations are in contact with one another, it is generally not difficult to arrive at a decision as to whether or not they are conspecific; the isolated forms are the ones that puzzle us.

A practical species definition, and this is after all what the taxonomist wants for his work, will have to compromise by combining the criteria of several species concepts. I have recently (Mayr 1940a) proposed the following formulation:

A species consists of a group of populations which replace each other geographically or ecologically and of which the neighboring ones intergrade or interbreed wherever they are in contact or which are potentially capable of doing so (with one or more of the populations) in those cases where contact is prevented by geographical or ecological barriers.

Or shorter: Species are groups of actually or potentially interbreeding natural populations, which are reproductively isolated from other such groups.

As can be seen from these definitions, it is necessary in the cases of interrupted distribution to leave it to the judgment of the individual systematist, whether or not he considers two particular forms as "potentially capable" of interbreeding—in other words, whether he considers them subspecies or species. This is necessary, because it is often impossible, for practical reasons, to test to what extent reproductive isolation exists. The life of a *Drosophila* individual is very short. A population of *Drosophila melanogaster* of the year 1942 is reproductively isolated from a *Drosophila melanogaster* population of the year 1932 by a complete time barrier. Still, nobody would call them two different species. The same is true (to a slightly less absolute degree) for many geographically isolated populations. They may be reproductively isolated by a geographic barrier, but still they are not necessarily different species. Reproductive isolation is thus an immediate, practical test only for sympatric,[1] synchronically reproducing species. The conspecifity of allopatric[1] and allochronic forms, which depends on their potential capacity for interbreeding, can be decided only by inference, based on a careful analysis of the morphological differences of the compared forms. This does not mean that I am retracing my steps and now propose to accept a morphological species definition; no, it means simply that we may have to apply the degree of morphological difference as a yardstick in all those cases in which we cannot determine the presence of reproductive isolation. To use this method in doubtful cases is justified for the following reasons. If we examine the "good" species of a certain locality we find that the reproductive gap is associated with a certain degree of morphological difference. If we find a new group of individuals at a different locality, we use the scale of differences between the species of the familiar area to help us in determining whether the new form is a different species or not. These scales of differences are empirically reached and differ in every family and genus. An ornithologist knows by experience that the differences between good species of *Empidonax* and *Collocalia* are much slighter than the differences between male and female or between subspecies in birds of paradise or humming birds. The important point is that the biological gap between species (reproductively isolated groups) is, in general, correlated with certain morphological differences. This correlation, which naturally has exceptions like every biological phenomenon, permits the experienced taxonomist to determine in many cases whether to describe a new form as a new species or a subspecies, even though he knows nothing about its biology. When such information becomes available at a later period, it nearly always confirms the judgment of the competent taxonomist. To the adherent of a morphological species concept, any clear-cut morphological difference is a species difference. To the supporter of a biological species concept, the degree of morphological difference is simply considered as a clue to the biological distinctness and is always subordinated in importance to biological factors.

The application of a biological species definition is possible only in well-studied taxonomic groups, since it is based on a rather exact knowledge of geographical distribution and on the certainty of the absence of interbreeding with other similar species. It seems to work well not only in birds, but in all bisexual animals (vertebrate and invertebrate). There is, however, some question as to whether this species definition can also

[1] See p. 148 for a definition of these terms.

be applied to aberrant cases, such as the mating types of protozoa, the self-fertilizing hermaphrodites, animals with obligatory parthenogenesis, and certain groups of parasites and host specialists. A much more intimate knowledge of the taxonomy and biology of the doubtful groups is needed before this point can be settled. The known number of cases in which the above species definition may be inapplicable is very small, and there seems to be no reason at the present time for "watering" our species definition to include these exceptions. It will always be possible to add supplementary clauses, should a need for them arise.

The Plant Species

It is also doubtful whether this species definition applies equally well to plants. Plants differ from animals in a number of highly important biological attributes. An animal can move around, while a plant is fixed to one spot from the moment of the germination of the seed to its death. In consequence, fertilization is a more or less mechanical process in plants, and, since the pollen is generally transported by wind or insects, "mistakes" are frequent, that is hybrids are common in nature. The possibility of such mistakes is largely eliminated in animals by the development of courtship patterns and by other means, described in Chapter IX. Still, even in plants, fertilization is not entirely a mechanical process, as Dr. Anderson points out. Polyploidy, apogamy, and sympatric hybrid swarms are phenomena which are common in plants and unknown, or at least decidedly rare and unimportant in animals. The "small species" (jordanons) found among plants do not seem to have an exact homologue in animals either.

Compared with all these other modes of speciation, geographic speciation does not seem very important in plants. In fact, there are many botanical taxonomists who even today pay no attention to geographic subspecies. A study of various works on plant taxonomy has convinced me, however, that there are many genera the classification of which would greatly benefit by the introduction of a polytypic species concept, based on the criteria of geographic distribution. The revisions of the North African species of *Biscutella* (Manton 1934), of the species of *Selenia* (Martin 1940), of most of the Spanish species of *Antirrhinum* (Baur 1932), and many species groups in *Calochortus* (Ownbey 1940) are a few recent pieces of work which have come to my attention and which might be quoted in this connection.

CHAPTER VI

THE POLYTYPIC SPECIES, IN NATURE AND IN SYSTEMATICS

WE HAVE LEARNED in the preceding chapter that a revolutionary change of the species concept is in the making, a change which not only affects taxonomic procedure, but which also contributes considerably toward a better understanding of the speciation process. Our findings were largely based on the rather small field of bird and butterfly taxonomy, and on selected examples at that. A number of questions will have to be answered before we can recommend, without reservation, the broad application of the new concept. Such questions are:

1. How prevalent are polytypic species?

2. Does the new concept really contribute toward a simplification of the taxonomic system and procedure?

3. Is the new species concept applicable in all animal groups?

4. To what extent has the new species concept already been applied in animal taxonomy?

Let us see what information we have in answer to these questions.

THE PREVALENCE OF POLYTYPIC SPECIES

Some of the previous discussions may have fostered the impression that all species break up into geographic races. On the other hand, a considerable number of authors claim even today that, at least in the groups in which they are working, geographic variation is an exceptional phenomenon, if not altogether absent. It seems necessary, in view of this apparent discrepancy, to undertake a survey of some of the better-known families and genera and determine exactly how many species are polytypic and how many monotypic. Naturally, in making such a survey one is at once confronted with the differences in the species concept among the various groups. Such a survey of the New Guinea birds, if undertaken in 1850, would have resulted in the statement that only 2 percent of the species are polytypic; the same survey repeated in 1941 shows that fully 80 percent of the species are polytypic. Kinsey's (1937b) claim that geographic variation is not a widespread phenomenon, since only 5 local races (or 3.2 percent) are found in 158 insular species of gall wasps, does not carry much weight. Goldschmidt (1937) and others have pointed out that most of Kinsey's insular "species" are nothing but members of widespread polytypic species and that they strengthen rather than weaken the concept of the polytypic species.

The attempt in Table 7 to determine the percentage of monotypic species in various groups of animals must be taken merely as an approximation, since absolute accuracy cannot yet be reached, owing to the divergence of the species concepts. The basic figures in this tabulation were provided by Rensch (1933), but they have been rearranged and augmented by me.

TABLE 7

THE PREVALENCE OF MONOTYPIC SPECIES IN A NUMBER OF GROUPS OF ANIMALS

SYSTEMATIC GROUP	TOTAL NUMBER OF SPECIES	NUMBER MONO-TYPIC	PERCENT MONO-TYPIC
European Mammals (Miller 1912)	196	145	75.8
N. Amer. Mammals (Miller 1924)	1,364	995	73.0
European Mammals (Ökland 1937)	168	92	54.7
Clausilia Snails (Rensch 1933)	37	21	56.8
European Reptiles (Mertens and	91	48	52.7
European Amphibia (Müller 1928)	37	19	51.8
Cypraea Sea Shells (Schilder and Schilder 1938)	165	81	49.1
Indo-Austr. Butterflies (Jordan *et al.* 1927)	695	283	40.7
Palearctic Passeres (Hartert 1923)	522	197	37.7
Palearctic Passeres (Hartert 1936)	516	153	29.7
New Guinea Passeres (Mayr 1941a)	309	64	20.4
New Guinea Non-Passeres (Mayr 1941a)	240	47	19.6

Two obvious conclusions can be drawn from this tabulation. The first is that a certain number of species are definitely monotypic. There is very little chance that future discoveries or changes in our species concept will materially reduce the number of monotypic species of New Guinea birds now set at 111. These species either have such a small range that within it there is no opportunity for geographic variation or else they are exceedingly stable for some reason which is still unknown to us. Such species, with very limited geographic variability, seem to exist in most groups of animals. The second conclusion which we can draw from these figures is that the percentage of monotypic species recorded in a certain group at a given period depends to a considerable extent on the degree of finality which the classification of the respective group has reached. The figure dropped in Palearctic song birds (Passeres) from 38 to 30 percent within thirteen years. In European mammals it dropped in twenty-five years from 76 to 55 percent, and there is every reason to believe that a considerable further drop is to be expected in the next tabulation. Birds seem to have the highest prevalence of polytypic species, according to the present figures, but this is due merely to the more advanced condition of avian taxonomy. Some poikilothermal animals, such as certain insects and most snails, being more sedentary and more dependent on their local environment than birds, seem to have many more subspecies per species and per unit of area than birds. No actual comparative figures can yet be given to substantiate this claim, but one needs only to look at a distribution map of some polytypic species of snails, gall wasps, bumblebees, or carabid beetles and compare it with a distribution map of a species of birds from the same region to appreciate the truth of the above claim.

A few figures from recent monographs may be appended as additional illustrations. No finality of classification has yet been reached in the warbler genus *Phylloscopus* (Ticehurst 1938a). At present, 30 species with 67 geographic races are recognized, but 4 of these species are probably only subspecies. Even so, 39 percent of the species are monotypic, although among the polytypic species of this genus one has 6·and one has 8 races. In the butterfly genus *Coenonympha*, Davenport (1941) recognizes 17 species, of which 11 are monotypic, while one species (*tullia*) has no less than 31 geographic races. The number of 11 monotypic species in this genus will eventually have to be reduced, since it includes several geographic representatives. Only such forms are recognized by this author as subspecies as intergrade either in space or by individual variation. The same is true for a revision of the genus *Helicigona* by Knipper (1939), in which 53 monotypic and 18 polytypic species are listed. *Pachycephala pectoralis* from the East Indies and the Papuan and Australian regions seems to be the polytypic species of bird with the highest number of races; no less than 80 subspecies are recognized.

The conclusion from this evidence is that a high proportion of the species in the well-worked animal groups have been found to be polytypic, but that a certain percentage of species does not break up into distinct geographic races.

THE SIMPLIFICATION OF TAXONOMY

The Linnæan species was the lowest category; it was monotypic and could be defined on a strictly morphological basis. These attributes are considered great virtues by many taxonomists, who believe that no practical advantage would be gained by accepting the biological species concept. Such a claim cannot be upheld if we look at the better-known groups of animals (see above, Chapter V, p. 110). It is not only possible to present a much truer picture of relationships by calling geographic races subspecies rather than species, but it also leads to a considerable simplification of the system. Rensch (1934) has described very graphically, by means of a specific instance, how classifications were simplified by the introduction of the polytypic species concept:

Nineteen different species and one subspecies of the bird genus *Sitta* (nuthatch) had been described from the Palearctic region between 1758 and 1900. . . . All these species differed in size, color, proportions of bill, tail, wings, construction of the nest, etc. No intergradation was known among these forms. The areas of origin were different in most cases but some species also lived in the same region. The taxonomy of the Palearctic *Sitta*, thus, was clear and unequivocal. With the increasing exploration of the Palearctic, more and more forms of *Sitta* became known whose classification proved to be more difficult. These forms were still rather distinct but they were so close to named species that they were considered to be merely subspecies or varieties of these. Thus Reichenow (1901) described a form *caucasica* which he considered to be a subspecies of the central European *caesia*, while Witherby (1903) considered his new form *persica* to be a subspecies of the north European *europaea*. But there was no reason why one should not have made *caucasica* a subspecies of *europaea* instead of *caesia*, the more so as a superficially very similar form *S. europaea britannica* had been described by Hartert (1900). The species concept thus became vague; the specialists were no longer in agreement as to how to delimit *Sitta europaea* with its subspecies against *S. caesia* with its subspecies. Similar difficulties appeared with other species of *Sitta* and it seemed as if the increase in material would lead to chaos in nomenclature, particularly since a growing discrepancy developed between the species definitions of the various authors.

Chaos would certainly have prevailed if one had retained the old ideas concerning species. It was more than a coincidence that in this critical epoch a new school of thought appeared in ornithology which soon began to become dominant under the leadership of O. Kleinschmidt and E. Hartert. They put the study of the geographic distribution of the various forms into the foreground and they searched systematically for forms which were both morphologically and geographically transitional between two "species." In the case of the forms of *Sitta* it was possible to unite thus not only *persica*, *britannica*, and other races, but also the central European *caesia*, with the species *europaea*. The difference of opinion, mentioned above, was thus removed: *caucasica* was a geographical representative of *caesia* as well as of *europaea*. In this way many "species" were combined into groups of forms, mutually replacing each other geographically,—so called geographical rassenkreise. . . . When E. Hartert began (1904) publication of "Vögel der paläarktischen Fauna" he was able to simplify the chaos of twenty-four known *Sitta* species into four rassenkreise, leaving three isolated species. The number of geographical races has still increased since then and today the rassenkreis *Sitta europaea* alone contains twenty-six geographical races (without the contested "subtilrassen").

Taxonomy thus has become definite again: the new "large species," i.e. the geographic rassenkreise, are clearly defined, are natural units. There are no transitions from one rassenkreis to another one: the rassenkreis *Sitta europaea* extends across the whole of the Palearctic region. All of its races (which are usually connected with each other by gliding intergradation) are distinguished from the races of the rassenkreis *neumayer* (which is distributed from the Balkans to Baluchistan) by chestnut-colored flanks in the male, or from the races of *S. canadensis* by the lack of a black crown, etc. [Rensch 1934:7–9, from Goldschmidt 1940].

Ornithologists have revised, in the same manner, genus after genus with a corresponding simplification. What is now a single polytypic species, *Zonotrichia capensis*, composed of 23 geographical races, consisted formerly of 8 separate species (Chapman 1940). In 1910 was published the last complete list of all birds, recording 19,000 species of birds. Since that time about 8,000 additional forms have been described, but they are now arranged in 8,500 species, many of which are polytypic, instead of in 27,000 species. The total number of species to be memorized by the taxonomist has thus been cut by two-thirds. The practical advantage of this simplification is so obvious that nothing more needs to be said. The scientific advantage of the method is that the species has become once more a uniform and unequivocal concept, instead of a mixture of two different categories, true reproductively isolated species and morphologically distinct geographic races.

THE OCCURRENCE OF GEOGRAPHIC VARIATION THROUGHOUT THE ANIMAL SYSTEM

The polytypic species concept is based on the principle of geographic variation; it can therefore become of importance only if geographic variation is widespread among animals. The same is true for geographic speciation, a process which depends on geographic variation. We have quoted in the preceding chapter cases of geographic variation in mammals, birds, frogs, butterflies, turbellarians, and a few other groups, but the task remains of making a complete survey of all orders and classes of animals, in order to find out exactly in what animal groups geographic variation is found and to what extent it is absent. Such a survey, however, is possible only if we apply a uniform terminology to the lower taxonomic categories. It is obvious, for example, that an author might deny the existence of intraspecific geographic variation if he calls the species the lowest recognizable unit. He would simply divide every species into two, as soon as he found that it contained two recognizable geographic races.

Rensch, in 1929, made the first systematic survey of the occurrence of geographic variation. During the last twelve years geographic variation has been found to occur in many additional groups. The main difficulty of an even more general application of the geographic principle lies in the fact that the species in many animal groups are known from such few specimens and localities that it is impossible in many cases to be certain whether two similar "species" from different localities are really good species or merely geographic races.

It is now certain that at least some species with geographic variation occur in all groups of terrestrial animals that have been sufficiently studied. More and more cases of geographic variation have recently been reported in marine animals, including even such ancient groups as the brachiopods. As a whole, of course, marine animals apparently show little variation in space, but this seems to be due primarily to our insufficient knowledge. The so-called cosmopolitan species appear to constitute another exception to the prevalence of geographical variation.

Certain species seem to extend from one end of the earth to the other without any noticeable change. This is sometimes due to insufficient taxonomic analysis, for in birds, for example, nearly all the cosmopolitan species are now known to break up into geographic races. Sometimes these widespread species are not naturally cosmopolitan, but owe their present wide distribution to human assistance. In still other cases, and this is particularly true for certain marine forms, the species are known to be very old (on paleontological evidence) and seem to have lost all evolutionary plasticity. They may be "dead-ends" of evolution. There are also the cases of very small organisms (certain protozoa, rotifers, and so forth) that owe their wide distribution to wind dispersal. Whether or not they are able to speciate without geographic variation will be discussed later (Chapter VIII). And finally there are forms with aberrant methods of reproduction, such as obligatory parthenogenesis and self-fertilizing hermaphroditism, which may speciate instantaneously, instead of through geographic variation.

THE PRACTICAL APPLICATION OF THE POLYTYPIC SPECIES IN MODERN ANIMAL TAXONOMY

The polytypic species principle has been employed more consistently in birds than in any other group of animals. This is not surprising, when we realize not only that more than 98 percent of all species probably existing are known and described, but that even subspecific variation has been well studied in most species and that the ranges of the various sub-species are mapped in detail. The primary reason that the polytypic species has not been adopted more generally by the specialists of other groups is the lack of material or of distributional information. Many species of spiders, insects, and so forth, are known from single specimens or from a single sex, or, if series are available, they come from localities that are separated by hundreds or thousands of miles of unexplored territory. Modern systematic methods cannot be applied to such inadequate material.

The transition from a purely morphological to a more biological species concept was a slow and gradual process, even in ornithology. It started about the middle of the last century and was more or less completed by 1930. In other, less well-known taxonomic groups, stages of this transition have now been reached (1942) which correspond to the ornithological species concepts of 1910 or 1890 or 1860, according to the degree of completeness to which the geographic variation is known. In the period during which the shift is made in a taxonomic group from one species "model" to the next, there is, of course, considerable uncertainty among the workers as to what forms to call species and what subspecies. This is well illustrated in the case of the birds occurring on the large island of New Guinea (Mayr 1941a).

The New Guinea bird fauna comprises a total of 649 species with 1,018 subspecies (not counting the typical race of each species). If we arrange these 1,018 forms according to the period in which they were described, we can see a steady decrease in the percentage of those that were originally described as species.

TABLE 8

HISTORY OF SUBSPECIES CONCEPT AS ILLUSTRATED BY NEW GUINEA BIRDS

PERIOD	TOTAL NUMBER OF SUBSPECIES DESCRIBED	ORIGINALLY DESCRIBED AS FULL SPECIES	THE PERCENTAGE OF SUBSPECIES ORIGINALLY DESCRIBED AS SPECIES
1758–1869	143	140	97.9
1870–1889	216	194	89.8
1890–1899	113	84	74.7
1900–1909	57	14	24.6
1910–1919	124	31	25.0
1920–1929	46	1	1.2
1930–1941	319	1	0.3
Total	1,018	465	45.7

Table 8 illustrates the changing species concept in ornithology better than anything else could do. Up to 1870 most geographic races were considered species; the change was made between 1870 and 1919, and since 1920 nearly all geographic races have been described as subspecies. In all, no less than 465 forms that are now considered subspecies were originally described as species.

The student of spiders may still (1942) have the species concept which the ornithologist had in 1880, and the student of weevils that of the ornithologist of 1900. This is one of the difficulties which we encounter when we want to compare the "species" of one systematic group with the species of another. Other difficulties are provided by ecological factors, as we shall see in a later chapter. There are certain conventions in every field, and, even though the worker in one systematic group may know exactly what is meant in his group by a "species," he may have but little knowledge and understanding of the "species" of other groups.

The present mature status of classification of birds into species and subspecies was reached only by the trial and error method. Some authors in their enthusiasm over the geographic principle, insisted on including all geographic representatives of common ancestry in wide polytypic species. The result was frequently quite absurd. According to this principle, all the Birds of Paradise of the genus *Paradisaea* (with the exception of the two mountain species *guilielmi* and *rudolphi*) would have to be reduced to subspecies. The composite species would contain, at least in this case, true geographic representatives. In other cases not even this was true. In their eagerness to apply the new ideas, some authors reduced to subspecies even widely overlapping species (*Meliphaga*, *Collocalia*, *Edolisoma*) or else they included mountain and lowland species in the same species, and so forth. Most dangerous is the attempt to try to base the new classification simply on published locality records, without actual comparison of the material. Wherever the polytypic species principle, based on geographic representation, is for the first time applied in a group, some authors go too far, as a few ornithologists did in the years 1920-1932. A healthy reaction will, however, soon set in and help to establish a balance.

THE APPLICATION OF THE POLYTYPIC SPECIES CONCEPT IN VARIOUS TAXONOMIC GROUPS

Rensch has made a number of surveys (1929, 1933, 1934, 1939a) on the application of the polytypic species in modern zoölogical writing. It would be useless repetition to cover the same ground again, but I advise those who are interested in this subject to consult not only Rensch's original papers, but also the summaries of Cuénot (1936), Dobzhansky (1941a), Goldschmidt (1940), Huxley (1940), and Robson and Richards (1936). We shall rather concentrate on those recent taxonomic works that have not yet been reported in the above-mentioned reviews. Furthermore, our presentation will not be very exhaustive, since it is impossible for the specialist in one particular taxonomic field to keep track of the publications in all the other fields. The extreme scattering of taxonomic zoölogical literature and the absence of review journals devoted to speciation or of any journal, with the possible exception of the *Archiv für Naturgeschichte*, that is entirely devoted to general systematics, makes serious omissions unavoidable. The interest of the taxonomist in questions of speciation and general systematics has reached such a degree, in recent years, that it would be exceptional for a taxonomic paper not to contain something that would justify its inclusion in the subsequent survey, but only a small fraction of them can be mentioned.

VERTEBRATES

Mammals.—The polytypic species is generally accepted by the mammalogist, but mammals as a whole are far less well known than birds. This is primarily due to the difficulties of preparation of the larger mammals and to the nocturnal habits of many of the smaller ones. The Archbold Expeditions discovered three new mammalian genera in New Guinea, as against one new bird genus, even though there are perhaps twice as many species of birds as mammals in that country. Many of the mammal taxonomists still insist on perfect intergradation as a subspecies criterion and treat every insular, morphologically separated population as a separate species. This results in the recognition of a high percentage of monotypic species. However, the new biological species concept is gradually gaining more and more adherents. Mammals are very favorable material for modern taxonomic studies, because many species (mice, for example) can be obtained in large series and their skulls can be measured much more accurately than any avian character. Good recent papers are those of Dice on *Peromyscus* (1936 ff.), of Orr on the California rabbits (1940), of Cowan (1940) on the American sheep, of Rümmler on the New Guinea Murids (1938), and of the Californian school (Grinnell, Hall, and others) on North American species. For additional literature, consult the *Journal of Mammalogy*, the *Zeitschrift für Säugetierkunde*, the *Proceedings of the Zoological Society of London*, and the various museum journals.

Birds.—It is generally agreed that birds are taxonomically the best-worked and best-known animal group. A striking feature of many monographs, particularly those concerning the Palearctic and Nearctic regions, is the close integration of the taxonomic facts with life-history data. See for example the papers of Blanchard (1941) on the Pacific White-crowned Sparrows (*Zonotrichia leucophrys*), of Lynes on the genus *Cisticola* (1930), of Lack (1942, unpublished) on the genus *Geospiza*, of Moffit (unpublished) on the Canada Goose (*Branta*), of Miller on *Lanius* (1931) and *Junco* (1941), and so forth. Good monographs are those of Ticehurst (1938a) on *Phylloscopus*, of Stresemann (1940a) on the Honey-Buzzard (*Pernis*), of Mayr *et al.* (1931 ff.) on Polynesian Birds, of Chapman (1940) on *Zonotrichia*, and of Stegmann on *Larus*, to mention just a few. Enough is known taxonomically to permit special studies, such as those of Stresemann and others on polymorphism (see p. 77) and of Meise and others on hybrid zones and populations (see p. 264). Modern lists, such as those of Hartert (1903-1938) on Palearctic Birds, that of the A. O. U. Checklist Committee (1931) on Nearctic Birds, of Chasen (1935) on Malaysian Birds, and of Mayr (1941a) on New Guinea Birds are valuable for the working out of percentages of monotypic species and genera, for the percentage of polytypic species in various families, and so forth. There is one respect in which ornithology has lagged behind other taxonomic fields and that is in the application of biometric methods and their statistical evaluation. A good start to overcome this deficiency was made in several papers of the California school (Linsdale, Miller, and others) and in Lack's *Geospiza* study (1942).

Reptiles.—The application of the polytypic species concept has made tremendous strides during the last twenty years, but, as with mammals, it too often excludes insular populations for which there is valid evidence of biological conspecificity. European herpetologists, under the leadership of Müller and Mertens, seem to have gone further than American authors in the combining of allopatric forms in polytypic species. Eiselt (1940) shows, in a study of the skink *Eumeces schneideri*, that what older authors (Taylor and others) had considered several species is really one polytypic species with five or six geographic races. The taxonomic procedure in herpetology has been discussed by Dunn (1934). American herpetology has produced in recent years some excellent papers, although it seems to me, as an ornithologist, that the terminology of the categories could be further improved and modernized (see p. 172, for a discussion of the work of Stuart [1941] on *Dryadophis*). Some authors are still guided in their nomenclature by similarities, rather than by relationships. Miss Cochran (1941) writes, for example: "In order to express the greater or lesser degree of difference between the Hispaniolan *Ameivas*, it seems best to recognize *taeniura*, *rosamondae* and *barbouri* as full and distinct species, to make *beatensis* a subspecies of *lineolata*, and *abbottii*, *affinis* and *woodi* subspecies of *chrysolaema*." But something seems to be wrong with this arrangement, since two *chrysolaema* subspecies (*affinis* and *chrysolaema*) occur in the same localities. To judge by the author's own data, it seems as if only two polytypic species were involved: *chrysolaema* and *lineolata* (including *taeniura*). All of the strongly differentiated island forms seem to be geographic representatives of one or the other of the two mainland species. An attempt by Fitch (1940a) to clear up the complicated classification of the Pacific garter snakes was presumably successful so far as the taxonomic analysis is concerned, but his strict adherence to the intergradation principle led to an absurd nomenclature. There are three groups of forms involved, as the attached diagram shows, the *ordinoides* group, the *couchii* group, and the *elegans* group. The ornithologist would call them three species. The forms that belong to each of the three groups constitute a morphological and biological unit. The only complications are the following. First, two forms of the *couchii* group (*hammondii* and *digueti*) are geographically isolated in southern California or Lower California and are thus physically unable to intergrade with the other forms of *couchii*. Secondly, one hybrid population is found between *atratus* and *elegans*, and another one between *biscutatus* and *hygrophilus*. In five of six cases in which an *elegans* race comes in contact with or overlaps a *couchii* race, no interbreeding takes place. This is likewise true in two of three cases of contact between *ordinoides* with *elegans* and in all three cases of overlap between *ordinoides* and *couchii*. But Fitch puts all three species in a single species, which he mistakenly calls an *Artenkreis*, simply because the isolating mechanism between the three species breaks down in two of the twelve instances of contact. On the other hand, he treats *hammondii* and *digueti* as separate species, even though he admits that they belong to the *couchii* group, merely because they happen to be isolated! (Table 9). I have treated this case in detail to show that the mere use of trinomials does not always indicate the proper application of the modern species concept.

Modern methods and terminologies are also employed in the paper of Grobman (1941) on the Green Snake and Gloyd's (1940) excellent monograph on rattlesnakes. Herpetologists are far ahead of ornithologists in the application of biometric methods and their statistical evaluation. The papers of Klauber (1936 ff.) are models of this type of work.

TABLE 9

INTERBREEDING AND OVERLAPPING IN THE THAMNOPHIS ordinoides GROUP

Thamnophis	ordinoides	atratus	hygrophilus	couchii	gigas	hammondii	digueti	vagrans	biscutatus	elegans	hueyi
ordinoides		X	O			O		O		O	
atratus	X		O							X¹	
hygrophilus	O	O		X	X	(X)			X²	O	
couchii			X		X	X		O		O	
gigas			X	X		X					
hammondii	O		(X)	X	X		X			O	O
digueti						X					
vagrans	O			O					X	X	(X)
biscutatus			X²					X		X	X
elegans	O	X¹	O	O		O		X	X		(X)
hueyi						O		(X)	X	(X)	

X = interbreeding; O = overlap without interbreeding; ¹ ² = hybrid zones.

Taxonomists tend to be somewhat suspicious of statistical methods, owing to the clumsy way in which these have frequently been applied to biological problems by authors who were not biologists, but if such methods are superimposed on a biological analysis, they can only be of advantage. They permit the expression of variability in absolute figures and the determination of the significance of differences between samples, to mention only two applications. For further information one should consult Klauber (1941a), Simpson and Roe (1939), and the standard statistical texts (Fisher, Snedecor, and others).

Amphibia.—Geographic variation in this class is very pronounced and has led to a widespread acceptance of a polytypic species concept (see Mertens and Müller 1928). The work of Witschi on the sex races of *Rana esculenta* and that of Moore on the geographic temperature races has already been reviewed by us (p. 47). W. Herre (1936) presents detailed data on geographic variation in salamanders and newts and points out the simplification of classification resulting from a recognition of this variation. Dunn (1940) shows that *Ambystoma tigrinum* breaks up into at least seven geographic races. Some other authors, however, still call every form a species which is separated by a gap from its next geographic representative. Goin and Netting (1940), for example, divide into three species, *Rana areolata, sevosa,* and *capito,* what seems to me to be merely one polytypic species of frog.

Fresh-water fish.—The work on geographic variation and the application of a more modern species concept have been reviewed in a number of recent papers (Hubbs 1934, 1940a, Worthington 1940). There are two principal difficulties that beset the student of fresh-water fishes. One is the strong and only rather recently appreciated phenotypical plasticity of many species. I have already quoted the very suggestive work of Hile (see p. 62) on this subject. This seems also to be the principal reason for the muddled state of the taxonomy of many genera. It was believed at one time that the classification of the difficult genus *Salvelinus* had been solved by Wagler (1937), who thought that there were four species in the Alpine lakes of Europe, each with numerous geographic races. The more recent work of Steinmann (1941), however, indicates that we are further away from a solution than ever.

The other difficulty is presented by the fact that many of the fresh-water habitats are as well isolated as oceanic islands and are, like them, inhabited by well-differentiated forms, separated by clearcut gaps from their nearest geographic representatives. Fish taxonomists, in general, have not been able to resist the temptation to call all such forms species, even though it would be biologically more correct to combine a number of such forms into polytypic species. This would simplify the classification and would, incidentally, also do away with the need for many recently created genera. The whole genus *Platypoecilus* seems to me to be just one polytypic species, or at best a superspecies (see p. 171), and in the family Goodeidae, also, most "genera" are based on groups of allopatric "species" which might just as well be considered subspecies of polytypic species (but see Hubbs and Turner 1939). The polytypic species concept has not yet been fully applied to North American fresh-water fishes. As far as Europe is concerned, Ökland's list (1937), which is primarily based on the work of Berg, renders a fair account of the status of fresh-water-fish systematics.

INSECTS

There is little doubt that insects, as a whole, offer a most promising field for modern species studies. They have a number of practical advantages; for example, their preservation for the collection requires no elaborate technique like that of birds or mammals, nor do they occupy very much space in collections. Thus they invite mass collecting, and this has been done for many species. The difficulty with insects is twofold: one is the tremendous number of species, variously estimated as between a half million and a million and a half; the other is our insufficient knowledge of the behavior and the ecology of nearly all but a few economically important species. Also, the network of collecting stations is rarely dense enough to provide sufficient information about the degree of geographic variation. Exceptions to this are found among the more common butterflies and large beetles of Europe and North America and among some groups that were assiduously collected by the worker himself, such as *Cynipidae* by Kinsey, *Ceuthophilus* by Hubbell, and so forth. There is every reason to believe that insects will gain an ever-increasing importance in the study of speciation.

Butterflies and moths.—Of all insects, the butterflies are perhaps the best known group, primarily because of the collecting activities of many enthusiastic amateurs. The large series of specimens gathered by them, combined with many workable taxonomic characters of color, size, proportions, and structure, makes them a particularly favorable material. These advantages are only partially offset by the high individual variability of many species, caused either by genetic polymorphism or by phenotypical plasticity (seasonal races, and so forth). Eller's (1936) analysis of the Palearctic races of the swallow-tail is perhaps the most detailed taxonomic study of any single species of butterflies. K. Jordan deserves much credit for promoting for more than forty years a sane, broad polytypic species concept, rather in advance of most of his contemporaries. His work on the Indo-Australian *Papilio* and related genera is exemplary. It would lead too far afield to list all the good modern lepidoptera papers, the authors of which have adopted the polytypic species. The *Parnassius* literature contains much interesting information, although the naming of local races (microsubspecies) has been carried to an extreme. The naming of all color variants, seasonal forms, and so forth completely obscures the major geographic trends in some recent papers, particularly those of Verity. Davenport (1941) has shown how much the classification in the genus *Coenonympha* could be improved by eliminating all such "nomenclatorial weeds."

There is a single genus of moths, the genus *Lymantria*, to which we must devote special attention, since it was recently made the basis of some very sweeping generalizations (Goldschmidt 1940). Unfortunately, the taxonomy of this genus is in a state of complete disorder, since the family to which it belongs has at the present time no specialist and the treatment in the leading catalogues (Seitz, Macrolepidoptera; Junk, Lepidopterorum Catalogus) are nothing better than uncritical compilations. It is clear enough that Goldschmidt was not in the least justified in saying, (*op. cit.*, p. 144): "The two nearest relatives of *Lymantria dispar* are the species *mathura* and *monacha.*" There is no doubt that *mathura* and *monacha* at least have tropical relatives with which they are much more closely related than with *dispar*, while the latter seems to be an isolated species without any close relatives. It is interesting in this connection that many of the older taxonomists, realizing the isolated position of *dispar*, kept it in a separate genus, *Porthetria*.

Lymantria dispar is a widespread species with many, but poorly characterized races. This is what we would expect from its range throughout the Palearctic Region, and it is paralleled in nearly all the bird species of similar range. The differences between most of its subspecies are so slight that Goldschmidt was able to deceive a specialist of moths by introducing a few mutations into the populations. This is rather a different picture from really well-defined subspecies which no specialist would misidentify, no matter how many mutations were introduced. On the other hand, in the few places where *L. dispar* has an insular range its subspecies are well defined and have, in fact, all the earmarks of incipient species. The subspecies *hokkaidoensis* is strikingly different from the other Japanese subspecies, as well as from the mainland forms. Some authors consider it a separate species, and Goldschmidt had difficulty for many years in producing the cross Honshiu ♀ x Hokkaido ♂ (*op. cit.* p. 124). But what is more important is the fact that the Hokkaido race and the population from the opposite shore of the main island of Japan produce extreme intersexes and sex inverts, when crossed. There is little doubt that a hybrid population resulting from a mixture of the two races in nature would be inferior in viability to the parental populations. The establishment of discontinuity between the Honshiu race and the Hokkaido race is thus almost complete.

The genus *Lymantria* is, primarily, a tropical genus. Seitz lists 13 other Palearctic species in addition to *dispar*, *mathura*, and *monacha* (*op. cit.*, II (1910), 126), 58 Indo-Australian species (*op. cit.*, X (1923), 320–328), and 44 African species (*op. cit.*, XIV (1927), 193–196). Of the tropical forms, probably not more than 25 percent are known and described at present, and many of the species listed in the present catalogues are unquestionably only subspecies of other species or perhaps only color phases. The illustrations of the various species published in the volumes cited seem to suggest that some of the Palearctic species are nothing but offshoots of widespread tropical superspecies: For example, *monacha* seems to belong to the *turneri* (Australia)-*novaeguineae-asoetria* (Java-Tenasserim)-*concolor* (Burma-Himalayas) chain. Many of the tropical "species" represent each other geographically and are so similar that one must assume that they are probably members of the same *rassenkreis*; for example, *viola* (Bombay)-*grandis* (Ceylon), *rhodina* (E. Himalayas)-*cerebrosa* (W. Him.), *lunata-ochorina-galinara-similis-niassica*, and in Africa the chain *albimacula-metella-marwitzi-mimiata-melia-banamoides*. Many others could be mentioned, but they would not prove anything that is in the least different from what is known from other and better-studied groups of animals. These examples are nothing but suggestions of probable relationship; they can not be proven as long as the present disorganized condition of the genus *Lymantria* continues. Many of the geographically representative species on the tropical islands cited above seem to be about as different as the two good species *dispar* and *monacha*, particularly if the far-distant links of the chain are compared. This condition corresponds exactly to that found in tropical species of mammals and birds, because the populations are old and the isolation is very thorough. When Goldschmidt speaks of "the relatively small differences of the subspecies," he refers to findings in *Lymantria dispar* occurring in a part of the Palearctic region in which we have almost exactly the same condition in the majority of species of birds. There is a considerable number of species of birds known in which the Japanese race is almost indistinguishable from the European one, and very few species in which there are striking differences that would suggest a high level of speciation. We may summarize our findings by saying that the taxonomic situation in the genus *Lymantria* supports rather than weakens our general thesis on the importance of geographic variation for speciation.

Beetles.—Very little is known, as yet, about the geographic variation of small-sized beetles, but the workers on the larger species employ the polytypic species concept widely. The work of Breuning, Krumbiegel (1932, 1936a,b,c), and Zarapkin (1934) on *Carabus*; of Strohmeyer (1928) on *Cypholoba*; of Koch (1940, 1941) on *Pimelia* and other flightless Tenebrionids; of Endrödi (1938) on *Oryctes nasicornis*; and of Dobzhansky (1933) on Coccinellids are a few of the many recent papers that have come to my attention. Delkeskamp (1933) was able to reduce the 28 oriental "species" of the genus *Encaustes* (Erot.) to 4 by applying the polytypic species concept. This process of synthesis and simplification is, however, possible only in genera in which sufficient material is available.

Hymenoptera.—The polytypic species occurs commonly among the hymenoptera. Most of Kinsey's (1930, 1936) species "complexes" of Cynipids are polytypic species, as defined by us, although in a few cases two or three overlapping species seem to be included in one species complex. In the *Cynips dugèsi* complex, for example, I would judge, on the basis of the data provided by Kinsey, that the following 20 forms are geographic races of a single species: *cubitalis, brevipennata, capronae, simulatrix, subnigra, pupoides, catena, cava, emergens, deceptrix, occidua, pictor, oriunda, vasta, oriens, pulex, pusa, vulgata, dugèsi,* and *pumilio.* All of them are allopatric except *vulgata* and *dugèsi,* which apparently overlap. The other 9 or 10 forms included by Kinsey in the *dugèsi* complex seem to belong to from 2 to 4 additional species, although some of them seem to be conspecific with what Kinsey calls the *bulboides* complex. Naturally, not being a student of Cynipids, I can supply only a paper analysis, with all its inherent weaknesses. I present it merely as an attempt at approximating the *Cynips* species to the polytypic bird species. A modern, up-to-date review of the species situation and of geographic variation in the genus *Bombus* (bumblebees) was recently presented by Reinig (1939), showing that the species there corresponds, indeed, very closely to the bird species, except that the geographic races in birds are rarely as localized. Furthermore, there is nothing in birds comparable to the enormous polymorphism found in *Bombus.* Geographic variation in the honeybee (*Apis mellifica*) was studied by Alpatov (1929) and in the wasp genus *Polistes* by Zimmermann (1931). Our knowledge of the parasitic hymenoptera is still largely in a confused state, as is that of the solitary bees. Sibling species are of common occurrence among ants, but most of them are still listed as "varieties" and this has impeded a more rapid acceptance of a modern species concept. The lack of color patterns and the reduction of external structural detail, particularly in the worker, is perhaps one of the reasons for the rather backward condition of ant systematics. Morphological evolution in the ants seems to have been rather stagnant since the Miocene.

Flies.—A few years ago geographic variation was practically unknown among diptera and the species was strictly that of 1758. In the meantime, subspecies have been described in several Syrphid species, and more modern taxonomic work has been undertaken in several medically important groups. Zumpt (1940) showed that the tsetse fly (*Glossina palpalis*) can be divided into three distinct geographic races (*palpalis, fuscipes,* and *martini*) and that there is complete intergradation in the contact zone of the three subspecies. The greatest progress, in regard to geographic variation among diptera, has been made recently in the genus *Drosophila*. It has been found that this genus possesses, in addition to semi-cosmopolitan and semi-domestic species such as *Drosophila melanogaster, D. immigrans, D. hydei,* and so forth, a number of truly "wild" species, which show a pattern of geographic variation not unlike that found in birds, butterflies, and the like. Work on these geographic races is made somewhat difficult by the fact that the morphological differences between many of the species of this genus are very slight; in other words, many sibling species occur. Cases like that of the three species *D. pseudoobscura* A—*D. pseudoobscura* B—*D. miranda,* or of *D. melanogaster* and *D. simulans,* or of the *D. affinis* complex, warn us to be cautious. The results of Spencer (1940, 1941) and of Patterson and his coworkers (1942) on the *D. mulleri, D. virilis,* and *D. macrospina* complexes cannot be interpreted with finality until much more collecting and breeding has been done. So much, however, is already clear: most of these *Drosophila* species are not uniform monotypic Linnæan species, but rather polytypic species with geographic races. The painstaking analyses of the salivary gland chromosomes, as well as the determination of partial sterility between distant geographic races of the same species, may shed considerable light on the evolutionary history of the *Drosophila* species and on the development of isolating mechanisms in this genus. We are, however, still a long way from knowing how far such results are applicable to other orders and classes of animals.

Other insects.—Orthoptera seem to provide suitable material for the study of geographic variation, as indicated by the papers of Ramme, Rehn, and Uvarow, although lack of series has so far prevented a more general adoption of the polytypic species. Hubbell's (1936) excellent review of the cave cricket genus *Ceuthophilus* indicates the widespread occurrence of geographic variation and of polytypic species in this genus. Lack of material from intermediate localities and a too-strict adherence to a purely morphological species concept has prevented the author from a broader application of the modern species. Groups such as (1) *divergens*, *rogersi*, *peninsularis*, and *carolinus*; or of (2) *spinosus*, *walkeri*, and *armatipes*; or of (3) *fusiformis*, *elegans*, *silvestris*, *occultus*, *carlsbadensis*, *polingi*, and *umbratilis*; or of (4) *caudelli*, *perplexus*, *vicinus*, and *inyo*; or of (5) *ensifer*, *saxicola*, *brevipes*, *williamsoni*, *pallescens*, and *agassizi* have all the earmarks of polytypic species. A consistent application of the polytypic species concept would probably reduce the number of species in this genus from the 80 (or more) that are now known to less than 30.

Lieftink (1940) showed how the application of the polytypic species principle simplifies dragon-fly taxonomy, Spieth (1941) did the same for a genus of mayflies, and Usinger (1941) for hemiptera, to cite just a few examples from other insect groups. It is safe to predict that a general and consistent application of the modern biological species concept will reduce the total number of insect species from the present one million or more to one-third of that number or less. Such synthetic work is, however, very tedious and will not proceed very rapidly unless the entomological staffs of museums are considerably expanded.

ARACHNIDS

Lack of material rather than lack of geographic variation has so far prevented a broader acceptance of the polytypic species. If Rensch said in 1934 that geographic variation was unknown in spiders, this is no longer true today. My colleague, W. Gertsch, called my attention to a paper by Chamberlin and Ivie (1940), which indicates widespread occurrence of geographic races in the genus *Cicurina* (even though they were described as species in the original paper). Such forms as (1) *ludoviciana* and *varians*, or (2) *itasca*, *arcuata*, and *colorado*, or (3) *tortuba*, *garrina*, and *robusta*, or (4) *simplex* and *shasta*, or (5) *sierra*, *jonesi*, *nina*, *arcata*, and *nevadensis*, and many others, seem to form polytypic species. Subspecies seem to be of widespread occurrence among spiders, but have been neglected merely on account of the presence of large numbers of undescribed good species. Geographic variation seems to be extreme in some of the cave spiders, with every cave possessing a particular "species" representative of some other "species" found in a neighboring cave. The polytypic species principle is already firmly established among students of scorpions (see Rensch 1929, Meise 1932). Kratz (1940) found that among the 27 species of the tick genus *Hyalomma*, no less than 9 have geographic races (up to 10 subspecies per species). These figures indicate the importance of geographic variation in this poorly known taxonomic group. Diplopods and myriapods also show strong geographic variation, but the percentage of the known forms is too small to permit a general application of the polytypic species concept.

MOLLUSKS

Land snails were perhaps the first animals in which large polytypic species were recognized, even before this was done in birds. The pioneer work was done by Rossmässler (1836), Kobelt (1881), F. Sarasin and P. Sarasin (1899), and Gulick (1905), and although most of these authors used the conventional term species for geographically representative forms, they nevertheless had a clear concept that the members of these groups of allopatric "species" had a taxonomic and evolutionary status different from that of ordinary sympatric species. Rensch (1929) treats the history of the development from these beginnings to recent monographs in which the term species is employed in the modern sense as consistently as the available material permits. It was believed for a long time that the almost incredible localization of geographic races, as found among the species of *Achatinella* (Gulick, D'Alte Welch) and *Partula* (Crampton) in the Polynesian islands was a phenomenon peculiar to that region, but a study of the land snails of other tropical islands and even continents has shown that a more or less pronounced localization is rather typical for tropical snails. In fact, wherever environmental factors favor isolation, strongly localized races have been found, as recorded by Fuchs and Käufel (1936) for the Ægaean Islands, by Knipper (1939) for the Balkans, by Klemm (1939) for the southern slopes of the Alps, by Degner (1936) for southern Italy, by Rensch (1937) for Sicily, to mention only a few of many similar investigations. Diver (1939) presents a general treatment of local variation in snails. The polytypic species concept is equally applicable to fresh-water mollusks, as shown, for example, by Riech (1937) for some of the Papuan and Melanesian species and by Boycott (1938) for British *Lymnaea*. To date only a beginning has been made and it may take several generations, devoted to additional collecting and to painstaking museum work, before all the mollusks of the world are classified in biological instead of morphological species.

OTHER GROUPS OF INVERTEBRATES

Rensch stated in 1934: "There are only few groups in which geographical variability has not been recorded: the protozoa, the 'worms,' the tentaculata, echinoderms, and a few smaller or larger groups in the other classes of animals." The field of the geographically not variable animal groups has been narrowed down considerably within the last seven years. Geographic variation has, for instance, been found in several species of earthworms and planarians (for example, Pickford 1937, Thienemann 1938, and Husted and Ruebush 1940). The existence of geographic variation in spiders has already been discussed. Crustaceans show considerable geographic variation, as shown in numerous recent papers. In protozoa also the study of geographic variation is beginning to play an important role (Gause *et al.*, 1942).

Geographic variation also seems to be of wide occurrence among parasites, as proven by Ewing's (1926) work on the human head louse, by K. Jordan's work on fleas (1938), as well as by circumstantial evidence recorded in a number of recent helminthological papers.

MARINE ANIMALS

The study of geographic variation in marine animals is made difficult by their pronounced phenotypical reaction to water conditions. It is known, for example, that the form of sessile coelenterates is strongly influenced by the waters in which they grow (Stephenson 1933). Individuals of a species that grow in a quiet lagoon appear very different from other members of the same species that grow in the surf zone. These factors were, unfortunately, disregarded in a study of the coelenterate "sea-feather" (*Pennatula phosphorea*), in which Jaworski (1939) attempts to distinguish a number of geographic races. The author tells in no case in what depth his animals were found, nor how many specimens were available to him, nor does he record the exact locations. A "Mediterranean" race is described that is so different from one from the "Marmara Sea" that one might expect that several races have developed in the Mediterranean, but the author does not even state what the type locality is of his Mediterranean form.

Rensch (1929, 1933:23) has reviewed some of the literature on geographic races in marine animals, referring to investigations on fish, on crustacea (cumacea, copepods, on mollusks (cypraeids), on bryozoa, and on coelenterates (anthipatharias). L. Doederlein (1902), in an excellent paper that was far ahead of the time in which it was published, establishes a number of polytypic species. According to him, there are four geographic races in the coral *Fungia fungites: agariciformis* (Red Sea), *indica* (Indian Ocean), *concertifolia* (Samoa), and *stylifera* (Marshall Islands). The sea urchin *Leiocidaris pistillaris* Lam. has three geographic races: *erythraea* (Red Sea), *pistillaris* (Indian Ocean), and *annulifera*

(Sunda Islands to New Guinea), while another species of sea urchin (*Echinometra lucunter*) does not vary in these same areas. In the asteroid genus *Culcita* there seem to be three geographically representative species in the respective areas: *coriaceos* (Red Sea), *schmideliana* (Western Indian Ocean), and *novaeguineae* (from the Sunda Islands to New Guinea). In the sea star, *Solaster papposus*, the northernmost population in the Arctic Ocean (*affinis*) has ten arms, the more southerly populations (Norway, Greenland, England) have eleven, twelve, and thirteen arms, while the Kattegat race has fourteen arms. Work with more extensive modern collections may show that some of Doederlein's (nomenclature and) interpretations are not valid, but it seems worth while to follow the trail blazed by this pioneer.

Helmcke (1940) showed that there is indication of geographic variation even in the amazingly conservative group of the brachiopods. The three "species" of the genus *Cryptopora* seem to represent a single polytypic species, consisting of three geographic races: (1) *gnomon* (North Atlantic), (2) *boettgeri* (South Africa), and (3) *bratzieri* (Southern Australia). Stiasny thought that he could divide the common jellyfish, *Aurelia aurita* L. into four geographic races, but this seems somewhat problematical, in view of Thill's work (1937) on this species. Phenotypical responses again obscure the picture. As far as marine mollusks are concerned, the work of Engel (1936) shows that the Aplysiidae show very little geographic variation; in fact, many species are cosmopolitan. There are frequently slight differences between the West Indian and the East Indian populations, but most of them are below the taxonomic threshold. Riech (1937) also calls attention to the wide range of the marine (as compared to the fresh-water) *Melania*. Schilder and Schilder (1938), on the other hand, find that more than half of the species of cowrie shell (*Cypraea*) are divided into geographic races. Several species have as many as 5, 6, or 7 subspecies (Fig. 14). Cuénot (1933) claims to have found 2 races in the common cuttlefish *Sepia officinalis*, but these are definitely not geographic races (see p. 253).

The most extensive racial studies of marine organisms have been made on fishes, from the pioneer work of Heincke and Schmidt to the most recent studies of Russian, Scandinavian, German, British, and American workers. Unfortunately, no agreement has yet been reached concerning the proportion of phenotypical and geno-geographic characters of these races. There is no doubt that water temperature and salinity affect phenotypically the growth of the young fish. Jensen (1939) states for example:

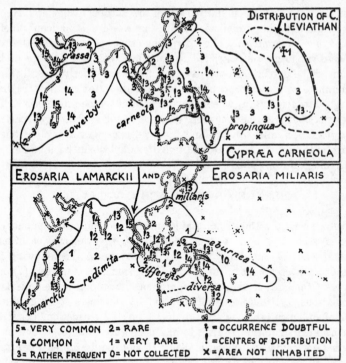

Fig. 14. Polytypic species of marine shells in the western Pacific. *Cypraea carneola* divides into four subspecies, of which the easternmost is overlapped by a closely allied species (*C. leviathan*). *Erosaria miliaris* consists of two groups which are usually treated as distinct species: *miliaris* with four subspecies and *lamarckii* with two. (From Schilder and Schilder 1939.)

As regards both the plaice (*Pleuronectes platessa*) and the dab (*L. limanda*) the number of anal fin rays seems to be positively correlated with the temperature of the water during the time at which the larvae are quite small. 1° C. corresponds to about 0.4 anal fin rays. The currents are of great importance to the racial character of the individual localities because the influx from the various hatching areas varies from year to year.

Schnakenbeck (1931), on the other hand, believes that he can distinguish 13 geographical races of the herring (*Clupea harengus*) in eastern Atlantic waters between the western exit of the Channel and Iceland (including the North Sea). The principal characteristic of each race is the percentage of individuals with 52, 53, 54, 55, 56, and more vertebrae. Each of these races has its peculiar spawning area and breeding season.

Lissner (1938) draws a similar picture of the European mackerel. Herald (1941) distinguishes 4 subspecies in the western American pipefish *Syngnathus californiensis*. The interesting aspect of this case is that one of these subspecies is restricted to the kelp beds and is more or less pelagic, while two intergrading eel-grass forms are strictly coastal. There is complete intergradation in the few localities (for example Elkhorn Slough, Monterey Bay) where the two habitats come into contact. The differences between the races relate to size, number of fin rays (particularly dorsal), number of tail- and body rings, as well as proportions of head, body, and tail. Many additional examples can be found in the ichthyological literature.

ABSENCE OF GEOGRAPHIC VARIATION

Some species without noticeable geographic variation (monotypic species) seem to exist in every one of the higher categories of animals. This absence of variability may be due to one of the following factors or to a combination of them: (1) Insufficient analysis, (2) high dispersal facilities leading to a continuous swamping of semi-isolated populations, (3) uniformity of habitat, (4) smallness of range due to lack of other suitable habitat or due to partial extinction, (5) recent expansion of a formerly very localized species, and (6) evolutionary stagnation (reduction of mutability). It will require much more taxonomic, ecological, and genetic research to determine in any given case which one of the above factors is responsible for the absence of geographic variation.

All this evidence may be summarized in the statement that geographic variation seems to be present in at least some species of every major animal group. Every new investigation not only adds more cases of geographic races, but it also leads to simplification of the system by showing that many of the previously recognized "species" are nothing but subspecies of widespread polytypic species. The acceptance of the modern biological species concept, based on the principle of geographical replacement, has resulted in an extraordinary simplification of the system in all those groups in which it has been employed consistently.

CHAPTER VII

THE SPECIES IN EVOLUTION

DARWIN entitled his epoch-making work not *The Principles of Evolution*, or *The Origin and Development of Organisms*, or by some other title which would stress the general problems of evolution. Apparently he considered these titles too speculative and therefore chose the more concrete one, *On the Origin of Species*. To him this was apparently more or less synonymous with these other titles, which is not surprising if we remember that Darwin drew no line between varieties and species. Any pronounced evolutionary change of a group of organisms was, to him, the origin of a new species. He was only mildly interested in the spatial relationships of his incipient species and paid very little attention to the origin of the discontinuities between them. It is thus quite true, as several recent authors have indicated, that Darwin's book was misnamed, because it is a book on evolutionary changes in general and the factors that control them (selection, and so forth), but not a treatise on the origin of species. Obviously it was impossible to write such a work in 1859, because the whole concept of the species was too vague at that time. This has changed in the intervening years, as we have tried to show in the preceding chapter, and we are now in a much better position to examine the role which the species plays in evolution and how the origin of discontinuities is correlated with evolutionary changes as a whole. The authors who have devoted themselves to a study of these questions during recent decades have come to the conclusion that the problem of the "origin of species" is one of the cardinal problems in the field of evolution.

Somebody might ask at this point if it was not exaggerated to attribute so much importance to the species. This question seems justified when we remember how much the species concept has changed between 1758 and today and how impossible it is to find a completely adequate and satisfactory species definition. There are actually some authors for whom species are merely abstractions and who consider the individual the only unit in nature which possesses any reality. They claim that all organisms form a continuity, which the taxonomist breaks up into species merely for the sake of expedience, to be able to handle them better in the museum drawers. Species are, according to this opinion, merely fancies of the taxonomist, created by him for his own convenience and amusement. Such a point of view may have some justification in poorly known groups, but is it true in nature? This question can be tested only by investigating groups which are well known taxonomically and biologically, as, for example, birds. If we ask ourselves whether bird species are objective, that is, whether they are units with a reality in nature, we must ask at once what the criteria are by which the objectivity of a systematic unit can be determined. Thinking this over, we come to the conclusion that such a unit is objective, or real, if it is delimited against other units by fixed borders, by definite gaps.

GAPS BETWEEN SYMPATRIC AND ALLOPATRIC SPECIES

Do such gaps exist and how complete are they? Let us look at some common eastern North American birds. The ornithologist unites, for example, all the smaller thrushes of this region in the genus *Hylocichla*. If we examine the variation within the genus in more detail, we find that it clusters very closely around five means, to which we apply the familiar names wood thrush (*Hylocichla mustelina*), veery (*H. fuscescens*), hermit thrush (*H. guttata*), gray-cheeked thrush (*H. minima*), and olive-backed thrush (*H. ustulata*). All five species are similar, but completely separated from one another by biological discontinuities. Every one of the five species is characterized not only morphologically, but also by numerous behavior and ecological traits. Two or three of them may nest in the same wood lot without any signs of intergradation; in fact, not a single hybrid seems to be known between these five common species. I could list genus after genus of familiar North American or European birds and demonstrate exactly the same. Aside from some rare exceptions, which will be treated later (p. 260), there is a clear-cut discontinuity, or to use Goldschmidt's term, a "bridgeless gap" between the species of a given locality. Such clear-cut discontinuity is, however, frequently lacking between species that represent each other geographically. *There are thus two ways of delimiting species: (1) against other species that coexist at the same locality, and (2) against species with mutually exclusive geographic ranges.* This difference in the geographic relationship of species is of the utmost importance and will be referred to frequently during our subsequent discussions; it will therefore be convenient to coin some technical terms for it. Two forms or species are *sympatric*[1], if they occur together, that is if their areas of distribution

[1] This term was coined by Poulton (1903).

overlap or coincide. Two forms (or species) are *allopatric*, if they do not occur together, that is if they exclude each other geographically. The term allopatric is primarily useful in denoting geographic representatives.

The gaps between sympatric species are absolute, otherwise they would not be good species; the gaps between allopatric species are often gradual and relative, as they should be, on the basis of the principle of geographic speciation. The few exceptions to this rule will be discussed subsequently. The failure to recognize the fundamental difference between the two kinds of gaps between species seems to be at the bottom of nearly every controversy between taxonomists on the nature of species and speciation. Goldschmidt (1940) quotes one fact after another in confirmation of the fixity of the "bridgeless gap" between sympatric species, but as soon as this is safely established, he states that "the species limit is characterized by a gap," but meaning, in this case, a gap between allopatric as well as sympatric species.

The delimitation of allopatric species will occupy us during the greater part of this chapter, but first a few more words may be said about the gap between sympatric species.

THE DELIMITATION OF SYMPATRIC SPECIES

What difficulties are encountered by the taxonomist when he attempts to delimit sympatric species? The answer is that there are very few difficulties in well-known genera. If a taxonomist of such a group receives a series of specimens from a particular locality, he is almost never in doubt as to whether they belong to one or to several species. "Dans une contrée donnée, il est facile de définir rigoureusement la grande majorité des espèces par leur caractères morphologiques constants, par leur habitat particulier dont elles ne sortent qu'exceptionellement, par le fait qu'elles ne se croisent pas habituellement entre elles, ce qui est prouvé par leur permanence et l'absence d'intermédiaires." Cuénot (1936:14) with these words very graphically describes the situation which is typical for most animal genera. Unusual cases, such as apomicts or hybrid swarms, found in so many plant genera (*Hieracium, Rubus, Salix,* and so forth), are exceptional or absent in animals. Nearly all the known hybrid swarms in animals occur at the meeting zone of otherwise allopatric forms. Serious difficulties in delimiting sympatric species are encountered, in general, only in poorly known systematic groups. After such difficulties have been completely analyzed, the final decision usually shows that either (1) several stages or phases (*individual variants*) of a species are so different that they had been mistaken for different species, or (2), just the opposite, that several species which occur at the same locality are so similar (*sibling species*) that they had been considered individual variants of one species.

Individual variants.—The striking individual variation of many animals, which we discussed in Chapter II, including the pronounced polymorphism (Chapter IV) typical of many species, have caused the systematist many difficulties. Among the few species of birds which Linnæus describes in the *Systema Naturae* are no fewer than 4 or 5 that are nothing but the immature or female plumage of another already described species. Most of these doubtful cases have now been cleared up in the better-known groups; the number of the remaining ones is exceedingly small in birds. Among the 568 species of New Guinea birds, *Meliphaga albonotata* is the only species whose validity is doubtful; it is possibly only an individual color variety of *Meliphaga analoga*. If such color phases are restricted to definite parts of the range of the species, particularly to the exclusion of the "wild" type, the difficulty is still greater. Two well-known pairs of "species" of North American birds seem to fall into this category (only 2 out of about 755). The Great White Heron (*Ardea occidentalis*) of the Florida Keys is currently considered to be specifically distinct from the Great Blue Heron (*Ardea herodias wardi*), and the Lesser Snow Goose (*Chen h. hyperboreus*) from the Blue Goose (*Ch. caerulescens*), but I am confident that in both cases it will eventually be shown that the white partner of the pair is merely a color phase (mutant), which has become the exclusive type of coloration over a smaller or larger part of the range of the species. Two additional doubtful species of North American birds are *Buteo harlani* and *Dendroica potomac*. The former is either a good species or a color phase of *Buteo jamaicensis krideri*, and the latter (known from only two specimens) seems to be a hybrid between the Yellow-throated Warbler (*Dendroica dominica*) and the Parula Warbler (*Parula americana*). Interspecific hybrids, rare as they are in most families of birds, have been the cause of some confusion. A full discussion of the problems of hybridization will be given later (Chapter IX).

Individual variation affects, in general, invertebrates much more than homoiothermal higher vertebrates. This is primarily due to their greater phenotypical plasticity, but is to some extent also due to the frequency of genetic polymorphism. Individual variation poses many difficulties to the working taxonomist, but these are being overcome steadily, as the available material and our knowledge of the various taxonomic groups increases. However, it seems that a few cases are so difficult that it will be impossible to analyze them satisfactorily, even with help of the finest collections. A study of the ecology and ethology of the doubtful forms or a breeding experiment will usually provide the solution, when the analysis of the morphological characters fails.

Sibling species.—Much more troublesome to the taxonomist and more interesting to the student of evolution is another class of difficulties caused by pairs or even larger groups of related species which are so similar that they are considered as belonging to one species until a more satisfactory analysis clears up this mistake. I call such morphologically similar and closely related, but sympatric species, *sibling species.* This corresponds to the "dual species" of Pryer and of Hering (1935), to the *"Doppel"*- or *"Geschwister"-Arten* of some German taxonomists, or the *"espèces jumelles"* of Cuénot (1936:236). The category of sibling species does not necessarily include species which are phylogenetically siblings, for example, the members of a superspecies. The term sibling species is arbitrarily limited to species which are as similar as are twins or quintuplets. The term is merely a convenient label for a not-infrequent taxonomic situation and has been adapted from the equivalent German and French terms. It is used only as a practical category, not clearly separable from other groups of similar species. In poorly analyzed groups it happens not infrequently that three, four, or five species are lumped under one species name, because the diagnostic characters of these species have not yet been discovered. An early worker in such a genus might call this group of species sibling species, but subsequent workers might find more and more distinguishing characters showing that these species are no more similar than most related species. In spite of this uncertainty, we recognize and emphasize the existence of sibling species for two reasons. First, because they demonstrate clearly that the reality of a species has nothing to do with the degree of its distinctness. Subspecies show more conspicuous visible differences in many genera than full species in other genera. The second reason for their importance is that many of them were considered "biological races" of one species in the bygone days of a purely morphological species definition. In view of this confusion between sibling species and biological races, it will be best to treat the two subjects jointly in a later chapter (p. 200). At present it may be said only that there is no reason to believe that sibling species evolve in a manner that is in the least different from that of other species.

THE DELIMITATION OF ALLOPATRIC SPECIES

The difficulties in delimiting sympatric species, which we have just discussed, are of a technical and temporary nature. They are due to the incompleteness of our knowledge of these species and disappear as soon as the missing information becomes available. They do not in the least affect the objective reality of these species. In addition to these clear-cut and "bridgeless" gaps between sympatric species, there are, however, the gaps between allopatric forms, and the unbridgeability of these gaps is very often doubtful. Nearly every well-isolated population which has developed some characters of its own may be considered a separate species on the basis of certain criteria. The decision as to whether to call such forms species or subspecies is often entirely arbitrary and subjective. This is only natural, since we cannot accurately measure to what extent reproductive isolation has already evolved. In fact, such cases are logical postulates, if the divergence of isolated populations is one of the important means of species formation. A species evolves if an interbreeding array of forms breaks up into two or more reproductively isolated arrays, to use Dobzhansky's terminology. If we look at a large number of such arrays (that is species), it is only natural that we should find a few that are just going through this process of breaking up. This does not invalidate the reality of these arrays; just as the *Paramecium* "individual" is a perfectly real and objective concept, we find in most cultures some individuals that are either conjugating or dividing. Such intermediate stages are very troublesome to the taxonomist. We have no way of telling whether the isolated forms that belong to the *Monarcha castaneoventris* group (Fig. 10) or to the *Tanysiptera galatea* group (Fig. 15), are still members of the nominate species, biologically speaking, or have already acquired reproductive isolation. Morphologically, such forms are often as different as good species and have been regarded as such by the older taxonomists. Reproductive isolation is, however, frequently absent, as is proven by the existence of hybrid populations, such as those found between *Pachycephala dahli* and *bougainvillei* on Whitney Island (Mayr 1932c), *Pachycephala torquata* and *aureiventris* on Rambi, Fiji (Mayr 1932d), for *Megapodius affinis* and *eremita* on Dampier Island (Mayr 1938b), and for many continental species (Meise 1936b).

It is of practical as well as of theoretical interest to learn how common these border-line situations are. We can study this if we examine all the possible gaps between the species of a genus and then segregate the doubtful allopatric gaps. In the North American warbler genus *Vermivora* there are 9 species, which means that there are 36 interspecific gaps $\frac{n(n-1)}{2}$. Of these only 2 (or 5.6 percent) are possibly incomplete; the other 34 are unquestionably complete. In the related genus *Dendroica* there are 23 species, with 253 interspecific gaps, of which 2 (or 0.5 percent) are doubtful. A very high number of doubtful gaps exist in the

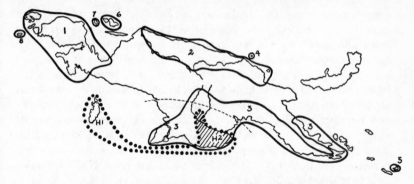

Fig. 15. The insular races (4-8) of the New Guinea kingfisher *Tanysiptera galatea* have developed almost specific rank in their small isolated ranges. The three mainland races (1-3) are very similar to each other. 1 = *galatea;* 2 = *meyeri;* 3 = *minor;* 4 = *vulcani;* 5 = *rosseliana;* 6 = *riedelii;* 7 = *carolinae;* 8 = *ellioti.* Range expansion of *minor* into south New Guinea has led to an overlap with *hydrocharis* (H₁ and H₂) which was formerly isolated by an arm of the sea.

genera in which all the species belong to one superspecies, as, for example, in the genera of birds of paradise *Astrapia, Parotia,* and so forth. If we were to add the figures of all genera of birds, I believe that the figure of doubtful gaps would be not more than 5 to 7 percent of the total number of intrageneric interspecific gaps.

We may summarize this discussion by saying that the allopatric species borders are not always sharply defined, but that this lack of clear-cut delimitation of some geographic representatives is an inevitable consequence of the continued operation of evolution.

THE DELIMITATION OF ALLOCHRONIC SPECIES

Hitherto we have spoken only of the delimitation of contemporary (synchronic) species. The delimitation of species which do not belong to the same time level (allochronic species) is difficult. In fact, it would be completely impossible if the fossil record were complete. The species of each period are the descendants of the species of the previous period and the ancestors of those of the next period. The change is slight and gradual and should, at least theoretically, not permit the delimitation of definite species. In practice, the fossil record is fragmentary, and the gaps in our knowledge make convenient gaps between the "species." In the few cases, in which an almost complete record of a continuous line is already available, the paleontologist follows the reasoning of the taxonomist who is confronted with an unbroken intergrading series of geographic populations. He breaks them up for convenience. It is obvious from these remarks that the "species" of the paleontologist is not necessarily always the same as the "species" of the student of living faunae. Breaks in series of intergrading "species" from subsequent geological horizons are not infrequent, even when the complete stratigraphic series from a certain locality is known. It is obvious in such cases, as several authors have pointed out, that the break must be due to a shift in geographic distribution (caused by a climatic or other environmental change), resulting in the replacement of a species or subspecies by a related one which had differentiated in a different region. Such a sudden break in a stratigraphic sequence is by no means proof of the instantaneous evolution of a new species.

THE PROCESS OF GEOGRAPHIC SPECIATION

The term speciation includes two processes: the development of diversity and the establishment of discontinuities between the diverging forms. To be sure, the two processes are correlated and frequently go hand in hand, but nevertheless they represent two rather different aspects of the course of evolution. The development of diversity, which is the more obvious of the two, has been discussed by us in detail in Chapters III and IV, under the heading of geographic variation. But variation and mutation alone do not necessarily produce new species. After all, it is quite thinkable that such variation might lead only to a single, interbreeding, immensely variable community of individuals. But this is not what we find in nature. What we find are groups of individuals that share certain characters, and that are more or less sharply segregated from other groups with different character combinations. These groups of individuals, these populations, races, or subspecies can be combined into species, and the latter into higher categories. This is a rough description of the situation as it occurs in nature. But we are not satisfied with mere description; we are interested in the dynamics of this process of speciation. Therefore, we want the answers to certain questions, such as: (1) Do species originate from individuals or from infraspecific units, and, if the latter, from which units? and (2) Is there any evidence for a broadening of intraspecific gaps, to the extent that they become interspecific gaps?

The answer to the first question is not simple, since it involves indirect proof. Even if no new species had ever developed under domestication or under other conditions of close observation, somebody might still insist that the spontaneous production of individuals representing new species was the usual process of species formation and that this had never been observed, merely because no interested observer had happened to be present when the new species first appeared. When De Vries described his first mutations, it seems that he was convinced that they demonstrated spontaneous species formation, and Lotsy insisted on this point even at a much later date. In the meantime the species concept has been clarified by the taxonomist, and we know now that species differ by so many genes that a simple mutation would, except for some cases in plants, never lead to the establishment of a new species. Goldschmidt, therefore, modified the simple De Vriesian concept and replaced it by the hypothesis of speciation through systemic mutations: "Species and the higher categories originate in single macroevolutionary steps as completely new genetic systems." To him a species is like a Roman mosaic, consisting of thousands of bits of marble. A systemic mutation would be like the simultaneous throwing out of all the many thousands of pieces of marble on a flat surface so that they would form a completely new and intelligible picture. To believe that this could actually happen is, as Dobzhansky has said in review of Goldschmidt's work, equivalent to "a belief in miracles." It seems to me not only that Goldschmidt did not prove his novel ideas, but also that the existing facts fit orthodox ideas on species formation so adequately that no reason exists for giving them up. This statement requires proof and there is perhaps no better way to introduce our arguments than to state briefly how we visualize the course of geographic species formation:

A new species develops if a population which has become geographically isolated from its parental species acquires during this period of isolation characters which promote or guarantee reproductive isolation when the external barriers break down.

This definition contains a number of postulates which we shall now discuss. To begin with, it involves the concept of the "incipient" species. Geographic speciation is thinkable only, if subspecies are incipient species. This, of course, does not mean that every subspecies will eventually develop into a good species. Far from it! All this statement implies is that every species that developed through geographic speciation had to pass through the subspecies stage. There is, naturally, a considerable infant mortality among subspecies and only a limited number reaches adulthood, or the full species stage. We shall see in Chapter IX under what conditions subspecies are most likely to be successful. At this point a few figures may be helpful. There are, in the entire world, approximately 8,500 species of living birds, with probably 35,000 recognizable subspecies. Apparently all the present orders of birds already existed at the beginning of the Tertiary period, some fifty-five million years ago, and we can think of no reason why the number of species should have increased materially during the last ten or twenty million years. As some became extinct, others took their place. This replacement is apparently a rather slow process, since there is much evidence that most of the present species or the "lines" to which they belong have existed for considerable periods (Miller 1940). Occasionally a species succeeds in entering a previously unoccupied ecological niche. We are forced to the conclusion, on the basis of such considerations, that probably less than 10 or 15 percent of the existing subspecies of birds will both diverge sufficiently and survive long enough in isolation to become good species. The statement that subspecies are incipient species should therefore be emended to read: Some subspecies are incipient species, or subspecies are potentially incipient species. Furthermore, the isolated incipient species may consist of several subspecies or of a subspecifically as yet unmodified population.

We have called the theory of geographic speciation an orthodox theory, and this is correct when we realize how old it is and how widespread its acceptance. It had considerable support among thinking biologists, even long before Darwin. Leopold von Buch, for example, in a description of the fauna and flora of the Canary Islands (1825), writes as follows:

The individuals of a genus spread out over the continents, move to far-distant places, form varieties (on account of differences of the localities, of the food, and the soil), which owing to their segregation [geographical isolation] cannot interbreed with other varieties and thus be returned to the original main type. Finally these varieties become constant and turn into separate species. Later they may reach again the range of other varieties which have changed in a like manner, and the two will now no longer cross and thus they behave as "two very different species."

We can hardly improve on this statement, except for choosing a few different terms. The two points which von Buch makes, namely that geographic isolation was needed to permit the species difference to "become constant" and that proof of the species difference was given by their reproductive isolation, were, curiously enough, not recognized with the same clarity by later authors. Darwin, for example, was primarily interested in the development of the diversity which precedes species formation and he therefore neglected to explain the development and maintenance of discontinuities. M. Wagner seems to have been the first author to realize this gap in Darwin's argumentation, and it led him to propose in 1869, his "Migrationsgesetz der Organismen," which he later called more correctly the "separation theory" (Wagner 1889). On the basis of his extensive collecting experiences in Asia, Africa, and America, Wagner emphasized the nonexistence of sympatric speciation and stated that "the formation of a real variety which Mr. Darwin considers as 'incipient species,' can succeed in nature only where some individuals can cross the previous borders of their range and segregate themselves for a long period from the other members of their species." Darwin himself, in a letter to Wagner, admitted later that he had overlooked the importance of this point.

The speciation process does not need to be completed during this isolation. Dobzhansky (1940, 1941a) has pointed out that selective mating in a zone of contact of two formerly separated incipient species (zone of secondary intergradation, p. 99) may play an important role. The two incipient species must be sufficiently distinct, so that the hybrid offspring of mixed matings has discordant (unbalanced) gene patterns; in other words, the individuals produced in such matings must have a reduced viability and survival value.

Let it be assumed that two incipient species, A and B, are in contact in a certain territory, and that mutations arise in either or in both species which make their carriers less likely to mate with the representatives of the other species. The nonmutant individuals of the species A which cross to B will produce a progeny which is, by hypothesis, inferior in viability to the pure species; the offspring of the mutant individuals will have, other things being equal, a normal viability. Since the mutants breed only or mostly within the species, their progeny will be more numerous or more vigorous than that of the nonmutants. Consequently, natural selection will favor the spread and establishment of the mutant condition [Dobzhansky 1941a],

until only conspecific pairs are formed or, in other words, until complete discontinuity (a bridgeless gap) has developed between the two species. Dobzhansky presents a plausible case, and we agree that such a selective process may help to complete the establishment of discontinuity, in those cases in which some interbreeding has taken place between incipient species.

The question is, however, whether or not this is the only way by which reproductive isolation can be established. Naturalists, from L. von Buch down to our contemporaries, have always believed that good species can complete their development in isolation. They find an abundance of cases in nature which seem to permit no other interpretation. The most conclusive evidence is, of course, presented by the multiple invasion of islands by separate colonizing waves coming from the same parental stock. Let us, for example, take Norfolk Island, 780 miles from the coast of Australia, and surely never in continental connection with any of the surrounding island areas or continents. Among its scanty bird fauna (about 15 species of land birds) there are 3 species of *Zosterops*: *norfolkensis*, *tenuirostris*, and *albogularis*, which in the same order are progressively more different from their only close relative, *Zosterops lateralis*, from the Australian mainland. The island is about 44 square kilometers in area and can easily harbor several thousands of pairs of each species. The following interpretation of this situation is obvious, and there seems no other interpretation nearly so convincing (Stresemann 1931). There were three waves of immigration. The first had already become specifically distinct when the second wave arrived. If the single or the two pairs of *Zosterops* which comprised the second colonization had hybridized with the more-than-thousand-pair population of the first wave, they would have been swamped out of existence within one or two generations. The second wave had developed into a separate species when the colonizing pair of the third wave appeared. The discontinuity between the three species could not have become established through a slow, selective process, as described above by Dobzhansky. The bridgeless gap must have been there already, when the second and third set of colonists arrived; otherwise there would not be three species on the island. The distance of 780 miles between Norfolk and the mainland precludes the possibility of numerous attempts at colonization, by which an isolating mechanism could have been built up gradually through selection. The same explanation applies, *mutatis mutandis*, to all other cases of double or triple invasions (see p. 173). It is also the best interpretation of many other situations in which two related species now have partly overlapping ranges, owing to the breakdown of former barriers (p. 176).

Some geneticists endorse the viewpoint of the naturalist, that the accumulation of small genetic changes in isolated populations can lead in the course of time to a new integrated genetic system, of such difference that it thereby acquires all the characters of a new species, including reproductive isolation. S. Wright (1941c) describes this in the following words:

If isolation of any portion of a species becomes sufficiently complete, the continuity of the fabric is broken. The two populations may differ little if any at the time of separation but will drift ever farther apart, each carrying its subspecies with it. The accumulation of genic, chromosomal and cytoplasmic differences tends to lead in the course of ages to intersterility or hybrid sterility, making irrevocable the initial merely geographic or ecologic isolation.

For a more detailed discussion of the genetic aspects of the establishment of biological discontinuity, we refer to Muller (1940). We maintain, therefore, that the discontinuity between species is due to their divergence (difference), both in regard to their cytogenetics and in regard to their crossability (ecological and ethological). The establishment of discontinuity is closely associated with the process of divergence, and, to make a pun, one might say: "The establishment of discontinuity is a continuous process."In other words, the big gaps which we find between species are preceded by the little gaps which we find between subspecies and by the still lesser gaps which we find between populations. Of course, if these populations are distributed as a complete *continuum*, there are no gaps. But with the least isolation, the first minor gaps will appear.

Stages of speciation.—That speciation is not an abrupt, but a gradual and continuous process is proven by the fact that we find in nature every imaginable level of speciation, ranging from an almost uniform species at one extreme to one in which isolated populations have diverged to such a degree that they can be considered equally well as separate, good species at the other extreme. I have tried in a recent paper (Mayr 1940a) to analyze this continuous process and to demonstrate its different phases by subdividing it into various stages. I am well aware that these divisions are somewhat artificial and that a polytypic species may be in different stages in different parts of its range at the same time. Still, this analysis is useful, as we shall see in the subsequent discussion. The classification of my 1940 paper has been somewhat modified, since I now realize that what I then called stage (1) is as much the final as the first stage of speciation. A species may have a small range because it is so new that it has had as yet no time to expand (Willis's age and area concept), or because it is adapted to a unique situation, or because it developed in a particularly isolated location (island, cave), or because it became extinct in the other parts of its range. A widespread species is more likely to represent the first stage of speciation than one with a narrowly restricted range.

There are many cases in nature which cannot be fitted very well into this scheme, but still it will be possible to take the entire number of species of a systematic group (let us say birds or butterflies) from one particular region and classify them according to the stage of speciation to which they belong. The resulting figures of such an analysis shed much light on the degree of speciation and, in particular, on the degree of geographic isolation in the respective region.

Stage 1. A uniform species with a large range

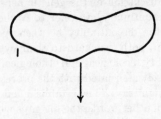

Followed by:
Process 1. Differentiation into subspecies

Resulting in:
Stage 2. A geographically variable species with a more or less continuous array of similar subspecies (2a all subspecies are slight, 2b some are pronounced)

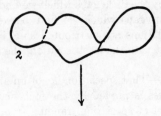

Followed by:
Process 2. a) Isolating action of geographic barriers between some of the populations; also b) development of isolating mechanisms in the isolated and differentiating subspecies

Resulting in:
Stage 3. A geographically variable species with many subspecies completely isolated, particularly near the borders of the range, and some of them morphologically as different as good species

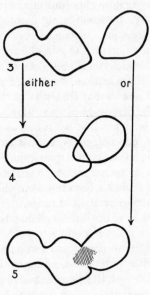

either   or

Followed by:
Process 3. Expansion of range of such isolated populations into the territory of the representative forms

Resulting in either
Stage 4. Noncrossing, that is, new species with restricted range or

Stage 5. Interbreeding, that is, the establishment of a hybrid zone (zone of secondary intergradation)

FIG. 16. Stages of speciation.

To demonstrate the value of this method, which is applicable only to well-known groups, I have listed in Table 10 the passerine birds of three geographic regions, including the extraterritorial range of each species. Stage 5 was omitted and in stage 4 every uniform species with small range was included.

TABLE 10

STAGES OF SPECIATION IN DIFFERENT GEOGRAPHICAL REGIONS

STAGE	MANCHURIA (CONTINUOUS RANGES)		NEW GUINEA REGION (PARTLY CONTINUOUS RANGES)		SOLOMON ISLANDS (DISCONTINUOUS RANGES)	
	SPECIES		SPECIES		SPECIES	
	Number	Percent	Number	Percent	Number	Percent
I	15	14.0 ⎫	21	7.2 ⎫	I	2 ⎫
2a	59	55.1 ⎭ 69	118	40.7 ⎭ 48	11	22 ⎭ 24
2b	30	28.0	84	29.0	12	24
3	1	1.0 ⎫	33	11.4 ⎫	17	34 ⎫
4	2	1.9 ⎭ 3	34	11.7 ⎭ 23	9	18 ⎭ 52

An analysis of this tabulation shows that stages 3 and 4, which indicate the final stages of evolution, are almost nonexistent when geography and geology favor continuous ranges, while stages 1 and 2a, indicating the early stages of evolution, reach a definite high in such continental areas. In contradistinction, we find that where geographic factors break up the species ranges to a high degree, as, for example, on an old tropical archipelago such as the Solomon Islands, a great number of the species are in the final stages of evolution (3 and 4) and comparatively few in the early stages (1 and 2a). A student of speciation must study regions with continuous ranges as well as those with discontinuous ranges before he can generalize on the dynamics of the speciation process. To base all conclusions on the temperate zones of the large Old World and New World continents leads inevitably into error or to a very one-sided viewpoint, because these two regions are characterized by special conditions. Not only are there very few effective geographic barriers, but most of the populations are also comparatively young, because they occupied their present ranges only after the rather recent retreat of the ice. So far as I know, all workers who minimize the importance of geographic variation for species formation base this opinion on work done in the Holarctic region. On the other hand, von Buch, Darwin, Wallace, and others derived their clear ideas on evolution from a study of both continental and insular species. Kinsey (1937b) has presented us with a particularly graphic description of the differences between these two types of species.

THE PROOF FOR GEOGRAPHIC SPECIATION

The conclusion of the taxonomist of birds, mammals, butterflies, and other well-known groups that geographic isolation is in most groups of animals one of the necessary conditions of speciation has not remained unchallenged. Rensch (1939a) recently has cited a whole list of books and papers by authors who deny the importance of geographic speciation (allopatric speciation). Goldschmidt (1940) devoted most of the first half of his book (183 pages) to a refutation of this thesis. It may be in order, therefore, to gather additional proof for the existence and importance of geographic speciation. But what is proof? Is it not sufficient to point out, as we have done, that the majority of well-isolated subspecies have all the characters of good species and are indeed considered to be such by the more conservative systematists? Is it not sufficient to show that subspecific characters are of exactly the same kind as specific characters? Is it not sufficient to point out that certain *Rassenkreise* clearly merge into each other?

All this evidence is highly indicative, but it may not be completely convincing. The fact that Goldschmidt and others, who know this evidence, deny the importance of geographic speciation makes it necessary to present additional proof. The evidence in favor of geographic speciation can be summarized as follows:

ALL DIFFERENCES BETWEEN SPECIES ARE SUBJECT TO GEO-
GRAPHIC VARIATION; THERE IS NO DIFFERENCE OF KIND
BETWEEN SPECIFIC AND SUBSPECIFIC CHARACTERS.

The discussion as to what characters are subject to geographic variation (Chapter III), proves this point so conclusively that nothing need be added. If species formation and subspecies formation were two fundamentally different processes, we should find that two different classes of characters were subject to variation in the two categories (geographic race and species). But this is not what we found in our analysis of geographically variable characters. Not a species character is known, be it morphological, physiological, or other, which is not subject to geographic variation. As a general rule it can be said that characters separating full species tend to be more pronounced, and that there are often more differences between species than between subspecies. But this criterion breaks down completely in all the really doubtful cases, and many subspecies are characterized by more striking differences than some "good" species. It is therefore obvious that there is no "gap" between subspecies and species, as far as systematic characters are concerned.

REDUCED FERTILITY BETWEEN GEOGRAPHIC RACES OF ONE SPECIES

We have already called attention to a number of mistakes in logic in the discussion of sterility as a species criterion (p. 119). Lack of interbreeding in nature between two forms of animals (in breeding condition) may be due to two different obstacles, sexual isolation and sterility. Even though these two factors are frequently correlated, they actually belong to two entirely different fields: ethology and cytogenetics. It has been proven again and again for birds and many other animals that several species can live side by side in nature without normally hybridizing, even though they are highly or completely fertile with one another in artificial crosses. It is therefore not to be expected that fertility should always be reduced between the geographic races of all the species. Still, the number of cases of partial sterility between geographically distant races of the same species is surprisingly high, particularly among insects. Rensch (1929:93–94, 1933) has listed a number of them and new ones are being discovered and described continually. Very striking are the intersexes or otherwise less viable forms which occur if certain subspecies of *Lymantria dispar* are hybridized (Goldschmidt 1934). A considerable degree of sterility occurs also between some of the geographic races of many of the "wild" species of *Drosophila* (excluding *melanogaster* and other cosmopolitan "domestic" species). These data have been summarized by Spencer (1940) and Dobzhansky (1941a). Pictet (1937) found reduced fertility, in certain species of butterflies and moths, between populations that are not even separated into different subspecies. This is true for *Nemeophila plantaginis* and for the geographic and altitudinal races of *Lasiocampa quercus*. Neighboring races are highly fertile, but the wider their geographic separation, the more pronounced is the reduction of fertility, some races being almost or completely sterile. It does not require much imagination to picture what would happen, if such races should meet in nature. The presence of even partial sterility would speed up considerably the establishment of biological isolating mechanisms between the two incipient species. The most recent work on Drosophila proves that not only may fertility be reduced in geographic races of the same species, but also the sexual attraction (Patterson 1942, Stalker 1942). This also proves that reproductive isolation (misogamy) is a by-product of genetic divergence.

THE BORDER-LINE CASES

It is a logical postulate of our thesis (that species originate from geographic races) that we should find certain subspecies which have just about reached the threshold of the species. Such cases are usually called border-line cases, since it is impossible in these situations to decide whether the questionable form is "still" a subspecies or "already" a species; they are in the border zone between the two categories. There are a number of different situations which can be included with the border line cases. For example, a form may be a species on the basis of one species definition and a subspecies on the basis of another definition. Or certain forms may behave like subspecies of a single species in part of their range and like good species in other parts of their range. Border-line cases are by no means exceptional; in fact, we find a surprisingly high proportion of such situations in all the regions in which geographic or ecological conditions promote active speciation. Border-line cases may be classified as follows:

No criteria permit satisfactory distinction between species and isolated subspecies.—The ranges of two allopatric forms are often separated by a geographic gap, a form of distribution which is particularly common among island, mountain, and cave species, where there is, in all cases, a discontinuous distribution of the habitat. The taxonomist who adheres to a strictly morphological species definition is not particularly baffled by such cases. Every isolated form that is separated from its nearest relative by a clear-cut discontinuity of taxonomic characters is regarded by him as a good species. He is, in consequence, forced to admit as good species many isolated forms, which differ by very minute, but constant and unbridged differences. Such a procedure is defensible, as long as we are merely interested in the pigeonholing of specimens in the correct collection cases. It becomes an absurdity when we view the species as a biological unit.

In the Atlantic Ocean, about one hundred miles east of Nova Scotia, there is a small, isolated land mass, Sable Island. On this island, and only on it, lives a sparrow, the Ipswich Sparrow (*Passerculus* (*sandwichensis*) *princeps*), which is unquestionably derived from the same stock as the Savanna Sparrow (*Passerculus sandwichensis*) of the mainland of North America. The differences are, however, very striking; the Sable Island bird is much larger (wing, ♂ 73.5–79.5, against 66–72 mm.), and of a distinctly different coloration (much more whitish) from the races of the neighboring mainland. Even in the field the two forms can be told apart at a glance.

Some ornithologists hold that the Ipswich Sparrow is nothing but a subspecies of the Savanna Sparrow, whereas others insist that the morphological gap should be recognized as a species gap. Similar situations are encountered in nearly every well-worked taxonomic group.

It is of interest to find out how common such cases are. I have made an analysis of all the North American birds listed in the A. O. U. Checklist (1931), a work which is rather conservative in its taxonomic point of view. I have omitted only introduced species and the purely marine order Tubinares. In 374 genera there are 755 species with a total of 1,367 species and subspecies. At least 94 of the listed 755 full species of North American birds will be considered by some authors to be merely subspecies of other species. In other words 12.5 per cent of the species of North American birds have reached a very interesting taxonomic stage: They still show by their distribution and general similarity that they had been only recently geographical forms of some other species, but they have, in their isolation, developed morphological characters of such a degree of difference that the majority of authors now prefers to call them good species. Typical examples in the North American bird fauna are: Ipswich and Savanna Sparrow (*Passerculus*), Red-shafted and Yellow-shafted Flicker (*Colaptes*), Audubon's and Myrtle Warbler (*Dendroica*), the various species of the genera *Junco* and *Leucosticte*, etc. The majority of these forms are more or less isolated, either on the islands off the California coast or on the various mountain ranges of the Rocky Mountains or in the lowlands east and west of the Rocky Mountains. These "semi-species" comprise 12½ per cent of the total of species in the rather continental fauna of North America. For a typically insular region, namely the Lesser Sunda Islands, Rensch (1933) thinks that not less than 47 species are intermediate among a total of 160 species. I have analyzed the birds of the Solomon Islands and find that if we employ a narrow species concept there are 174 species of land and freshwater birds; if we, however, employ a wide species concept (=include within one species all geographical representatives) there are only 125 species. In other words, of 174 species there are 49 of intermediate status, that is 28.2 per cent [Mayr 1940a].

An even clearer impression can be gained if we analyze, in a similar manner, the entire bird fauna of a single island (Table II).

The percentage of border-line cases depends on a number of factors (size, distance from mainland, and so forth) which will be treated in a later chapter. Only one of the birds of the British Islands, the red grouse (*Lagopus scoticus*), is a border-line case. It is by many authors considered to be a race of the continental *Lagopus lagopus*.

There is no doubt that similar conditions prevail in other animal groups and even in plants, but the taxonomy of most of these groups has not yet been clarified to the point where we can express the number of

THE SPECIES IN EVOLUTION

TABLE II

PERCENTAGE OF BORDER-LINE CASES ON ISLANDS IN THE PAPUAN REGION

NAME OF ISLAND	TOTAL NUMBER OF SPECIES	MAY BE CONSIDERED EITHER ENDEMIC SPECIES OR SUBSPECIES OF MAINLAND SPECIES	BORDER-LINE FORMS, PERCENT OF TOTAL
Biak Island (+Numfor)	69	21	30
Rennell Island	34	7	20
Waigeu* (+Batanta)	71	3	4.2
Aru Islands*	72	2	2.8

* Passeres only.

border-line cases in actual percentage figures. Kinsey (1937b) divides species into two classes, continental and insular. A study of his data has convinced me that an ornithologist would call most of his "insular" species either subspecies or border-line cases. Kinsey's data are therefore of interest to us in this connection. According to him the percentage of insular species in various taxonomic groups is as follows: the gall wasps (*Cynipidae*) 76 percent, the salamanders of the family *Plethodontidae* 74 percent, the cave crickets of the genus *Ceuthophilus* 62 percent, the pond weeds of the genus *Potamogeton* 15 percent, the spiderworts of the genus *Tradescantia* 9 percent, and so forth. On the basis of these data, it seems as if animals tended more to the formation of localized, isolated forms than plants, although both *Tradescantia* and *Potamogeton* are rather "weedy" plants, and perhaps not typical for all plants.

These isolated forms, or "insular species," are excellent evidence in support of geographic speciation and, as such, welcome to the student of evolution; but, on the other hand, they are also very troublesome to the modern taxonomist, as far as their practical treatment is concerned. Our species definition included the statement: "A species consists of a group of populations which replace each other geographically which are potentially capable of interbreeding . . . where contact is prevented by geographical . . . barriers." The question remains, how can we determine which of these isolated forms are "potentially capable of interbreeding"? Unfortunately, there is no way of testing this in most cases, and we may as well admit that a decision is then possible only by inference. We must study other polytypic species of the same genus or of related genera and find out how different the subspecies can be that are connected by intermediates, and, vice versa, how similar good sympatric species can be. This scale of differences is then used as a yardstick in the doubtful situations. And even after all these data have been given due consideration, the decision will often be, to a large extent, as Stresemann would say, "a matter of taste." Such arbitrary decisions have to be made in all modern taxonomic work. In a revision of the genus *Megapodius*, I proposed to unite, into one polytypic species, the seven species *nicobariensis, tenimberensis, reinwardt, freycinet, eremita, affinis*, and *layardi*, which had been recognized even by such progressive authors as Peters and Stresemann. The reasons were that I found not only that all these species were strictly allopatric, but also because the form (*macgillivrayi*) from the Louisiade Islands combined the characters of *reinwardt* and *eremita* and because members of a hybrid population between *affinis* and *eremita* (Dampier Island) were, by convergence, similar to *freycinet*.On the other hand, it was decided to retain as full species the forms *lapérouse* (Micronesia) and *pritchardi* (Niouafu, central Polynesia), which, although strictly allopatric, are separated from all other forms of the genus by very striking morphological as well as geographic gaps (Mayr 1938b). Meinertzhagen (1935:765) lists *Alauda arvensis* and *A. gulgula, Apus apus* and *A. pallidus*, and *Riparia obsoleta* and *R. rupestris* as typical border-line cases among birds.

Extreme morphological development of terminal subspecies.—The isolated forms of *Megapodius*, which are considered separate species, differ only in size, color, and proportions. But sometimes such isolated forms develop such a degree of difference that they might be considered different genera if they were judged only on morphological criteria. As a matter of fact, many of these forms have originally been described as separate genera, and their true systematic position has become clear only recently. That they are nothing but subspecies, or at best allopatric species, is particularly evident in cases in which the widely diverging species are the extreme ends of a long chain of intermediate subspecies.

The distribution map (Fig. 17) of the barking pigeon (*Ducula pacifica*) of Polynesia well illustrates the geographic conditions under which such extreme morphological development may occur. This species has developed a form (*galeata*) on the Marquesas Islands which, on account of its peculiarly developed bill, was, until nine years ago, considered a good genus (*Serresius*).

Other genera that are based on morphologically distinct geographic forms are: in pigeons, *Oedirhinus* (of *Ptilinopus iozonus*) and *Chrysophaps* (of *Chrysoena luteovirens*); in kingfishers, *Todirhamphus* (of *Halcyon chloris*); in birds of paradise, *Taeniaparadisea* and *Astrarchia*

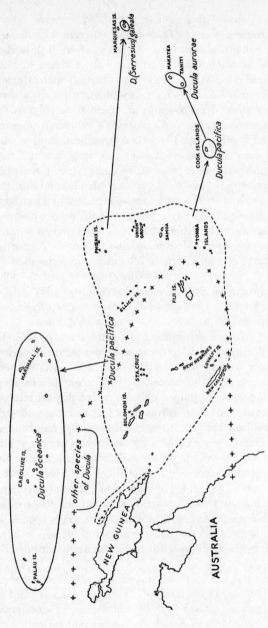

Fig. 17. "Genus" *Serresius*, a member of the superspecies *Ducula pacifica*. Extreme morphological differentiation of the most isolated form in the group.

(of *Astrapia nigra*), *Schlegelia* (of *Diphyllodes magnificus*), *Uranornis* (of *Paradisaea apoda*); in drongos, *Dicranostephes* (of *Dicrurus bracteatus*); in rails, *Porphyriornis* (of *Gallinula chloropus*); in Passeres, *Galactodes* (of *Erythropygia*), *Conopoderas* (of *Acrocephalus*), *Pinarolestes* (of *Clytorhynchus*), *Papuorthonyx* (of *Orthonyx*), *Allocotops* (of *Melanocichla lugubris*); and so forth.

I could quote many other similar cases in which subspeciation, that is geographic variation, has actually brought about the formation of unquestionably new species of birds. Unfortunately, the systematics of most other groups of animals is not sufficiently well known to justify our drawing comparable conclusions, but Kinsey reports exactly the same situation in cynipid gall wasps (Kinsey 1930, 1936, 1937a, 1941).

The superspecies, a border-line situation.—Nobody will deny that all the strongly specialized allopatric forms which we have just listed are merely "glorified" geographic races, and it seems possible to combine groups of them into single species if one wanted to carry the principle of geographic representation to an extreme. This is just about what Kleinschmidt does in his *Formenkreise*. Rensch (1929, 1934) realizing that two rather different taxonomic concepts were hidden under the term *Formenkreis*, namely ordinary polytypic species and groups of allopatric species, proposed the term *Artenkreis* for the latter. I have suggested the replacement of this term, for more convenient international usage, by the term *superspecies*[2] since it is the supraspecific counterpart to the infraspecific unit, the subspecies (Mayr 1931a).

A superspecies consists of a monophyletic group of geographically representative (allopatric) species which are morphologically too distinct to be included in one species. It is inconsequential whether the species of which the superspecies is composed are monotypic or whether some of them break up into geographic races. The principal feature of the superspecies is that it presents, geographically, the picture of an ordinary polytypic species, but that morphologically these allopatric species are different to such a degree that reproductive isolation between them may be suspected. One of the most important aspects of the superspecies is that it is the highest category which can be delimited objectively, as is appar-

---

[2] *Super*, beyond, is the counterpart of *sub*, below (or within); *supra*, above, is the counterpart of *infra*, below. The term supraspecies, used by several recent authors, seems to me to be an unfortunate combination. We can speak of supraspecific categories, as we speak of infraspecific factors, but as we use the term subspecies for a specieslike category that is below the species, we must use the term superspecies for a specieslike category that goes beyond the species. This corresponds to a similar usage of these prepositions in subgenus and supergenus, in subfamily and superfamily, and so forth.

ent from the definition. Rensch has pointed out that the adoption of this concept affects in no way the nomenclature of the species which are involved and that no objections can be raised against it on this basis. On the other hand, it offers a number of considerable advantages in the preparation of faunal lists, in zoögeographic studies, and in discussions on speciation. Some critics (for example Meise 1938:63) have proposed the elimination of the term superspecies by broadening the scope of the polytypic species to the point at which it includes all geographic representatives. If we go back to these Kleinschmidtian views, we shall have to include in one species the red and the yellow birds of paradise; we shall have to call all the *Astrapia*, all the *Parotia*, and all the juncos one species, to mention some avian examples. To call all these forms subspecies not only obscures their distinctness, but it violates even our species concept. There is some evidence that many of the species of which the superspecies are composed are reproductively isolated. On the other hand, it may also be called a mistake to list them merely as ordinary species, without combining them into superspecies, because this ignores an important relationship. The superspecies should be employed only in cases of strikingly different allopatric species. It would be an abuse of this concept if an author were to call every polytypic species, composed of insular and thus well-marked subspecies, a superspecies.

The members of a superspecies form a taxonomic and phylogenetic unit, all being descendants of one ancestral population. The recognition of the superspecies helps very materially to reduce the gap between subspecies and species, and, since every superspecies is a border-line case, it calls attention to these intermediate situations. The superspecies has its greatest practical importance in zoögeographic work. It is unwarranted to count the members of superspecies as separate species, if we compare two faunas. For example, it is altogether misleading to say that Polynesia has more species of fruit doves (*Ptilinopus*) than New Guinea. Current check lists record 17 species from Polynesia and 11 species from the mainland of New Guinea, but there are only 3 superspecies in Polynesia as compared to 11 on New Guinea. The comparison of the number of superspecies indicates, therefore, much more accurately how rich the New Guinea fauna is in fruit doves than does a comparison of the number of species.

The ranges of several typical superspecies have been illustrated by me in a recent paper (Mayr 1940a, Figs. 2, 3, 4, 7). The superspecies *Zosterops rendovae* consists of three species: *Z. rendovae, Z. luteirostris,* and *Z. vellalavella*; the superspecies *Ducula pacifica* consists of the species *galeata, aurorae, pacifica, oceanica,* and perhaps *myristicivora,* and so forth.

The 10 species of the genus *Junco* which Miller recognizes in his recent revision of the genus (Miller 1941) comprise one extensive superspecies. In fact, it would seem proper to reduce the number of species of this superspecies to 3 or 4, since several of them interbreed freely in their zone of contact and would not pass as species on the basis of a biological species definition.

We have already encountered, in our discussion on the application of the polytypic species principle, many situations in which groups of closely related forms are best characterized as superspecies. Just a few cases from groups other than birds may be added. The Mediterranean lizard *Lacerta lepida* forms a superspecies with *L. atlantica* (eastern Canary Islands), *L. galloti* (western Canary Islands), and *L. simonyi* (Gran Canaria) (Mertens 1928a). Most of the species of the genus *Orcula* seem to belong to one superspecies (St. Zimmermann 1932). Usinger (1941) lists superspecies in the hemipteran genus *Neseis* from Hawaii, and the 4 species of the Central American fish genus *Platypoecilus* (*couchianus, xiphidinus, variatus,* and *maculatus*) are another example, although these 4 "species" could equally well be considered subspecies of a polytypic species. The *Drosophila macrospina* group, as described by Patterson (1942), can also be cited as an illustration of a superspecies.

Superspecies are not exceptional cases. On the contrary, they comprise a regular and sometimes rather high percentage of every fauna. Rensch (1933:29) has tabulated their occurrence among birds and snails and has found, as is to be expected, that they are particularly frequent where effective geographic barriers are present, that is, where insular ranges are involved. There are 17 superspecies (or 13.6 percent) among the 125 species of Solomon Island birds. Among the 9 widespread, mountain-inhabiting species of birds of paradise from New Guinea 3 are superspecies (33 percent). But even among continental species, the number of superspecies is rather high. Among the Palearctic Corvidae (crow family) there are 4 superspecies, in addition to 40 polytypic species; in the Palearctic starlings, one superspecies and 2 polytypic species; among the finchlike birds of the Palearctic there are 6 superspecies in addition to 70 polytypic species; and so forth (Rensch 1934:50). At least a dozen superspecies of birds occur in North America (in the genera *Branta, Larus, Otus, Colaptes, Lanius, Dendroica, Leucosticte, Junco,* and so forth). The percentage of superspecies may be expected to be even higher among animals, which are more sedentary than birds. Among the European Clausiliidae (snails) there are no less than 10 superspecies, in addition to 16 polytypic species (Rensch, *loc. cit.*).

The superspecies is, of course, only a stage in the speciation scale, and it is to be expected that it also has its border cases. The species pairs, *Acanthiza pusilla* and *ewingi*, *Tanysiptera hydrocharis* and *galatea*, *Ptilinopus dupetithouarsi* and *mercieri*, and *Lalage maculosa* and *sharpei*, which we shall discuss later in this chapter, must be mentioned here. Each of these pairs of species would be considered as belonging to the same superspecies if there was not some overlap of ranges. The superspecies is the stage at which the transition from allopatric to sympatric species is most likely to occur.

The indivisible gradient of the lower systematic categories.—We have stated repeatedly that every one of the lower systematic categories grades without a break into the next one: the local population into the subspecies, the subspecies into the monotypic species, the monotypic species into the polytypic species, the polytypic species into the superspecies, the superspecies into the species group. This does not mean that we find the entire graded series within every species group. It simply means that in the absence of definite criteria it is, in many cases, equally justifiable to consider certain isolated forms as subspecies or as species, to consider a variable species monotypic or to subdivide it into two or more geographic races, to consider well-characterized forms as subspecies of a polytypic species or to call them representative species.

In a revision of the neotropical snake genus *Dryadophis*, Stuart (1941) recognizes 17 forms in 6 monotypic and 3 polytypic species, belonging to 4 species groups. Isolated forms which do not intergrade are considered full species. Many ornithologists would not recognize this criterion and, by considering some of the "species" subspecies, they would reduce the total number of species to 4 or 5 (*bifossatus, pulchriceps, pleei, amarali,* and *boddaerti* (with *heathii, melanolomus,* and *dorsalis* as subspecies). In the bunting genus *Junco* there are about seven or eight possible ways of delimiting the species, and none of the disagreeing authors can prove that his arrangement is more correct than the others. The presence of graded series and the absence of all decisive criteria makes it necessary to rely on subjective judgments. But the fact that so many geographic races stand on the border-line between subspecies and species is further proof of the importance of geographic speciation.

A similar gradient of categories may be observed, if we compare the degree of geographic variation of a number of related species in the same geographic region. Usinger (1941) describes very graphically such a situation among the hemiptera which have colonized the Hawaiian Islands. After arrival on the islands, these species

proceeded to diverge, and have now reached varying degrees of differentiation, the extent of which can not be determined without breeding experiments. Thus the various species in the endemic genera fall into a series, ranging from (1) the widespread and variable *Oceanides nimbatus* Kirk., not yet broken up into distinguishable forms on the various islands, through (2) the scarcely differentiated *Neseis saundersianus* Kirk. to (3) the "polytypic species" (Huxley 1938) or "Rassenkreis" (Rensch 1929) *Neseis nitidus* White, which has structurally distinct but closely allied races on each island, then to (4) the "supra-species" (Huxley 1938) *Neseis hiloensis* Perkins, the Oahu form of which was unhesitatingly called a distinct species, until a connecting link was discovered on Molokai, and finally to (5) that which Huxley (1938) has called a "geographical subgenus" and Rensch (1929) has called an "Artenkreis," namely, the *Neseis mauiensis* Blackburn group which has diverged to such an extent that the Oahu and Kauai forms have attained the status of full species and had not even been recognized as belonging to this group previously.

A similar gradient of systematic categories was described by me for some islands and mountains of the Papuan Region (Mayr 1940a:267).

DOUBLE INVASIONS

Oceanic islands are defined as all those islands that have received their fauna from other islands or from neighboring continents by transoceanic colonization, and not over land bridges (Mayr 1941b). The immigrants soon start to diverge from the original parent population (a process which is speeded up by the small size of most of these island populations) and if, after a sufficient time interval, a second set of immigrants arrives from the same source, the two waves of immigrants will behave like good species.

Simple cases.—Cases of double colonization are known from nearly every sufficiently isolated oceanic island, for example among birds, from Tenerife (*Fringilla teydea* and *F. coelebs canariensis*), western Canary Islands (*Columba laurivora* and *C. bollii*), Norfolk Island (*Zosterops albogularis, Z. tenuirostris, Z. lateralis norfolkiensis*), and Samoa (*Lalage maculosa* and *sharpei*). Double invasions also occur on continental islands, for example Ceylon (*Brachypternus erythronotus* and *B. benghalensis intermedius*), Luzon (*Pitta kochi* and *P. erythrogaster*), and Celebes (*Dicrurus montanus* and *D. hottentottus*). Isolated mountain peaks may present exactly the same phenomenon, since they act as distributional islands. *Dendrobiastes bonthaina* (together with *D. rufigula*) on the Pic of Bonthain (S. Celebes) and several of the endemic species of Mount Kina Balu (Borneo) may be explained in this manner. Willis (1940) has listed a number of endemic plant species on the mountains of Ceylon, for which the same manner of origin is probable.

Not a single case of double colonization is known to me from recent continental islands, such as Britain or Ireland, or from any oceanic island (such as Biak or Rennell) which is situated close to a continent. The reason for this is obvious. Two species can develop from immigrant descendants of the same parent species only if the time interval between the first and the second colonization was sufficient to permit the earlier arrivals to develop sexual isolation. The new arrivals are simply absorbed by the earlier ones if this condition is not fulfilled. This is the reason why such twin species are absent from incompletely isolated islands.

Double colonizations of islands are, of course, not restricted to birds; it is only that the advanced condition of avian systematics makes their detection easier. I know of at least one well-analyzed case in butterflies. The common European Swallowtail (*Papilio machaon*) occurs as a single species in all of the Mediterranean countries. Two species of the *machaon* group are found only on the islands of Corsica and Sardinia, *Papilio machaon* subsp. and *Papilio hospiton* (Eller 1936:79). *P. machaon* subsp. is closest to the Italian and southern French races of the *mediterraneus* group, and *P. hospiton* to the North African races (*saharae* group) of *P. machaon*. When the two sets of colonists met on Corsica and Sardinia, they had diverged sufficiently from each other not to interbreed. Some of the species of the hemipteran genus *Nysius* reported by Usinger (1941) seem also to belong here.

A particularly puzzling case is presented by the Tasmanian thornbill, which reveals how difficult it is to decide, purely on the basis of morphological criteria, whether an island form is a species or a subspecies (Mayr and Serventy 1938). On the island of Tasmania (AE) south of Australia, there are two very closely related species of *Acanthiza* (thornbill). One of these (A), *Acanthiza pusilla diemensi*, is very similar to the subspecies *Acanthiza pusilla pusilla* (B), of the mainland of Australia, opposite. The other species *Acanthiza ewingi* (E), which lives beside *diemensi* like a perfectly good species without any signs of interbreeding, is also fairly similar to B (*Acanthiza pusilla*) and clearly an earlier offshoot of B. However, E is as different from C (western Australia) as is B, but B and C are completely connected by intergradation and interbreeding. E is morphologically closer to B than is C, but since A also occurs on Tasmania, E cannot be considered a subspecies of B. There is no question that we would list E as a member of the species B . . C, if the second invasion (A) had not taken place on Tasmania and revealed the specific distinctness of E. This teaches us that analogy is a poor tool in analyzing these cases, and that in many of these border-line cases one guess is as good as another.

Archipelago speciation.—The chances for double invasions are particu-

larly favorable in archipelagos consisting of two or three good-sized islands. The representative subspecies which develop in isolation on these
islands have a good chance to become in time so different that they can
spread to the neighboring island without mixing. This probably explains the presence of two species of related hummingbirds (*Eustepha-*

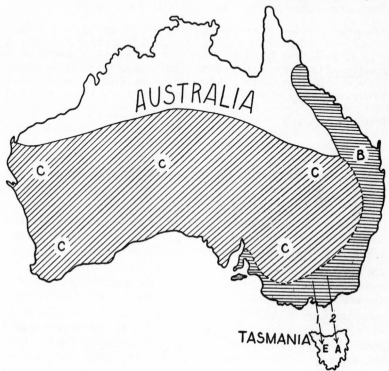

FIG. 18. Double invasion of Tasmania by *Acanthiza pusilla*. Completion of
the speciation process proved by successful second colonization. A = *Acanthiza pusilla diemenensis*; B = *A. pusilla pusilla* group; C = *A. pusilla api-
calis-albiventris* group; E = *Acanthiza ewingi*.

nus fernandensis and *galeritus*) on Masatierra Island of the Juan Fernandez group; of two species of related doves on Hivaoa and Nukuhiva
Islands in the Marquesas Islands (*Ptilinopus dupetithouarsi* and *mercieri*); of two related flycatchers (*Mayrornis versicolor* and *M. lessoni orientalis*) on Ongea Levu, Fiji; and of two species of finches (*Nesospiza
acunhae* and *Nesospiza wilkinsi*) on Nightingale Island, Tristan da
Cunha.

These cases are forerunners of that amazing speciation which has taken place on ancient archipelagos, such as Hawaii or the Galápagos Islands. The case of the Geospizidae on the Galápagos Islands has been excellently reviewed by D. Lack (1940a, 1942), while the more ancient and more complicated case of the Drepanididae on Hawaii has, so far, defied adequate analysis. Even richer species swarms than those of the Drepanididae have developed among the Hawaiian invertebrates.

The *Proterhinus* weevils with one hundred and fifty species, Cerambycids of the genera *Plagithmysus* and *Neoclytarhus*, Lygaeid bugs of the genera *Nysius*, *Neseis* and *Oceanides* in the tribe Orsillini and a host of other genera in all the principal orders of Hawaiian insects, have developed unique branches of from six to over one hundred species. Each of these is a small phylogenetic world in itself. Here we find geographical replacement, well developed, with distinct forms on each separate island and often on each host [Usinger 1941].

The same is true for the Hawaiian snails and in particular for the genus *Achatinella*. There is no doubt that archipelago speciation presents some of the most instructive examples of geographic species formation.

PARTIAL DISTRIBUTIONAL OVERLAP

Border invasions.—Another class of border-line situations is presented by cases in which two otherwise allopatric species show a slight overlap of ranges. Particularly interesting are those cases in which the two representative species are so similar that they would probably be considered subspecies, if it was not for the existence of the area of overlap. Even so, the entire distributional picture indicates the former subspecific relationship. Cases of this sort are not frequent, because, aside from some ecological competition, there is no reason why the two species should remain largely allopatric after the biological isolating mechanisms have developed to the point of complete reproductive isolation. As soon as such a species moves back into the range of a sister species (stage 4, p. 160), it is likely to spread so fast that all traces of the original allopatric condition are soon wiped out. This is particularly true for all large genera (with numerous species). Cases of slight overlap, as we shall presently see, therefore indicate generally a rather recently completed establishment of discontinuity between species.

The overlap is usually due to the recent breakdown of a geographic or ecological barrier. *Tanysiptera galatea* now lives in South New Guinea side by side with *hydrocharis*, because the arm of the sea that had separated them previously (Fig. 15) recently dried up. *T. hydrocharis* lived on an island which connected the Aru Islands with the Oriomo River plateau. *T. galatea* was restricted to the mainland of New Guinea and offshore islands. When the erosion debris of the rapidly rising central range of New Guinea filled the sea, *T. galatea* was enabled to intrude into the formerly isolated range of *hydrocharis*, but no interbreeding took place. A similar situation exists in a Venezuelan snake (Stuart 1941). *Dryadophis amarali* developed apparently from *pleei* stock during insular isolation on Tobago Island or on the Paria Peninsula. Recent geological events have led to an overlap of its range with that of *pleei*, but there are no signs of interbreeding. A third situation of the same sort has been described in the case of a Florida dragon fly. The Florida species *Progomphus alachuensis* and the Cuban species *P. integer* developed in insular isolation from the eastern North American species *P. obscurus*.

The reunion of the central Florida Island (Pleistocene) with the mainland of North America brought the ranges of *P. obscurus* and *P. alachuensis* in contact with each other . . . and *P. obscurus* invaded north and north-central Florida. In north-central Florida the invading species overlapped the range of the endemic one, but remained ecologically distinct, inhabiting the rivers and streams, leaving the lakes for the species already established [Byers 1940].

More frequent than the joining of an island with the mainland is range expansion due to the breakdown of ecological barriers in connection with climatic changes. The coming and the going of the ice during the Pleistocene age has been responsible for a great many such changes, of which very few have as yet been analyzed. It is not always clear whether the isolation was due to glaciation or occurred at an earlier date. Some authors, notably Salomonsen (1931), list a very high number of European species pairs as being due to Pleistocene separation; other authors hold that this separation was only in exceptional cases long enough to permit the development of interspecific gaps. The final decision cannot be reached until we know more details as to climate and plant distribution during Miocene and Pliocene. Until such time, cases discussed below will have to be treated with some reservation. There is an eastern and a western species in many genera of European birds. Stresemann (1919), who studied the distribution of the western Tree Creeper (*Certhia brachydactyla*) and the eastern Tree Creeper (*C. familiaris*), suggested that this peculiar pattern of distribution was of Pleistocene origin. When, at the height of glaciation, the Scandinavian and the Alpine ice caps approached each other in central Europe to within a distance of about 200 miles, they forced all European animal life into a southwestern (southern France, Spain) and southeastern (Balkans) refuge. During this period of isolation, the parental *Certhia* population developed specific differences and reproductive isolation and did not interbreed when the ranges of the expanding species finally met. (But see Steinbacher 1927.) Today the two creepers occur side by side without interbreeding, in a broad zone which extends from northwestern Germany to the Alps. Salomonsen (1931) explains on the same basis similar species pairs in the avian genera *Hippolais* (*polyglotta* western, *icterina* eastern), *Luscinia* (*megarhyncha* western, *luscinia* eastern), and *Muscicapa* (*hypoleuca* western, and *albicollis* eastern). A number of parallel situations exist among European amphibia. The western toad, *Bombina variegata*, became a mountain form during the glacial separation, while the eastern toad, *Bombina bombina*, remained a lowland species. Range expansion after the retreat of the ice led to a considerable distributional overlap, but the two species remain effectively isolated, since they occur at different altitudinal levels. At a few localities there is an overlap of the altitudinal ranges, and it is in such places that intermediate (hybrid) individuals have been found. The two species can be hybridized in captivity without difficulty (Mertens 1928a, b). A similar overlap of ranges is shown in the case of two central European frogs, but the ecological factor which keeps the two species separate is, in this case, the breeding season. The western species (*Rana esculenta*) breeds from the end of May well into June, while the eastern species (*Rana ridibunda*) completes its breeding season before the end of May (Mertens 1928a). The two species of newts *Triturus cristatus* and *T. marmoratus* developed apparently during glacial separation. There is now a narrow zone of overlap in central France, in which a few hybrids with reduced fertility have been observed ("*T. blasii*"). A similar case in presented by *Triturus vulgaris* and *T. helveticus*. The present overlap between these two species is very considerable, comprising the British Isles and the region between eastern France and western Germany. *T. helveticus* prefers the mountains, *T. vulgaris* the lowlands, but both have been found in the same waters, where lack of sexual affinity prevents interbreeding (W. Herre 1936). The glaciers, which at the height of the Pleistocene era advanced into the Po basin from the southern foot of the Alps, separated very effectively a number of snail and insect populations, which lived on southern spurs or foothills of the Alps. These populations expanded when the ice retreated, and, even though they are still largely allopatric, there are now a number of places where two of such "forms" overlap without any signs of interbreeding. Good examples of this can be found in the work of Klemm (1939) on the snail genus *Pagodulina* and of St. Zimmermann (1932) on *Orcula*.

A few similar cases have also been described from North America, although isolation was not as long-continued and effective as in Europe, where the formidable barrier of the Alps has been so important. The geographic ranges of the two mice *Peromyscus leucopus* and *gossypinus* are exclusive except for some areas of overlap in the Dismal Swamp of Virginia, in northern Alabama, and, more widely, in the lower Mississippi Valley. They occupy, in part, the same habitats, where their ranges overlap, but there is no evidence of any interbreeding in nature, except for two presumed hybrids reported from Alabama. The two species are very similar and fully fertile in the laboratory (Dice 1940b). Quite a number of similar cases have been described from North American snakes, of which I shall report only a few.

The polytypic species (or species group) *Crotalus atrox* (diamondback rattler) exhibits very clearly the effects of isolation during the height of the Pleistocene age (Gloyd 1940). The species became separated into three portions, one on the west coast of North America, which developed into *ruber*; a second one in Mexico, which developed into *atrox*; and a third one in Florida, which became *adamanteus*. Additional populations were isolated on the tip of Lower California (*lucasensis*) and on some islands near Lower California (*exsul* and *tortugensis*). After the retreat of the ice, the populations expanded northward, but the gap between *adamanteus* and *atrox* in the lower Mississippi Valley was never closed. However, *atrox* moved westward until it reached the border of the range of *ruber* in the western part of San Diego County, California. There are no hybrids or intergrades known from this district, but the forms (species?) seem to be ecologically separated. Another interesting case of speciation is presented by the species *Crotalus viridis* and *mitchellii*, which are very similar and the ranges of which are still largely exclusive. In southern California there is, however, a considerable area of overlap, without any signs of intergradation or hybridization. Among the North American bull snakes (*Pituophis*) there is an overlap of the ranges of the species of *catenifer* and *sayi*, which species indicate by their pattern of distribution that they were formerly subspecies of a single polytypic species (together with *melanoleucus*) (Stull 1940). The overlap results occasionally in a limited amount of hybridization without an actual breaking down of the species limits. This happens for example, where the moth *Platysamia cecropia* overlaps the ranges of the closely related species *nokomis*, *columbia*, and *gloveri* (Sweadner 1937).

All these cases have one feature in common, namely, that owing to range expansion two formerly allopatric forms begin to overlap and to prove thereby to be good species. If no overlap existed and if we had to classify these forms merely on the basis of their morphological distinctness, we would probably decide, in most cases, that they were subspecies. But overlap without interbreeding shows that they have attained species rank.

Overlap of the terminal links of the same species.—The perfect demonstration of speciation is presented by the situation in which a chain of intergrading subspecies forms a loop or an overlapping circle, of which

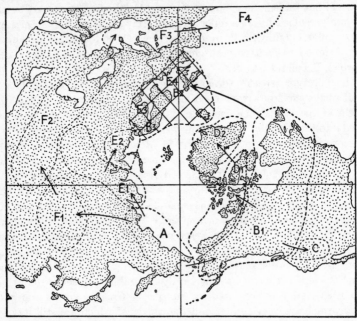

FIG. 19. Circumpolar projection of the ranges of the forms of the *Larus argentatus* group, showing overlap of the terminal links of a chain of races. A = *vegae;* B1 = *smithsonianus;* B2 = *argentatus;* B3 = *omissus;* C = *californicus;* D1 = *thayeri;* D2 = *leucopterus;* E1 = *heuglini;* E2 = *antelius;* E3 = *fuscus;* E4 = *graellsi;* F1 = *mongolicus;* F2 = *cachinnans;* F3 = *michahellis;* F4 = *atlantis.*—*L. fuscus* (with *graellsi*) lives now beside *L. argentatus* (with *omissus*) like a good species. (From Mayr 1940a.)

the terminal forms no longer interbreed, even though they coexist in the same localities. To be sure, such speciation by force of distance is much rarer than speciation by strict isolation, but at the same time these cases demonstrate species formation by geographic variation in the most perfect manner. One of the reasons why such cases have not been recorded in the literature more frequently is a purely psychological one. The puzzled systematist who comes across such cases is tempted to "simplify" them by making two species out of one ring, without frankly telling the facts. Overlapping rings are disturbing to the orderly mind

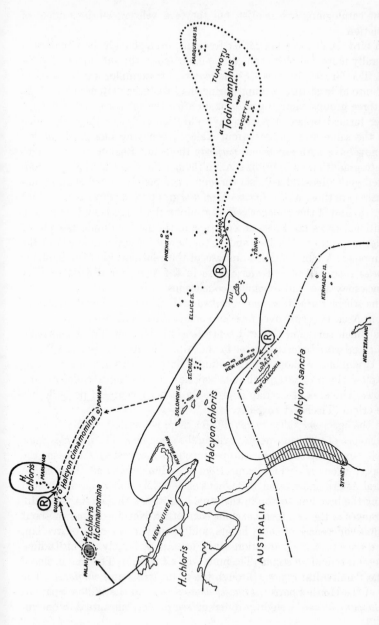

Fig. 20. The closely related species of kingfishers of the *Halcyon chloris* group still replace each other geographically (R), except in two places: Palau Island and the coast of eastern Australia. At both localities two forms live side by side as good species. (From Mayr 1940a.)

of the cataloguing systematist, but they are welcome to the student of speciation.

In birds such cases are rather frequent, even though the situation is generally more complex than can be indicated in the subsequent discussion. The Great Titmouse (*Parus major*), for example, was apparently split into at least three groups during the Pleistocene (Rensch 1933). As the three groups came together again after the retreat of the ice, they either formed broad or narrow hybridization zones or they expanded into the same area (upper Amur Valley), behaving like good species. We now have both *minor* and *major* in the Amur Region, without signs of intergradation or hybridization, although the two "species" are connected via China-India-Persia through a completely linked chain. Similar cases are those of the *Larus argentatus* group in northwestern Europe (Fig. 19) and of the *Halcyon chloris* group in the Palau Islands (Fig. 20). Additional cases are those of *Zosterops* in the Lesser Sunda Islands, of *Lalage* in southern Celebes, and of the honey buzzards (*Pernis*) in the Philippines. A more detailed analysis of the relationship of the babblers *Eupetes caerulescens* and *nigricrissus* in the Wanggar district of New Guinea may also lead to similar conclusions.

The warbler *Phylloscopus trochiloides* (Fig. 21) has a wide distribution in Asia. It occurs over most of northern Asia and also on the mountains which surround the arid central-Asiatic plateau. Two forms (*viridanus* and *plumbeitarsus*) meet in the Altai Mountains (western Sayan and Uriankhai) without interbreeding. The two forms are connected by a gapless chain of intergrading subspecies: *obscuratus*, *trochiloides*, and *ludlowi*. The area of overlap is probably rather recent—of post-Pleistocene origin (Ticehurst 1938a).

In the species *Phylloscopus collybita* there is another possible case of coexistence of two "subspecies" within the same area. The race *abietinus*, which came from northern Europe, meets in the western Caucasus the subspecies *lorenzii*, which came from the Himalayas and the western central Asiatic mountains. Specimens of both forms have been collected during the breeding season in the same localities, although, in the main, the ranges of the two forms exclude each other. Nothing is known about possible differences of song, habits, and habitat in the area of overlap, but there are some indications that *lorenzii* is largely an altitudinal representative of *abietinus* (Ticehurst, *op. cit.*:42–52). The ring is closed in the Pamir-Altai region, through the forms *tristis* and *sindianus*. The case of the House Sparrow (*Passer domesticus*) and the Willow Sparrow (*P. hispaniolensis*) is slightly different (see p. 268), but agrees in one re-

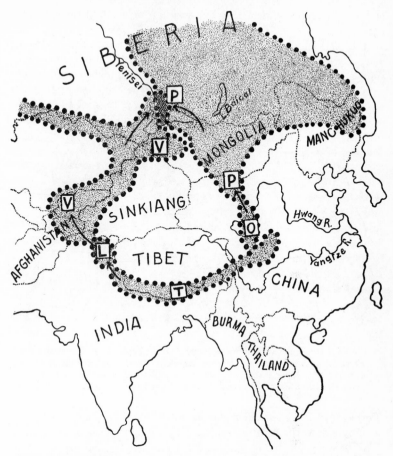

FIG. 21. Overlap of two terminal links in a ring of subspecies of the warbler *Phylloscopus trochiloides*. The subspecies of this ring are: V = *viridanus:* L = *ludlowi:* T = *trochiloides:* O = *obscuratus:* and P = *plumbeitarsus*. The overlap between *viridanus* and *plumbeitarsus* in the district between the western Sayan Mts. and the Yenisei River is indicated by cross-hatching. (From Ticehurst 1938a.)

respect, namely, that two forms may have reproductive isolation in part of their range and may be interbreeding in other parts.

The known number of cases of circular overlap in other animal groups is constantly increasing. The butterfly *Junonia lavinia* colonized the West Indies from South America and from North America (W. T. M.

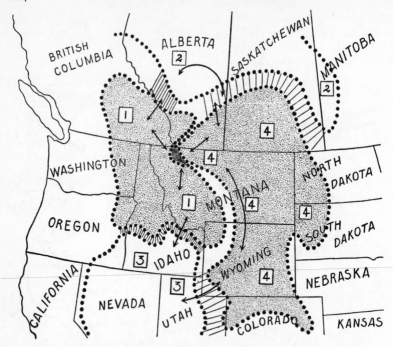

Fig. 22. Overlap (without interbreeding) of subspecies of the deermouse *Peromyscus maniculatus* in Glacier National Park. 1 = *artemisiae;* 2 = *arcticus;* 3 = *sonoriensis;* 4 = *osgoodi.* Habitat segregation is more or less maintained in the zone of overlap. (After Osgood 1909 and other sources.)

Forbes 1928). The two colonizing lines met in Cuba, where they now live side by side without interbreeding. Goldschmidt's question (1940:120): "Would they be able to mate and produce fertile offspring, if brought together?" is beside the point. The point is not what they would do under the artificial conditions of captivity, but what they do in nature. Many good species can be crossed in captivity, but that does not in the least weaken their status as good species. A very interesting overlapping circle of races exists in the mouse *Peromyscus maniculatus.* In Glacier National Park, Montana, a forest-inhabiting subspecies, *P. m. artemisiae*, meets a grassland race, *P. m. osgoodi*, with no evidence of interbreeding (Murie 1933). The failure of the two subspecies to interbreed in the zone of overlap is only partly due to the differences in their ecological requirements, for at some places near the margins of their habitats the two races live together without interbreeding. The two forms would undoubtedly be considered good species if the chain of intergrading races, now connecting them, were broken. (Fig. 22).

The evidence discussed by me on pages 162 to 185 is, it seems to me, conclusive proof for the existence of geographic speciation: If an isolated population of a species remains long enough in this isolation, it may acquire biological isolating mechanisms which permit it, after the breakdown of the isolating barrier, to exist as a separate species within the range of the parental species. The reproductive isolation, which originally was maintained by the extrinsic means of a geographic barrier, is being replaced during this isolation by intrinsic isolating barriers. One species has developed into two.

CHAPTER VIII

NONGEOGRAPHIC SPECIATION

WE HAVE SPOKEN of geographic speciation, up to this point, as if it were the only way by which new species can originate. This is correct for birds, so far as we know, and may have something to do with the fact that in birds the species, as such, is a very homogeneous natural phenomenon. The species of Australian or of North American birds, of mountain or of lowland birds, of terrestrial, fresh-water, or oceanic birds, the species of humming birds or of vultures, all of them are, biologically speaking, comparable units. There is no certainty that all other animal species can be considered as strictly equivalent to the species of birds. Many kinds of species are known in plants (apomicts, allotetraploids, hybrid swarms) for which there is no counterpart among the bird species. But are there, perhaps, some unusual types of species among the invertebrates, and particularly among the lower forms? Taxonomic refinement in these groups has not yet reached the point where this question could be answered with any degree of positiveness. The mating types of protozoa, the hermaphrodite and parthenogenetic species, seem to represent species types which are different from the bird species, but these forms may be considered exceptional and their total number is apparently negligible in proportion to the high number of ordinary bisexual species.

ALTERNATIVES TO GEOGRAPHIC SPECIATION

However, the fact that most species of animals have the same method of reproduction does not necessarily imply that all speciation is also of only one kind. The possibility is not to be disregarded that reproductively isolated populations, e.g., species, may develop even in bisexual animals by several independent and basically different processes, which have in common only the final result, the origin of new species. In addition to this possibility, one may also expect aberrant types of speciation in all animals with aberrant types of reproduction, as in self-fertilizing hermaphrodites and budding coelenterates. In view of this Hogben (1940) has recently proposed to speak of "origins of new species." To me this seems an unnecessary refinement of terminology. No doubt there are many different origins of species, particularly if we include plants, but the word origin in "origin of species" is used as equivalent to a collective noun, like, for example, the word behavior. Different animals have different behaviors, but this has never been considered sufficient reason for speaking of the "behaviors of animals." We prefer, therefore, to continue to speak of the "origin of species," even if species originate by a number of different processes.

Let us now examine what other kinds of speciation are thinkable and what evidence exists for their actual occurrence. To repeat, geographic speciation is characterized by the gradual building up of biological isolating mechanisms during geographic isolation. The primary factor is thus geographic segregation and isolation, and the secondary factor is the gradual accumulation of genetic differences leading to morphological, physiological, ecological, and ethological differences. If we are trying to find an antithesis to "geographic speciation," it cannot be "genetic speciation" or "ecological speciation," because these categories are not contrasting; in fact, they are largely overlapping. There is no geographic speciation that is not at the same time ecological and genetic speciation. To separate these factors into different categories would be as erroneous as to classify animals into (1) vertebrates, (2) marine animals, and (3) flying animals. The opposite of geographic speciation is obviously nongeographic speciation, e.g., speciation without geographic isolation, a process which might also be called "sympatric speciation." Another alternative classifying principle for speciation processes would be the speed by which reproductive isolation is acquired. Speciation can be either instantaneous (polyploidy, "systemic mutations," and so forth) or gradual (accumulative), as is all geographic speciation. This criterion may be used for a further subdivision of the phenomena of sympatric speciation, and we arrive then at the following classification:

A. Geographic speciation
B. Semigeographic speciation
    (Origin of species gaps in zones of intergradation)
C. Nongeographic speciation (sympatric speciation)
    (1) Instantaneous
    (2) Gradual

This is a logical classification of speciation processes from the viewpoint of the naturalist, and we shall follow this general outline in our subsequent discussions. Geographic speciation has been fully dealt with in the preceding chapter, and this leaves us with the topics listed under headings B and C.

ORIGIN OF SPECIES GAPS IN ZONES OF INTERGRADATION

We understand by "semigeographic speciation" the development of species gaps between populations not completely separated geographically. Very little concrete information on this process is available, and we must limit ourselves to a discussion of the basic points of this problem.

Let us go back to our distinction between primary and secondary zones of intergradation (p. 99). A secondary zone of intergradation develops if (after a period of isolation) two forms meet which have diverged to a lesser or greater degree, but which have not yet acquired complete reproductive isolation. Dobzhansky (1941a) shows that there will be a premium on homogeneous matings if there is the least reduction in the viability of the hybrids. The slight original cleavage between the two forms will develop under this condition into a complete gap between species. No logical or actual difficulties are encountered in these cases of secondary zones of hybridization. The unfinished process of geographic speciation is merely completed by selective factors.

The question as to whether species gaps can develop along zones of primary intergradation is more difficult to answer. Huxley (1939:511), for example, visualizes the following situation:

> Whenever two relatively large and uniform areas were separated by regions of relatively rapid environmental change, the effect of selection would be to produce two main types of gene-complex, each stabilized by its own set of modifiers giving maximum harmony and viability. So long as the population is continuous these will interbreed where they meet. But the recombination between them being *ex hypothesi* less well adapted and harmonious than either of the two main complexes will remain restricted to a narrow zone and will not spread progressively through the population.

Huxley cautiously stops at this point, but some other authors have postulated that a "tension" of such force might develop in this zone of abrupt intergradation that it would lead to a breaking of the single species into two. It seems to me that this is too great a simplification of what actually happens in nature. To begin with, there is a continuous gene flow in the zone of intergradation (working in both directions), in connection with the normal dispersal of individuals within populations. This will prevent the development of harmoniously balanced gene systems which are integrated to such a degree that interbreeding between them necessarily leads to a reduction of viability. More important, however, is the possibility that a third balanced (and locally superior) gene combination will develop in the zone of changing environment. The existence of such a local population would guarantee an unimpeded gene flow between the two neighboring balanced gene systems. It seems very unlikely on these premises, provided normal population densities prevail, that a biological "tension" would develop in the zone of environmental change which would lead first to a partial biological discontinuity and eventually to a complete species gap.

On the other hand, Huxley (*ibid.*) is on safe ground if he postulates that discontinuity could develop through partial isolation

e.g. where an area of relatively sparse population is interposed between two areas of greater density which are further distinguished by some degree of environmental difference. The obstacle to free gene-flow will render it easier for selection to build up distinctive gene-complexes in the two dense areas, and their greater harmony and viability, once established, will extend their ranges so as to decrease the intermediate area to a narrow zone.

However, this is merely a special case of subspeciation in connection with incomplete dispersal barriers. The fact that so many viable hybrid populations have formed in areas of secondary intergradation (p. 263) warns against overrating the reduction of viability in zones of primary intergradation.

It would seem advisable that an author should keep the above considerations in mind before announcing cases of sympatric speciation along ecological "fault lines." It seems to me that nearly all such cases listed in the recent literature can be explained much better by considering them cases of secondary breakdown of an interspecific reproductive isolating mechanism. Furthermore, there is no need for the assumption of sympatric ecological speciation, now that we know that ecological differences, such as we find between closely related species, can be acquired by way of geographic variation. The extreme reduction or complete stoppage of gene-flow effected by geographic isolation provides for a much-better-substantiated development of biological isolating mechanisms (including ecological differences) than sharp breaks in the environment within the range of widely distributed species. In fact, no case is known to me that could be cited as irrefutable proof for the latter type of speciation.

SYMPATRIC SPECIATION

We are now ready to consider the question as to whether it is not possible in some animal groups to have speciation without geographic segregation. The isolation would have to be effected in such cases either instantaneously or by ecological specialization and the discontinuities would have to develop within a single local population, that is within a single interbreeding unit. We call this *sympatric speciation*.

The question whether and to what extent sympatric speciation occurs among animals is one of the most controversial subjects in the field of speciation. Unfortunately, most of the discussions of this subject have been largely speculative, and, if one attempts to gather well-substantiated data, one is surprised to find how little concrete knowledge exists. The deplorable confusion of terms used in this field makes an adequate treatment even more difficult. Terms such as "ecological races," "biological races," "speciation by ecological specialization," and so forth have been used freely, but they are not based either on adequate definitions or on an analysis of the concepts which they are supposed to support. This field is in such utter confusion that it seems impossible at the present time to render a well-classified presentation of the data, based on a searching analysis of the available knowledge. Furthermore, most of the recorded examples concern insects or marine invertebrates, and this makes a treatment of the subject even more difficult to an ornithologist. It seems impossible, in view of all these obstacles, to give more than a tentative survey of the field. We shall in the main content ourselves with an analysis of certain phenomena, such as ecological and biological races, sibling and cosmopolitan species, and "explosive" speciation. A better-balanced treatment will have to be postponed until more data are available, but we hope that our discussion will stimulate the collecting of such data.

Darwin thought of individuals when he talked of competition, struggle for existence among variants, and survival of the fittest in a particular environment. Such a struggle among individuals leads to a gradual change of populations, but not to the origin of new groups. It is now being realized that species originate in general through the evolution of entire populations. If one believes in speciation through individuals, one is by necessity an adherent of sympatric speciation, the two concepts being very closely connected. However, fewer and fewer situations are interpreted as evidence for sympatric speciation, as it is realized more and more clearly that reproductive isolation is required to make the gap between two incipient species permanent and that such reproductive isolation can develop only under exceptional circumstances between individuals of a single interbreeding population.

Instantaneous Sympatric Speciation

The term instantaneous speciation means the production of a single individual (or the offspring of a single mating) which is reproductively isolated from the species to which the parental stock belongs. Such an individual would be the potential ancestor of a new species. Several processes are known in the plant kingdom, such as autopolyploidy and allotetraploidy, which result in the spontaneous and instantaneous production of new species. Polyploidy is rare among animals, since it interferes with the sex-chromosome mechanism. Its occurrence is restricted to parthenogenetic and hermaphroditic species or to such races of normally bisexual and diploid species (Vandel 1934). Species produced in this manner have all the earmarks of blind alleys of evolution. However, the fact that polyploid individuals occur indicates that the production of individuals that are reproductively isolated from their parental stock is possible. Hogben (1940) lists seven such possibilities: "(I) hermaphroditism combined with the possibility of self-fertilization, (II) the existence of a separate spore-forming generation, (III) parthenogenesis, (IV) production of individuals of either sex by clones from the same soma, (V) polyembryony, (VI) obligatory close-inbreeding, (VII) the occurrence of an epidemic of similar mutations at the same time." Let us now make a rapid survey of the evidence that would support the existence of these speciation processes.

I.—Hermaphroditism is common in certain groups of animals (Platyhelminthes, Oligochaeta, Hirudinea, and Pulmonate Mollusca), but, so far as the evidence goes, it is, with the exception of a few cases, connected with obligatory crossbreeding. The occurrence of instantaneous speciation (including polyploidy) is, in this case, as unlikely as in ordinary bisexual reproduction. Self-fertilizing hermaphroditism has real potentialities for the instantaneous production of new species, but, curiously enough, most of the known cases concern single species in a genus or single genera in a family, as for example the coccid *Icerya purchasi* or the nematode *Anguiostomum*. Self-fertilizing hermaphroditism is of wider distribution only among the parasitic cestodes, all of whom seem to be primarily self-fertilizing (except in heavy infections). The other cases mentioned are more in the nature of freaks and are rather to be considered evolutionary dead ends than starting points.

II.—Spore formation does not occur in animals. However, certain animals alternate between sexual and asexual stages of which the latter correspond, as far as speciation is concerned, to the spore-forming generations in plants. Asexual reproduction proceeds either by simple division or by various methods of budding. It is of widespread occurrence not only among protozoa, but also among the lower metazoa (sponges, sessile coelenterates, turbellarians, entoprocts, annelids, bryozoa, and tunicates). Its evolutionary significance is exactly the same as that of parthenogenesis (see below).

III.—Parthenogenesis is, in most of the animal groups in which it occurs, a condition that alternates with ordinary bisexual reproduction. Plant lice (aphids), gall wasps (cynipids), and daphnias are well-known examples in which one or several parthenogenetic generations are followed by a bisexual one. The importance of this phenomenon for speciation lies in the possibility that a mutation which affects fertility or crossability can build up a population of such size during the asexual generations that it can survive afterwards as the ground stock of a new species (see p. 213). This is a potential mechanism, but how far it is of actual importance in speciation remains to be seen. It is significant that cynipid gall wasps with such alternating parthenogenesis show perfectly normal geographic variation, of a degree comparable to the most striking cases in bisexual animals (Kinsey 1930, 1936), but that, on the other hand, parthenogenesis is of wide occurrence among the cosmopolitan animal groups and may be of importance in their speciation. Permanent parthenogenesis is always an exceptional, freaky condition and seems to have no potentialities as a speciation mechanism.

IV and *V. Clones and polyembryony.*—Hogben lists some cases in which these reproductive processes might contribute toward the origin of new species, but these cases are entirely hypothetical. The probability is exceedingly small that a mutant would be produced that would be both viable and either cross-sterile or reproductively isolated from the parent. Furthermore, the examples cited were taken from families in which geographic variation is known to occur and geographic speciation may be expected.

VI and *VII. ("Obligatory close-inbreeding" and "an occurrence of an epidemic of similar mutations at the same time").*—These are purely genetic phenomena and I do not feel qualified to discuss them. The present evidence indicates that they can play at best a very minor role in the speciation process. As far as VI ("obligatory close-inbreeding") is concerned, it seems to be merely a restatement of the "Sewall Wright effect" of evolution in small populations.

Summarizing all this evidence, we might say that there are a number of processes known, particularly among parthenogenetic and hermaphroditic animals, which permit instantaneous speciation, but such speciation is apparently rare, even where it is hypothetically possible.

Gradual Sympatric Speciation

In addition to instantaneous speciation, sympatric speciation is supposed to be possible also through the formation of ecological or biological races that continue to accumulate differences until they have reached the level of specific distinctness. Some authors believe that this type of speciation is of widespread occurrence. Careful recent studies tend to disprove this assumption, since most of the cases that were formerly quoted as proof for sympatric speciation have now been found to have been erroneously interpreted. It has frequently been overlooked (by the exponents of gradual sympatric speciation) that biological races can continue to exist as separate sympatric conspecific units only if they can develop isolating mechanisms to prevent swamping. On the other hand, the reproductive isolation must not be complete, or else we shall have to consider these "races" good species. It will therefore be our first task to analyze the published cases of ecological and biological races, to separate them clearly from similar but unrelated phenomena (sibling species), and to study their isolating mechanisms. The speciation literature makes, curiously, a distinction between ecological races (habitat specialization) and biological races (host specialization). We shall adopt this classification for purely practical reasons, even though no sharp line can be drawn between the two categories. All biological races could equally well be called ecological races, and vice versa.

The Ecological Race

We have treated the geographic race, to this point, as if it were the only infraspecific category and have used the term subspecies as synonymous with it. This is possibly an oversimplification, and other authors prefer several subspecific categories. Rensch (1929, 1934), primarily on the basis of his experience with mollusks, distinguishes between two kinds of subspecies, the geographic race and the ecological race. Dice (1940a:219), on the other hand, says: "The subspecies should be considered primarily an ecologic unit." It seems to me that it is misleading to make a strict distinction between ecological and geographic races. All geographic races are, at least to some extent, also ecological races, since the environment of no two localities is exactly the same and since we know that local ecological factors participate in the shaping of all local geographic races. It is therefore evident that we cannot define an ecological race (if such a category exists at all) as being one that is influenced by the environment, as compared to the geographic race, "which is entirely due to geographical factors" (whatever that means). Such an antithesis is wrong and misleading. Botanists seem to be equally hazy as to how to distinguish between geographic races and ecotypes. This is obvious from a statement made by some of the leading students in this field (Hiesey, Clausen, and Keck 1942):

As we extend our studies to populations in different climates, we notice that the differences attain a larger order of magnitude. We arrive at a point where some taxonomists begin to wonder whether they are dealing with another species or merely with a variety or a subspecies. These are the climatic races, or ecotypes. Sometimes they are distinct enough morphologically to be named as subspecies.

It seems to me that any geographic race, is to be regarded a subspecies, whether it owes its principal characters to the selective properties of the local climate or not. More difficult to treat are habitat forms that are strictly localized.

An author may find, for example, in the same geographic district, two different, but very similar forms in two different ecological niches or under the influence of two different sets of ecological factors. The morphological differences are more or less constant, but the author may consider them too slight to suffice for specific separation. Neither can the two forms be geographic races, since they coexist in the same geographic district (which conflicts with the definition). Nor can they be considered merely individual variants, since the difference is associated with a habitat difference. Therefore the author concludes they must be "ecological subspecies." Such ecotypes, as have been described in insects, snails, and so forth, are usually restricted to distinct habitats, as meadow, forest, swamp, bog, sand dunes, and the like. Rensch, for example, describes in the snail *Arianta arbustorum* a meadow form which is high, pale, and opaque, a forest form which is flat, dark, and translucent, and a mountain form which is very much smaller (Rensch 1934: 74, fig. 19). Whenever similar ecological conditions reoccur in widely separated places, similar ecotypes may appear. At the edge of two habitats we generally find a broad zone of intergradation, such as Rensch has described for *Arianta arbustorum* at the edge of meadow and forest. Whether or not such very localized ecological races differ in their genetic basis cannot be determined except by breeding or transplantation experiments. There is much indirect evidence, which we have already discussed in Chapter II, that at least in animals the majority of such habitat races are primarily phenotypical, that is, they are modifications of a practically identical genetic background. It would be misleading to recognize such ecophenotypes as ecological subspecies.

A different situation exists when the habitat of the ecological race is sufficiently extensive or isolated to have permitted the development of genetic differences peculiar to this population. I know of no definition by which such ecological races, the true ecotypes, could be distinguished from typical subspecies or at least from microsubspecies. For example, should we call a mountain race, which has differentiated from a lowland race, an ecological race or a geographic race? The characters of such a race are, to a considerable extent, the direct result of selection by a specific set of environmental (ecological) factors, but would not this be equally true for most geographic races (except those that owe their characters to the Sewall Wright effect)? It might be possible to reach a better definition of the ecological race if we shift the emphasis from the factors which cause the differences (through selection) to those which permit the differences to remain localized. We might try to define a geographic race as a subdivision of the species which does not become obliterated ("swamped") by other populations of the species, because it is either geographically too distant or because it is effectively separated by geographic barriers. In contradistinction, an ecological race would be a form which does not mix with neighboring ones, because it is kept separated by ecological factors. So far so good! But as soon as we try to apply this concept to practical cases, we run into difficulties. Let us again compare a mountain and a lowland race of the same species. No great distance is involved, since they approach each other within one or two kilometers, or even less. There are no pronounced geographic barriers between the two, because their ranges meet on the slopes and show intergradation. On this basis we should consider them ecological races. This point of view is strengthened by the fact that similar races occur on other mountain ranges. However, if we base our considerations on the cruising radius of the individual, we come to different conclusions. We find that such genetically fixed races occur only in very sedentary or at least *"ortstreue"* (philopatric) species. Species with a considerable random dispersal do *not* tend to the formation of ecological races, at least not of genotypic ones. In other words, a mountain race, in a sedentary bird or mouse or beetle, is, biologically speaking, geographically isolated and thus a geographic race. This isolation is reenforced by habitat selection, as we shall see in the next chapter (p. 246). Ecotypes among animals are thus nothing but microsubspecies, which owe their principal characteristics to the selective effects of a very local environment.

The adherents of the ecological race concept overemphasize the correlation between environment and taxonomic characters. There are numerous instances reported of populations which live on mountains and in valleys, or in arid and humid areas, without any change in the subspecific characters. A single subspecies is thus distributed over several ecologic units, without breaking up into ecologic races. Furthermore, the local environment very often affects conspicuously only a single character, such as pigmentation, which is correlated in desert mammals and larks with the color of the soil, while other characters behave independently or else are correlated with an entirely different set of environmental factors. It would thus be erroneous to consider all the dark-colored races of certain rock mammals or all the small-sized pocket gophers as particularly closely related (as "belonging to a single ecologic race"). They may be composed of as many races as there are independent populations, no matter how difficult it may be for the taxonomist to distinguish them. A painstaking analysis will eventually show, in such cases, that the subspecies, which is recognized for practical reasons, is actually composed of a heterogeneous medley of populations, which have become similar by the convergent evolution of a few characters.

Mountain and lowland races are, at least to some extent, geographically isolated and can therefore not be quoted as typical ecological races. A number of cases have, however, been reported in the literature in which two (or more) so-called ecological races (which were clearly not ecophenotypes) were found at the same localities in which they were at least partially isolated. Is there any evidence that they developed *in loco*, and what is their prospective potentiality for speciation? Huxley has stated recently:

We know relatively few cases of ecological species *in statu nascendi*. However, Dice (1931) records two subspecies of *Peromyscus* in the same geographical area, but separated by their ecological preferences for woodland and open country respectively. Worthington (1940) cites cases among fish; Dementiev (1938) gives examples of bird subspecies separated by altitude [Huxley 1940:4].

The implication of this statement is that in these cases populations diverge and reach sympatrically the subspecies stage on account of their ecological preferences. Actually, this does not seem to be true. Geographic isolation preceded the formation of the ecological preference in every one of the quoted cases, so far as I was able to determine. Only after the geographic barriers had broken down was mutual swamping prevented by the establishment of ecological barriers. This is quite obvious if we examine these cases more closely. A *Peromyscus* overlap has already been treated by us in detail, and it is superfluous to add anything to our previous discussion. Neither can Worthington's or Dementiev's cases be quoted as evidence for sympatric ecological speciation, as we shall see presently. A study of some other types of ecological races will also show that they acquired their ecological specializations as (micro-) geographic races.

Altitudinal races.—We find in many mountain ranges, particularly in the tropics, that some species have different subspecies at higher altitudes than on the lower slopes. Rand (1936) has examined this in detail for the birds of southeastern New Guinea and has found:

Of the sixty species [of which he had sufficient material], nineteen species, or 31.6 per cent show some variation; in 15 or 25 per cent of the total number of species examined there is an increase in size with altitude; in two cases or 3.3 per cent of the total the representatives from the higher altitudes are darker. In only one case, 1.6 per cent, are the higher altitude specimens smaller. In one case, 1.6 per cent, the higher altitude specimens are of a paler color. Of the sixty species discussed, seventeen, or 28.3 per cent, show an increase in size or in pigmentation with increase in altitude, while in only two, or 3.3 per cent, of the cases is the reverse true.

The altitudinal variation is more common in the small, passerine birds. Thus, of the 22 non-passerine species, 5, or 22.7 per cent of them show altitudinal variation, and this in size only; of the 38 species of passerine birds, 14, or 36.8 per cent, show altitudinal variation.

The change is so gradual in most cases that it is impossible to recognize subspecies, even though the extremes may be quite different, a situation equivalent to that in *Cacatua galerita triton* described above (p. 37). Altitudinal subspecies are recognized in only 8 species, but the habitats of 3 of these are discontinuous (grassland birds) (Fig. 26).

Chapman (1931) found some altitudinal variation on the table mountains of southern Venezuela (Mount Roraima, Mount Duida). The clear-cut, unbridged difference which exists between some of the low-altitude and high-altitude races of these mountains is not surprising, since their habitats are separated in the most effective manner by a cliff which is more than a thousand feet high. No such barrier exists on most other mountain ranges, and the intergradation between the lowland and highland populations is therefore generally very gradual. Among the 8 species of southeast New Guinea birds with altitudinal races, there are only 2 the subspecies of which are separated by striking discontinuities (in the species *Melidectes belfordi* and *Ptiloprora guisei*), even though the habitat is continuous. Rand (*loc. cit.*) has therefore suggested that the contact between these conspicuously different forms is a secondary phenomenon and that the differences originated during a former period of much more effective isolation. The facts of the distribution of the related subspecies of these two species support this assumption. It is strengthened also by the findings yielded by an analysis of the fauna of the mountains of the Burma-Yunnan frontier in southeastern Asia (Mayr 1940b). Two faunas meet here at an altitude of from 5,000 to 8,000 feet, below a tropical fauna which came from northern India and above a subtropical fauna which came from southwestern China. In at least 10 or 12 bird species, pairs of subspecies come into contact in this zone, which are strikingly different, sometimes almost to the degree of specific difference. It seems reasonable in these cases to assume that the present contact is of rather recent date and that the ecological difference did not develop *in loco*, but rather as the by-product of a general divergence produced in geographic isolation, which probably took place during the last glaciation. In many of the cases listed by Dementiev (1938), we also find that the two altitudinal subspecies, which are separated by pronounced taxonomic gaps, belong to different faunas and can have reached their present proximity only recently. They certainly cannot be quoted as evidence for sympatric speciation. The ecological difference may become very pronounced in some of these cases and will give active support to biological isolating mechanisms, if by secondary expansion the ranges of such previously geographically separated forms come together again. If the break between the habitat is sharp and the two subspecies have developed strong ecological preferences during their isolation, they will remain as neatly separated as if they were living on two different islands.

Seasonal races.—Another type of ecological race is presented by the so-called seasonal races. It happens occasionally that two or more sympatric populations of one species are kept separate, because their reproductive periods do not coincide. The second annual generation of certain species of mayflies (*Ephemerids*) is sometimes the descendant, not of the first generation of the same year, but of the last one of the previous year. The same species may have in other streams merely seasonal peaks in the number of emergent individuals, instead of clearly separated generations. The various broods of periodic insects are good examples of isolation by breeding period. The seventeen-year cicada (*Magicicada septendecim*) has, for example, five major and four minor broods in West Virginia, which are independent of each other. Most of these broods have a wide range in eastern North America (Craig 1940). There are no morphological differences known between the members of the various broods, but certain distributional features suggest that the various broods, or at least some of them, might have been geographic races at former times. This is plausible, since locally adverse conditions may cause a postponement of the year of emergence. That the seasonal races of certain marine fish have developed as local populations is established without doubt. In the herring (*Clupea harengus*), for example, Schnakenbeck (1931) distinguishes thirteen geographic races in eastern Atlantic waters between the western exit of the Channel and Iceland (including the North Sea). The spawning grounds of several of these races overlap to a considerable extent, but the breeding seasons are different at these localities. In the southern North Sea two races overlap, the "bank herring," which breeds from August to October, and the "spring herring," which breeds from March to May. Even though they mingle in the same school in the zone of overlap, they are completely isolated and furthermore morphologically characterized by their different variation curves. Cuénot's (1933) case of two presumable races of the cuttlefish *Sepia officinalis* is not equally well established. A comparable situation is possible in migratory tropical birds. It is thinkable that a race, whose range extends from the equator southward and which nests from September to November, overlaps near the equator the range of another subspecies, whose range extends from the equator northward and which breeds from February to May. No definite cases are known, but Dr. Chapin tells me that some indirect evidence points to its occurrence in two African species. The breeding ranges of the north and south equatorial races of the kingfisher *Halcyon leucocephala* overlap perhaps at Buta, Uelle, Congo, and those of the hoopoe *Upupa epops* at Entebbe, Uganda. That certain subspecies occur as winter visitors in the breeding range (and during the breeding season!) of other subspecies of the same species is of common occurrence and will be discussed in a later chapter (*Eurystomus*, p. 253).

We may summarize our conclusions on ecological races as follows:

1. No evidence exists for most so-called ecological races which would indicate whether they are merely phenotypical or whether their morphological differences have a genetic basis.

2. There is no criterion by which well-localized and genetically characterized ecological races or ecotypes can be distinguished from microsubspecies. There is every degree of intergradation between subspecies of which the most obvious characters are the selected product of a local environment and those of which this does not seem true.

3. No process is known which would permit the development and perfecting of biological isolating mechanisms in "ecological races," as long as they are in wide contact with neighboring populations.

4. Whenever two neighboring (or even partly overlapping) subspecies are distinguished by strong ecological differences, it can nearly always be shown that these differences were acquired prior to the period of geographic contact and that the present contact is a secondary condition.

5. There is, at the present time, no well-substantiated evidence that would prove (or even make probable) the development of interspecicfi gaps through habitat specialization. The cases recorded as such have all the characteristics of zones of secondary intergradation.

Sibling Species

We have defined as sibling species sympatric forms which are morphologically very similar or indistinguishable, but which possess specific biological characteristics and are reproductively isolated (see p. 151). Sibling species and "biological races" have been so consistently confused by several recent authors that it is necessary to analyze the sibling species problem thoroughly before we can attempt to discuss intelligently what we consider bona fide biological races.

It is a fact well-known to the experienced taxonomist that, in addition to clear-cut species there are, in nearly every order and family of animals, groups of species which seem to resist analysis. The borders between species, subspecies, and varieties seem to be so vague that nobody knows just how many species should be recognized. The final analysis of such groups shows invariably that two, three, or more well-defined species are involved, which differ from "ordinary" species in only the one respect that the differences in the examined morphological characters are very minute. Several good species were listed under a single specific name until the time when the minute differences between them were discovered. Several such incompletely analyzed species groups occur in the genus *Drosophila*. *Drosophila "obscura"* and *"affinis"* are best known, but a number of additional sibling groups have recently been discovered by Spencer and by Patterson and his coworkers.

In birds, sibling species are not very common. Sympatric species are generally sufficiently different to permit easy recognition. Among 568 species of New Guinea birds we might quote the following as sibling species: *Collocalia vanikorensis* and *hirundinacea*, *Pachycephala pectoralis*, *soror* and *meyeri*, *Pachycephala schlegeli* and *lorentzi*, *Sericornis nouhuysi* and *beccarii*, *Manucodia jobiensis* and *chalybatus*, *Meliphaga analoga*, *gracilis*, *orientalis*, *flavirictus*, and *albonotata*, *Melanocharis nigra* and *longicauda*, *Zosterops minor* and *novaeguineae*, *Erythrura trichroa* and *papuana*. The specific distinctness is now well established in all these cases except that of *Meliphaga analoga* and *albonotata*, and is in some cases corroborated by field observations. Altogether the sibling species comprise less than 5 percent of the New Guinea bird fauna. In Europe and North America all the cases of sibling species among birds were cleared up more than forty years ago, and it is only in the tropics that such difficulties still exist. I have listed recently (Mayr 1940a:259) the principal bird genera in which such taxonomic difficulties have been cleared up in recent years. In some cases the coloration is almost identical, but there is a considerable difference in size between the two members of the sibling pair, for example in *Mearnsia*,

Erythrura, Myiarchus, Ramphastos, and *Phyllastrephus* (Chapman 1924). Sibling species in birds involve nearly always dull-colored forms. They are encountered only very rarely in genera containing species that are not only very bright and colorful but also possessing complicated color patterns. It was found recently (Mayr 1940c) that the common minivet *Pericrocotus "brevirostris"* of the taxonomist (from India, Thailand, Indochina, and south China), consists really of two species. These brilliantly colored birds had been studied by the leading ornithologists of the world, but all of them had been deceived. The differences between the two species (*brevirostris* and *ethologus*) are quite slight; in *brevirostris* there is less black on the third innermost tail feather than in *ethologus; ethologus* has some red along the outer margins of the inner wing feathers (which is absent in *brevirostris*); the red of *brevirostris* is a little deeper, less orange than in *ethologus*, and so forth. Ticehurst (1938b), discussing the similarity of two such sibling species, the babblers *Garrulax pectoralis* and *moniliger,* writes:

These two species afford one of the most remarkable cases of parallelism in ornithology. Apart from two small characters, the difference between the two is that of size, the largest *moniliger* practically overlapping the smallest *pectoralis.* If the two were separated geographically they would at once be considered races of one species. Yet so far from being separated geographically they are not even, like some closely-allied species are, separated by difference in terrain; indeed, where one is found the other frequently is also, even in the same hunting party. Their nests, habits, eggs, courtship, and terrain are identical; they share the same ecological niche. Furthermore, when the form of the one changes geographically—as it does in southern Burma, *pectoralis* to *meridionalis*—*moniliger* changes to *fuscata* in the same area, and the differences between these races and the typical forms are the same in both species—the substitution of buff-coloured tips to the tail for white. Farther east in Indo-China the forms are again changed, and both tend to show the same differences—a darkening and saturation in colour. Yet it is quite clear that we have here two species. I have never seen a specimen which was not definitely one or the other and, moreover, in parts of the distribution of the two the status is by no means equal, the one or the other being much more the commoner. In Burma the ear-coverts in both *pectoralis* and *moniliger* vary very much and may be black to almost white. The measurements are as follows:
Adult ♂♀ (*pectoralis*): wing 140–152; tail 130–144; bill from skull 31, 32–36 mm.
Adult ♂♀ (*moniliger*): wing 119.5–132; tail 120–132; bill from skull 27–32.5 mm.

On account of the excellent progress made in recent years, there are only a few avian genera left (for example, the cave swiftlet *Collocalia* with about 16 species) in which the species have not yet been com-

pletely analyzed. Considering that there are about 8,500 species of birds
in the world, the number of "difficult" species is so small that it does not
amount even to one percent. The eventual elimination of all such cases
may perhaps be considered the most tangible result of taxonomic work.

Sibling species are known from nearly every family of animals, although they seem to be more common in some groups, such as the
diptera, for example. *Cepaea nemoralis* and *hortensis* among the snails
and *Pieris napi, rapae*, and *brassicae* among the butterflies are well-
known European examples of sibling species. Alkins (1928) analyzed
biometrically the differences between the two similar snails *Clausilia
rugosa* and *cravenensis* and proved their specific distinctness. A study of
the diagnostic differences between the stone marten (*Martes foina*) and
the pine marten (*M. martes*) showed that they were not as similar as
had been believed. There are at least five characters that permit unmistakable diagnosis, and not a single intermediate or hybrid was found
among several hundred specimens examined (Streuli 1932). The two
European wood mice *Apodemus sylvaticus* and *flavicollis* are much more
similar, and some authors claim even today that the two forms are only
ecological races or color phases of one species. No single character of
size or of coloration is by itself clearly diagnostic, but by correlating all
the characters K. Zimmermann (1936) had no difficulty in assigning
definitely every single live specimen or well-prepared skin to one or the
other of the two species. The characters of the doubtful species *flavicollis*
are (as compared to *sylvaticus*): (1) greater size, (2) longer body appendages (tail, ear, foot), (3) more rufous upper parts, (4) a yellowish
mark on the fore-neck, (5) under parts purer white, (6) tail with more
rings, (7) skull larger and less rounded. In large parts of the range,
particularly in the northern parts there is also an ecological difference,
flavicollis lives in the woods or in scrubby growth, and *sylvaticus* in the
fields. No intermediates are found where the two habitats meet, as for
example at the edge of woodlands and open fields. This clear ecological
separation does not exist in the more southerly parts of the ranges of
the two species. All this proves their specific distinctness, and it is
therefore nonsense to call them ecological races, as some authors have
done. The fleas which parasitize these mice present equally puzzling
complications (Jordan 1938). Müller and Kautz (1940) consider the
differences between *Pieris bryoniae* and *napi* to be those of sibling species,
but it is also possible that *bryoniae* is an altitudinal subspecies of *napi*.

There is a difference between the ecological preferences of the sibling
species in all these cases. Diver (1940) has analyzed this difference more
closely with the help of modern ecological methods. The plant com-

munities of an area of 750 acres on the South Haven Peninsula, Dorset, England, were carefully plotted and the animals recorded on this background. Three species of the fly genus *Syrphus* were recorded, at one time or another, from 35 major habitat loci. But all 3 species co-occurred only in 9 percent of the stations, two in 31 percent, while only one species was recorded in the remaining 60 percent of habitat loci. Similar results were obtained in the genera *Crambus*, *Myrmica*, *Lasius*, *Sphaerophoria*, and *Cepaea*. In a few exceptional cases it was not possible to find even quantitative differences between the habitat preferences of two similar species, as for example between the hover flies *Sphaerophoria scripta* and *menthastri*. Similar but less accurate surveys have been undertaken by other authors: Kramer and Mertens showed (1938b) that each of the 3 closely related and very similar lizards *Lacerta muralis*, *sicula*, and *melisselensis* was ecologically characterized; Bragg and Smith (1941) showed that every one of the 7 forms of toads (*Bufo*) that occur in Oklahoma are restricted to one or several habitats with but little overlap.

Among students of ants it is customary to call sibling species "subspecies" or "varieties," even though they live side by side in the same habitat and behave like good different species. Cole (1938) attacks this convention with good reason, but then he proceeds to describe as a new subspecies what on the basis of his own data cannot be anything but a sibling species. In the genus *Pogonomyrmex* he finds one form (*owyheei*) restricted to sand dunes, where it makes small mounds, with single central entrances that are surrounded by borders of chaff. The other form (*occidentalis*) makes large pebble mounds in the sagebrush (*Artemisia tridentata*) areas surrounding the sand dunes. The workers differ in size (5.0–5.5 mm. against 7–10 mm.) and color, and even the queens show certain structural differences. The differences are slight, but clearcut, and no intermediates have been found, not even where the two habitats meet. We have no choice, on the basis of these data, but to consider the two forms as sibling species and not as ecological races or subspecies, as was done by Cole.

It is a widespread custom among entomologists to call two forms "biological races" if they occur at the same localities and show certain biological or ecological differences, but are very similar morphologically. This taxonomic terminology is the consequence of a purely morphological species concept, a concept which determines the rank of a form by the degree of its difference. When C. L. Brehm discovered, about 1830, that the common Brown Creeper of Europe actually consisted of two exceedingly similar sibling species of birds (*Certhia familiaris* and *brachydactyla*), his opponents called them ecological races and claimed that the differences in the length of toe and bill of the two forms were due to the fact that one lived on trees with a smooth bark and the other on rough-barked trees. Ornithologists refused for almost seventy years to admit *brachydactyla* as anything but a subspecies of *familiaris*, since they could not believe that two good species could be so similar. Numerous parallel situations have been reported in entomology. Emerson (1935) found two very similar species of termites (*Nasutitermes*), which differed more in the termitophile fauna of their nests than in morphological characters, and recorded them as sibling species. Thorpe (1940) refuses to accept this interpretation and lists the two forms as biological races. Fulton's so-called biological races of tree crickets are also obviously sibling species. Hering (1935) reports the case of two similar flies (*Ceriocera*) which parasitize the plant *Centaurea scabiosa*. The larvae of one live in the stem, those of the other in the flower. The adult flies differ primarily in size. Hering considers that the "stem fly" developed from the "flower fly" by ecological specialization. However, this interpretation is not very convincing, since he fails to indicate how sexual isolation could have developed between forms that live in different parts of the same plant and have flying imagines. It must not be forgotten, as Dobzhansky (1941a:281) points out, that mutants appear in populations at first as heterozygotes, and that therefore inviable or sterile heterozygotes are eliminated from further reproduction, regardless of how well adapted the new mutant might be in a homozygous condition. The newly arising stem flies would therefore have one of two fates, unless protected by geographic isolation. They would either be heterozygous for a potential isolating mechanism, but would be swamped for lack of spatial or ecological segregation, or they would be heterozygous for the factor controlling ecological preference, but would be eliminated for lack of an isolating mechanism. Homozygosity cannot develop for these reasons, unless mass mutation occurs, and geneticists are skeptical about this possibility.

Hering (1936) reports some additional similar cases, but they are open to the same objections. The different forms described by him are either phenotypes or sibling species. He presents no evidence that they are ecological subspecies and that they can be regarded as proof for ecological speciation. The same objections are valid in regard to most of the "biological races" reported by Thorpe (1940). *Drosophila pseudoobscura* "races" A and B constitute such a case. They are apparently not only completely reproductively isolated, but they are even partially sterile, if crossed artificially. Dobzhansky (1941a), who has studied these forms more thoroughly than anybody else, is now also convinced that they are two good species. They are characterized by a number of physiological differences, which concern the length of the pupal period, egg-laying curve, oxygen consumption, resistance to starvation, and so forth. There are significant statistical differences between the number of teeth on the proximal sex-combs of the males, and smaller, but still significant differences in regard to certain measurements (wing, tarsus) (Mather and Dobzhansky 1939). It was found recently (Reed *et al.* 1942) that the range of the wing-beat frequencies, which in turn depends on the size of the wing area and on the thoracic muscle mass, permits an accurate determination of the two sibling species.

The so-called "biological races" of the malaria mosquito *Anopheles maculipennis* are, in view of their medical importance, particularly famous and well analyzed and therefore deserve special attention. It may be mentioned at the outset that all the modern work proves conclusively that these "races" are nothing but sibling species, a view first advanced by de Buck, Schoute, and Swellengrebel (1934). According to the latest revision (Bates 1940), there are at least 5 but probably 6 good European species. These species (as well as some of their geographic races) differ in regard to their egg-floats, the larval chaetotaxy (or number of branches of the antepalmate hair of the fourth and fifth abdominal segments of the grown larva), number of maxillary teeth in the adults, larval tolerance for sea water, swarming behavior, other epigamic behavior patterns of the male, feeding behavior, ability to hybridize, and geographic and ecological distribution. The important point is that the form, color, and composition of the egg-floats is definitely diagnostic and that it was possible, by raising the mosquitoes in the laboratory as well as by studying them in their native habitat, to associate definite ecological and behavior characteristics with definite egg types and larval structures. The vast number of European "races" of the *Anopheles maculipennis* type, which have been described in the literature, may be grouped into 6 discrete units, which are characterized by morphological features of the egg, larva, and adult, and by ecological and ethological criteria. They are 6 natural sympatric units which are reproductively isolated and must therefore be considered good species. These species are:

1. *A. maculipennis* is apparently without significant geographic variation in Europe, where it is widely distributed. It is not, or but rarely, a malaria carrier; it prefers to lay eggs in small bodies of water (pools, ditches, and small streams).

2. *A. messeae* is a Continental European type which is absent from

the warmer parts of the Mediterranean. It likes great inland river valleys and large marshes, does not take blood during the cold part of the year, and is not (or but rarely) a malaria carrier. Possibly it has some geographic variation; larvae from Albania and Hungary have a smaller number of branches of the antepalmate hair (14.82) than German (16.9) or Dutch (18.2) larvae.

3. *A. melanoon* is a Mediterranean species which is not normally a malaria carrier. It breaks up into two well-defined (geographic) subspecies:

A. m. melanoon.—Italian Peninsula. Upper surface of egg dark, without pattern.

A. m. subalpinus.—Spain, northern Italy, and throughout the Balkans. Upper surface of egg with a pattern of light and dark areas: Two transverse black bars near the ends of the floats, with a few irregular black patches in the area between the bars.

4, 5. *A. labranchiae* and *A. atroparvus.*—The common malaria mosquitoes of Europe break up into a number of local races, which fall into two major groups, *labranchiae* and *atroparvus*. These two groups are very similar in most of their morphological and ecological characteristics and are almost completely allopatric. There is, however, some overlapping in central Italy, and no hybrids have been found in the mixed population. Furthermore, the F_1 males of an artificially produced hybrid population are sterile. There is also one striking ethological difference between the two: *atroparvus* males will mate with females without swarm formation, while *labranchiae* must swarm, although it will form a swarm in a cage only 1 m. high and 50 cm. wide. These data, as well as some other differences between the two forms, indicate to me that it is more correct to consider the two forms species than subspecies. The Morocco population of *labranchiae* has been separated as *siccaulti* by Roubaud, and the Sicilian population as *pergusiae* by Missiroli. In *atroparvus* Roubaud separates a Normandy population as *fallax* and a Portuguese population as *cambournaci*, but the work of Bates indicates that these geographic races may not really be distinct.

6. *A. sacharowi* (= *elutus*).—This is a very distinct species, well characterized in the egg and adult, but still clearly a member of the *maculipennis* group. It is very tolerant to salt water and lives in the eastern Mediterranean and the Near East.

Some of the important differences between the six species are as follows: *A. labranchiae*, *atroparvus*, and *sacharowi* are malaria carriers; *A. maculipennis*, *melanoon*, and *messeae* are not. *A. atroparvus* will mate in a very small cage without swarm formation, *labranchiae* in a small cage (1 x 0.5 m.), *sacharowi* in a room-sized cage, and *maculi-pennis* in a very large outdoor cage, while it has been impossible, so far, to induce *melanoon subalpinus* to mate and swarm in captivity. *A. maculipennis* and *A. messeae* have very low tolerance for salt-water, in *melanoon* it is slightly higher, in *atroparvus* and *labranchiae* it is still higher, and *sacharowi* larvae survive sometimes in a 50-percent sea-water solution. Every time that a new ecological, physiological, or ethological character has been analyzed, new differences between these species have been found. Further details can be found in the reports of Bates (1940, 1941a, b), where a review of the earlier literature is also given. As Bates (1940:349) states, it is certainly not admissable to quote the Anopheles evidence "as an argument against the role of geographical isolation in the formation of species." I have presented the case of the sibling species of the *maculipennis* complex in so much detail because this situation is of considerable help in understanding other cases of "biological races," reported in the literature.

Sonneborn, Kimball, and Jennings showed that the individuals of several species of ciliates can be divided into groups, the individuals of which will not conjugate with individuals of the other groups (Sonneborn 1941). In *Paramecium bursaria*, for example, 3 such mating types occur. All 3 groups have the general form, structure, and size that is characteristic of *P. bursaria*, all have the type of micronucleus known for this species, and all contain the characteristic green algae cells. In groups I and II mating reactions occur mainly or exclusively in the day-time, particularly in the afternoon, while in group III they may occur at any time of day or night. There is also a slight indication of differences in geographic distribution. Whether or not these mating types are equivalent to the sibling species of the higher animals must remain a moot question until we know more about speciation in protozoa.

The differences between sibling species are sometimes very slight; in fact, as Thorpe says (1940:343): "There seems no doubt that finally in certain cases no satisfactory structural differences will be discoverable, and it will be then essential to distinguish some perfectly good species on biological grounds alone." This puts the taxonomist in a quandary. Shall he recognize species which he cannot diagnose? An author who adheres to a strictly morphological species definition may and will refuse to recognize sibling species that are morphologically indistinguishable. In doing so, he ignores the fact that species are not his own artificial creations, but products of nature! A taxonomist who thinks in biological terms will accept these sibling species more readily. And in his museum work he will simply put the specimens of *Anopheles messeae* and *A. atroparvus* in the drawer where the mosquitoes of the *Anopheles maculipennis* group are kept. No reasonable person will ridicule him if he explains that the members of this group cannot be identified down to the species, unless additional differences between these species are discovered.

The fact that sibling species exist is, to my mind, not surprising. After all, our taxonomic characters are visual cues, and it is quite reasonable to expect that the species divergence (particularly in nonoptical animals) should affect different sensory fields, for example, the olfactory sense (special scents) or the auditory (wing vibrations, and so forth). There is little doubt that such sibling species as *Drosophila pseudoobscura* A and B show specific differences of this kind, but the human sense organs are simply not capable of discovering these differences. There is no reason why "reproductive isolation" (and that is, after all, what the term "different species" means in modern biology) can not develop without a conspicuous change of the basic pattern. Indeed, it is almost more puzzling that the acquisition of reproductive isolation is so often combined with the acquisition of distinct morphological novelties. Even in the most similar sibling species, morphological differences are nearly always found when looked for. The chromosomal differences between the two species *Drosophila pseudoobscura* A and B are as striking and reliable as the differences between the external characters of certain species of birds or the internal characters of certain species of nematodes.

BIOLOGICAL RACES

The fact that so many so-called "biological races" have recently been unmasked as geographic races or ecophenotypes or as sibling species does not mean that biological races are altogether nonexistent. It seems, however, appropriate to restrict the use of the term to the host races of parasitic and semiparasitic animals and of monophagous food specialists. "A biological race may be said to exist where the individuals of a species can be divided into groups usually isolated to some extent by food preferences occurring in the same locality and showing definite differences in biology, but with corresponding structural differences either few or inconstant or completely absent" (Thorpe 1930:177). Such biological races may live in the same localities without mixing, if reproduction takes only place on the host. New biological races may develop almost spontaneously as single individuals become conditioned to new hosts:

Certain experiments have been carried out whereby it has been possible to induce some kind of insects to feed upon an unusual food plant in the absence of their normal host. In the next generation the preference for the new food plant became so marked that the original host was refused. . . . Once an insect has fed upon a new food plant, from the youngest larva or nymph onwards, it has become conditioned to that plant. This conditioning impresses itself upon the chemotropic behavior of the female to the extent that she selects the same plant species for egg-laying. Her progeny feed upon this same host and this may go on generation after generation [Simms 1931:405.]

It is conceivable that species may evolve from these "chemically" separated races through mutations that affect reproductive behavior and sterility, although it seems as if nothing would prevent the random mating by males, in other words, swamping. The fact that the two races live in two different (chemical) environments should speed the divergence, once it has become firmly established. To what extent speciation actually proceeds along the above lines is still a moot question. Even in the latest reviews of biological races (Thorpe 1930, 1940), no definite distinction is made between geographic races, ecophenotypes, sibling species, and host races. Nearly all the cases described relate to insects, and it is impossible for an ornithologist to assort them critically.

Changes in food habits occur, even in birds. Famous is the case of the New Zealand parrot, the kea (*Nestor notabilis*), a species which fed largely on insects and vetegable matter before the island was colonized by Europeans. After sheep had been introduced, it developed a taste for their meat by feeding on dead sheep and eventually began to attack live animals. Changes of feeding habits are much more common in insects. In fact, most of the dangerous insect pests of cultivated plants originate through changes in the food preference of formerly harmless species. *Plesicoris rugicollis*, an English willow bug, turned to apples in 1918 and has become a serious pest. Thorpe (1940) and Dobzhansky (1941a) record a number of similar instances. It is known only in a very few cases whether any isolation exists between the two "races," that is between the population on the old and the population on the new host. Genetic differences are sometimes proven, but these may be credited to the small size of the samples or to geographic variation with as much reason as to the host change, since the breeding stocks always came, so far as I know, from different geographic districts. Experimental data are scanty also in regard to the possibility of transplanting individuals from one host to the other. There is some indirect evidence for the importance of "host races" for speciation. Petersen (1932) calls attention to the fact that monophagous and oligophagous genera of butterflies and moths are much richer in species than the polyphagous ones. Such highly polytypic genera (of monophagous species) are, for example,

Nepticula (about 140 Palearctic species), *Lithocolletis* (about 100 species), and *Coleophora* (about 140 species). The species in these genera are remarkably similar, and this has made a generic subdivision impossible.

Even less is known about the biological races in gall insects and gall mites. It is in most cases still undecided whether the similar (or indistinguishable) insects that produce different galls on different hosts are sibling species, genetic host races, or genetically identical (with the galls merely phenotypically different). Considerable experimental work must be done before this type of biological races can be considered as analyzed and understood. It is significant in this connection that among 300,000 individuals of 400 species of gall wasps only 10 (or 0.003 percent) were found on trees that were not their normal hosts (Kinsey 1937b).

Parasites.—It is only a small step from the monophagous food specialist to the parasite; in fact, many species (including some of the gall insects) could be recorded with equal justification under either category. Most species of parasites tend to form host races unless, of course, the species is restricted to a single host. Bischoff (1934) believes that the parasitic golden wasp, *Chrysis ignita*, forms about 8 or 9 host races. Wertheim (1936) tried to prove the existence of intraspecific variation of the ciliate species that live in the intestines of ruminants, but his data lose their value since he confuses sibling species, geographic and host races. On the other hand, there is no doubt that these ciliates should yield very interesting data on speciation. A puzzling picture is presented by the human louse (*Pediculus*), which has two races, the head louse (*humanus* L.) and the cloth louse (*vestimentorum* L.). They are connected by intermediates; they change their characters within three generations if transferred from one body part to the other, and they can be crossbred in captivity. Most of the hybrids are fertile, but a certain percentage of them are intersexes, which indicates a fair degree of genetic difference. Nothing is known about possible isolating mechanisms between the head and the body "races," and no recent author seems to support Ewing's (1926) division of the head louse into a number of geographic races.

The two races of bugs (*Cimex*) that parasitize man (*lectularius*) and the pigeon (*columbarius*) are so similar that many authors consider them indistinguishable. The only character that separates them consistently is the proportion between head-width and third antennal segment (Johnson 1939). Both forms are fully cross-fertile in captivity, but whether or not they are reproductively isolated in nature is not known. The round worm (*Ascaris lumbricoides*) has at least two host races, one in man and one in the pig. Morphological differences are not known, but cross infection is impossible (Goodey 1931). Are these biological races or sibling species? The same question can be asked in regard to the host races formed by the plant nematodes, *Tylenchus dipsaci* and *Heterodera schachti*. It is possible to raise some parasites for many generations on new hosts, "but an instant in which the parasite actually chooses its own [new] host species in preference to the ancestral host has yet to be described among entomophagous forms" (Salt 1941). A strain of *Trichogramma evanescens*, which for more than 260 generations had access to no other host than to *Sitotroga cerealella*, still chose eggs of the ancestral hosts *Ephestia* and *Agrotis* in preference to *Sitotroga*. There is no doubt that the chance for conditioning to new hosts is exceedingly slight, which makes the development of sympatric biological races a practical impossibility in this group.

Even though we have not been able to do more than barely skim the surface of a very extensive and important field, we hope to have made it clear in our discussion on biological races that conditioning to new hosts is potentially an important method of speciation in monophagous species and in particular in plant feeders. Much more experimental work needs to be done, however, before we can fully understand the complicated relationships between host and parasite. Geographic variation may play an important role, even in this field, since host races often seem to be geographically restricted. Our knowledge of sympatric speciation through ecological specialization will advance much more rapidly if future writers on the subject will make a determined effort to draw careful distinctions between a whole group of phenomena that are now lumped together under the terms "biological species" or "ecological races." At the present time these terms include morphologically similar sibling species, physiologically polymorphic species, phenotypically different populations, and populations conditioned to different food plants, as well as genuine host races.

The occurrence of sympatric speciation has been postulated by certain authors in order to interpret a number of taxonomic situations which geographic speciation does not seem to explain adequately. These will now be discussed.

COSMOPOLITAN SPECIES

It may be said, as a broad generalization, that the more sedentary a species of animals is, the more it will tend to differentiate into geographic races. Conversely, it should be true that the more easily the individuals of a species are dispersed, the less diversification into geographic races takes place. The extreme of this proposition would be species which cannot be stopped by any geographic barrier and in which no isolated population is even partly removed from the free interchange of individuals. We should expect that species formation cannot be accomplished via geographic races, if there are groups of animals that are dispersed with such ease. What is the evidence that they exist?

The most promising possibilities are presented by the "floaters," that is by animals which, either in their normal condition (aphids for example) or encysted (including the egg), weigh so little that they can be carried by wind currents for hundreds or thousands of miles. Freshwater forms and small terrestrial species among the protozoa, rotifers, tardigrades, cladocera, collembola, protura, and many others seem to be particularly well adapted to this type of transport. Ballooning spiders also belong potentially to this group, but, since many species with this habit have restricted ranges, other factors must counterbalance this easy dispersal.

Among the tardigrada Marcus (1936) quotes the following examples of typical cosmopolitan distribution: *Echiniscus wendti:* Greenland and other arctic countries, Europe, South America, South Pacific Islands, Antarctic; *Pseudechiniscus suillus:* Arctic, Europe, Himalaya, Malay Archipelago, Africa, Madagascar, Hawaii, Australia, New Zealand, South America; *Macrobiotus hufelandii:* Arctic, Europe, Pacific Islands, Australia, Africa, North and South America, Subantarctic. Not all these species are, of course, ubiquitous, since most of them are restricted to definite ecological niches, but at least they show no geographic isolation. Gislén (1940), who made a special study of the distribution of cosmopolitan forms, came to the following conclusions:

> Summing up we can state that the planctonic oceanic beings get their wide spread through the ocean currents, while the terrestrial and limnic microscopic faunas probably attain a world-wide or regional spread with transport by flowing water, by birds, but especially by air-currents.
>
> For microscopic or semimicroscopic beings the following rules, therefore, seem to be valid.
>
> (1) There exists no geographical, i.e. geomorphological, borders or barriers for the very small animals.
>
> (2) They are often cosmopolites, otherwise regionally distributed round the whole earth. Some of them are thus restricted to climatic regions.
>
> (3) Most of the microscopic animals are edafically [ecologically] very strictly specialized. However, because of their large spreading power they may be found in every locality of the whole earth or of a certain climatic belt where their demand on ecological necessities is fulfilled, provided only that there has been sufficient time to give a chance for the germs, transported through the air, to settle in the suitable locality.

The difficulty presented by these cosmopolitan species to the student of speciation lies in the fact that the continuous swamping of every population by new immigrants does not seem to permit the development of new forms. No adequate explanation for speciation in these families and orders has yet been advanced, but there are several possibilities. One is that there is actually no longer any speciation in the most success-ful and most widespread of these species. Speciation is restricted to the more-localized and, from the point of view of dispersal, less-successful species. It is difficult to test this hypothesis, since the taxonomic and faunistic exploration of these microscopic groups is still rather in the initial stages. Marcus (*loc. cit.*) lists, for example, among the tardigrades 84 doubtful species, in addition to the 176 that are well substantiated. The well-explored European countries have only about 50 species each of the known 176, and there are at least 15 well-known and widespread (American, African, and other) species which are probably absent from Europe. The evidence is therefore conclusive that at least some species have localized ranges, even in the cosmopolitan groups. In fact, there are one or two cases of geographic variation known in the tardigrades. The species *Echiniscus intermedius*, for example, has 3 geographic races, *intermedius* (Queensland, Australia), *laevis* (Thuringia, Germany), and *hawaiica* (Oahu, Hawaii). It is therefore possible that speciation, at least in the tardigrades, proceeds in an orthodox manner by geographic variation.

A second possibility exists for most of these cosmopolitan groups. Many of them have parthenogenetic (asexual) generations, sandwiched in between the bisexual ones. It is possible that a radically new mutation, affecting, for example, the mating behavior, can build up a sufficiently large population during the parthenogenetic period to be able to survive afterwards as the ground stock of a new species (see p. 192).

Explosive Speciation in Lakes

Sympatric speciation on a large scale has been postulated to explain the presence in certain fresh-water lakes of large flocks of closely re-lated species. There are, for example, 171 species of Cichlid fishes in Lake Nyassa in East Africa, and more than 300 species of Gammarid crusta-ceans in Lake Baikal. There are 17 or more species of Cyprinidae in Lake Lanao, on the island of Mindanao, in the Philippines. Several of these species have become specialized to the extent that they are now con-sidered as representatives of monotypic genera. Herre (1933), who studied this situation in detail, seems to be inclined to assume that these species developed from each other in this lake. The same assumption is made by E. Woltereck (1937) to explain the presence of 7 endemic species of fresh-water shrimps in the lakes of central Celebes. In fact, nearly all the authors who have studied species flocks in fresh-water lakes have come to the conclusion that these species developed by sympatric speciation. R. Woltereck (1931) has inferred, on the basis of these fresh-water situations, the existence of a previously unknown process of speciation, that of *"schizotypische Artzersplitterung,"* or explosive sympatric speciation. According to this hypothesis, species flocks originate through ecological specialization in localities where many empty ecological niches are present. The explanation is applied not only to flocks in fresh-water lakes, but also to a number of situations among land animals where many species of the same genus occur in one locality. Woltereck states, for example, that he cannot see any other explanation for the presence of 53 species of the genus *Achatinella* on Oahu (Hawaii). Rensch (1933:37) counters these assertions by pointing out that most of these so-called species are nothing but geographic races. He believes that the number of valid *Achatinella* species on Oahu is less than 12, but Dr. Welch informs me (*in litt.*) that it is probably nearer to 20 species, some of which are restricted to isolated localities. There is little doubt, as pointed out in an earlier chapter (p. 174), that the species flocks on isolated archipelagoes have developed by the normal process of geographic speciation. Usinger (1941), the latest student of Hawaiian species flocks, came to the same conclusion. Neither is there any need for the assumption of explosive speciation to explain species flocks among continental terrestrial animals.

Old fresh-water lakes are, for fresh-water faunas, very much what old islands are for terrestrial faunas. They permit the survival of old elements which have long since become extinct in the surrounding areas. It seems to me that students of fresh-water faunas have vastly underestimated the age of the species with which they are working. The evidence for this is quite overwhelming for Lake Baikal, Lake Tanganyika, Nyassa, and so forth. The statement by the proponents of explosive speciation that ecological specialization precedes the establishment of discontinuity is not in the least plausible, if we remember that these habitats are in continuous contact with each other and that there is no evidence for the establishment of biological isolating mechanisms as long as unrestricted interbreeding takes place between the inhabitants of the different sympatric ecological niches. On the other hand, no objections seem to exist against the assumption that species flocks originated by multiple colonizations, corresponding to the double and triple colonizations and the archipelago speciation among island animals discussed previously (p. 174).

The fish faunas of the East African lakes seem to offer particularly valuable material for the testing of these theories. It seems that the closest relatives of most of the species of fish in the East African lakes are not sympatric. Worthington (1937) is somewhat puzzled by the fact that the genus *Lates* (Nile perch) is represented by two forms in most of the East African lakes, a large one in the surface waters, and a small one in the deeper waters. He takes it for granted that the two forms evolved in a parallel manner, independently, in each lake, by ecological specialization. Would it not be much simpler to assume that all the lakes were colonized twice by Nile perches, once by a small-sized, deep-water-loving species, and once by a large-sized shallow-water species? An analysis of these lakes shows that their faunas are not uniform, and the older a lake is the more obvious is the composite character of its fauna. The accumulation of large numbers of related species in these lakes is apparently partly due to the fact that a number of different river systems have "washed" their own endemic species into the lake, and partly to the fact that some of these lakes originated by the amalgamation of a series of smaller lakes. Ecological specialization helps now to preserve the discontinuities between the species, but it is not responsible for their creation. Species flocks in fresh-water lakes cannot be considered as proof for "explosive" speciation.

Our discussion of ecological and biological races, of sibling and cosmopolitan species, and of so-called explosive speciation has revealed that bona fide evidence for sympatric speciation is very scanty indeed. Even if it should become evident that sympatric speciation through ecological specialization is largely nonexistent, we need not feel disturbed. The fact that geographic races can acquire considerable ecological differences, as we have seen in Chapter III (pp. 53-59), facilitates the explanation of strong biological differences between closely related species, without any recourse to a hypothetical process of sympatric speciation. Certainty as to the relative importance of sympatric speciation in animal evolution cannot be expected until a much greater body of facts is available than at present.

CHAPTER IX

THE BIOLOGY OF SPECIATION

THE VARIATION of taxonomic characters and the development of divergence and of discontinuities between the systematic categories are influenced by a number of factors. Some of these are internal, some external; some promote speciation, and others inhibit it. We have referred to them only casually in the preceding chapters, in order to be able to give a better-balanced presentation in the present chapter. This field is of vital importance to the systematist of today, in his capacity as classifier as well as student of speciation. The majority of the factors that we have to discuss are environmental, and we might therefore speak of an "ecology of speciation." However, since we have to include the internal factors (mutability), as well as factors that involve behavior patterns, such as crossability, sexual isolation, pair formation, and the like, it might be preferable to use the broader term, biology. We are still groping in the dark about much of this matter, and the following attempt to organize this subject should be considered merely as experimental.

The greatest difficulty with which we are faced in our discussion is to arrive at a convenient classification, as well as a balanced evaluation of the numerous factors. The mathematical calculations of Sewall Wright and the theoretical analysis that preceded them have been of particular value in this task. We may classify these factors as (1) those that either produce or eliminate discontinuities and (2) those that promote or impede divergence. The latter may be subdivided further into adaptive (selection) and nonadaptive factors (see Huxley 1941). Whatever classification we use will be exploratory and tentative and may have to be modified as more facts become known. I have decided to treat divergence and discontinuity together and to select instead a different scheme of classification.

FACTORS INFLUENCING SPECIATION

These are of two kinds, which may be designated for convenience as internal and external. It might be equally correct to call them physiological (or mutability) factors and environmental factors. It must not be forgotten, however, that internal factors are always involved, even though the primary factor may be environmental. All external factors, such as the isolating value of geographic barriers or of specific recognition marks, depend for their proper functioning on the reactions of the animal, that is, on internal factors. The classification of the observations relating to speciation factors into internal and external factors was adopted for the sake of convenience.

INTERNAL FACTORS

The reasons why certain species and genera are stable, while others that live under similar conditions change rapidly, are still shrouded in mystery. It is a very unsatisfactory explanation to say that this is due to differences in the mutation rates, because we may ask immediately what causes these different rates in the different species. Work in the genetic laboratories has established beyond doubt the fact that the mutation rate of certain stocks of *Drosophila melanogaster* is higher than in others, and it is also known that in certain species (maize, for example) there are genes which control or at least influence the rate of mutation of other genes. This field belongs to the domain of genetics, and we shall therefore not enter into a more detailed discussion of it, particularly since there are two excellent recent summaries which approach the field from different angles (Dobzhansky 1941a, S. Wright 1941a). We shall see later in this chapter that it would be a mistake to explain all differences of variability as differences of mutability, but there seems to be little doubt that some differences exist in the mutability of different species. As naturalists, we merely observe that some species (genera, families, and so forth) are plastic, others static. What the biochemical basis is for this static condition and whether such species consist of particularly well-integrated, genetic systems (or have reached a particularly tall adaptive peak), can not be stated on the basis of our present knowledge.

Degree of variability.—In certain genera of animals there are dozens or even hundreds of similar species, many of them with numerous subspecies. It appears in such cases as if an evolutionary explosion had taken place. In other genera we find just one or two well-defined, clearcut species, without appreciable individual or geographic variation, indicating almost complete evolutionary stagnation. The most frequently quoted case of stagnant evolution is that of the Brachiopod genus *Lingula*, which is reported to have survived without conspicuous changes from the Paleozoic, a period of 475 million years. Actually there are certain differences between the living and the paleozoic *Lingula* which cause most modern authors to classify them in different genera. Furthermore, nothing is preserved of the fossil species except their shells, and we cannot even guess how much the internal anatomy may have changed between the Paleozoic and today. Many brachiopod lines had a fairly rich development during the Mesozoic, but our knowledge of the history of the class is still very incomplete, as indicated by the more than 250 genera described during the last decade (A. Cooper *in litt.*). However, even with all these reservations in mind, there is no doubt about the slowness of brachiopod evolution in general, which is proven by the fact that all living brachiopods go back to similar forms in the Paleozoic. Even though this may be a record, there are among marine animals many almost equally astounding cases. Among the reptiles there has been very little change since the Triassic in the Crocodiles and Rhynchocephalians, while the present birds and mammals are totally unlike their reptilian ancestors of Triassic times. A number of additional comparisons have been listed by Robson and Richards (1936:131) and by Cuénot (1936).

We must compare equivalent groups if we wish to find intrinsic differences of variability. Marine animals, with their more uniform environment, show much less geographic variation and correspondingly fewer changes of taxonomic rank during geological time than terrestrial animals. But even if we limit our consideration to a single taxonomic group, let us say birds, we find considerable differences in the degree of variation, thus indicating intrinsic differences. A few examples will illustrate this:

SONG-BIRD SPECIES DISTRIBUTED OVER THE ENTIRE SOLOMON ISLANDS

SPECIES	NUMBER OF SUBSPECIES
Pachycephala pectoralis	10
Rhipidura rufifrons	7
Rhipidura cockerelli	7
Monarcha barbata	7
Monarcha castaneoventris	6

Yet *Cinnyris jugularis* and *Rhipidura leucophrys*, with equally extensive or even larger ranges, have only a single subspecies in the entire archipelago. There is a good reason to believe that these two species have invaded the Solomon Islands only recently and have not yet had time to break up into races.

The following tabulation arranges the 95 species of song birds which are widely distributed over the lowlands of the mainland of New Guinea in nine classes, according to the number of subspecies belonging to each species.

NUMBER OF SPECIES	NUMBER OF RECOGNIZED SUBSPECIES PER SPECIES
1	15
1	13
1	9
2	8
1	7
17	4
13	3
29	2
30	1 (monotypic)

This shows that some species (31 percent) show no pronounced geographic variation in the entire, extensive area of the lowlands of New Guinea, while other species exhibit varying degrees of subspeciation. The range of the individual subspecies of birds is rather large (even in the most subdivided species), as compared to the ranges of the subspecies among many of the small mammals and invertebrates. This is well illustrated on the maps of the species complexes in gall wasps (*Cynips dugèsi*, for example), published by Kinsey (1936), and even better by the Hawaiian snail *Achatinella musinelta*, which on an area of less than 20 x 5 miles has 26 named subspecies and about 60 additional recognizable microgeographic races (Welch 1938). Not all terrestrial invertebrates show an equal variability; in fact, many species have as extensive ranges as some birds without any signs of geographic variation.

Rensch (1933) compared the species that are geographically variable with those that are not and found that in birds the amount of subspeciation is greater in small-sized species than in large ones. This correlation is, however, not very strict, since the large sized geese (*Anser, Branta*) show more subspeciation than the small ducks (*Anas, Nyroca*, and so forth), and the large gallinaceous birds show more geographic variation than the small shore birds (Limicolae), to list a few of many exceptions. In general, it seems to be true that the small song birds have, on an average, more subspecies per species than the large Non-passeres, and this correlation holds, even if we allow for all extrinsic factors (population size, sedentary nature, and so forth). To say that these large birds show reduced geographic variation because they belong to old genera and families only shifts the explanation to another level, since the amount of active evolution is one of the main criteria for the age of a group.

SPEED OF SPECIATION

It would be interesting as well as scientifically important to know how many years or generations are required for the evolution of a new subspecies or species. A number of such estimates have been made, but it is constantly growing more evident that so many different factors influence the speed of speciation (either positively or negatively) that only guesses are possible at the present time. The most direct method would be to analyze and describe very carefully the characters of a local population and then to examine the same population again after a lapse of time, in order to determine whether or not it had changed. Crampton (1932) finds that the collections of snails of the genus *Partula* which he made in 1909 in certain valleys of Moorea do not agree with collections made at a later (1923) visit. He interprets this result as being due to rapid subspeciation in the interval (14 years). There is, however, a second interpretation possible, in the light of the recent work on the Hawaiian snail *Achatinella mustelina*. Welch (1938) found that not only every valley had its endemic forms, as had been maintained by earlier workers, but that within each valley (or along each ridge) numerous separate and different populations could be distinguished, many of them occupying areas of less than 50 and some of less than 10 acres in extent. The possibility cannot be ruled out that Crampton's parallel collections were made at slightly different localities within the same valley and that this is the reason for the differences found by him.

A number of changes of populations in historical times are known (Dobzhansky 1941a:190–196). Most of them refer to physiological characters, such as the resistance of scale insects to poisons. Other changes relate to various forms of polymorphism (in the widest meaning of this word). There are the annual changes of the percentage of chromosomal inversions in *Drosophila pseudoobscura* populations or the variable composition of fungi (rusts) populations. These changes only rarely reach the taxonomic threshold, as in the cases of industrial melanism in moths (see Goldschmidt 1940, Hasebroek 1934) and in the previously discussed changes of polymorphic species. The results of transportation experiments have frequently been quoted as evidence for quick subspecific changes. We have already rejected most of these claims (p. 60) by showing that some of these cases are not proven, while others can be explained on the basis of phenotypical changes. There are, however, a few cases that seem well established. The Faeroe house mouse (*Mus musculus faeroeensis*) seems to have developed its present distinct characters within the last 500 years and *Lepus* during the last 85 years (Degerbøl 1940), and there is also some evidence that some island populations of rabbits have changed during historical times. We must conclude from these facts that the attempts to determine the speed of speciation by direct observation of distinct populations have not yielded many tangible results.

There is, however, an indirect approach possible, since it is sometimes possible to prove or at least to make it seem very probable that a race or species could have developed only after a certain geological event had taken place. We can then determine the maximum age of such a form. The great difficulty of this method is the incompleteness of geological data, which in some cases are even contradicted by the zoölogical evidence. For example, Tutuila is the oldest of the Samoan Islands, according to geologists, but its bird fauna is much younger than that of the neighboring islands of Upolu and Savaii and lacks nearly all of the typical Samoan endemisms (Mayr 1941 b). Tutuila is, of course, somewhat smaller than the other two islands, but is it certain that the geologist is not mistaken? The areas in North America and Europe from which the ice has retreated since the last glaciation are about the only regions on the earth where alluvial deposits and geomorphological structures are sufficiently well known to permit even an approximate chronology of recent geological events. But if we were to limit our study of speciation to the temperate zone of the Holarctic, we would obtain a very one-sided impression, owing to the peculiar conditions of this zone. After the retreat of the ice, there was much mixing of populations, settlement of new territories by heterogenous elements, strong competition, and lack of geographic barriers. The killing effects of winter and seasonal migrations serve to promote a rather thorough mixing of neighboring or even distant populations before every breeding season. All these factors tend to prevent the development of strong subspecies and thus slow down the speed of speciation. We cannot generalize on the basis of figures derived from this region and say, for example, that it takes from 10,000 to 20,000 years for a subspecies of bird to develop, because this happens to be the estimated age of some Scandinavian subspecies. There is no doubt that speciation proceeds much more quickly where the external conditions are favorable, as on small tropical islands or on well-isolated mountain peaks. This is quite evident if we compare the size of the ranges of *Cynips* "species" from the southwestern United States and Central America with those from the northern and eastern United States. More evidence for this will be presented in our discussion of isolating factors (p. 234), and I mention these facts only to warn against accepting the following figures too literally.

Hubbs (1940a, b) states in regard to the fishes of the western United

States that "in several isolated waters evolution has proceeded far enough to produce new subspecies within what appears to be a few hundred years, at most a few thousand." Moreau (1930) studied the races of birds that are associated with the black alluvial soil of the Nile delta and concluded that 5,000 years is not far from the minimum time required for the development of these races, which are not entirely isolated from the surrounding races. There is valid evidence that some of the endemic races of Scandinavian birds developed within the last 10,000 to 15,000 years. Even shorter periods were probably needed for the endemic races of Iceland and the Faeroe Islands. Kramer and Mertens (1938a) concluded that the subspecies of the lizard *Lacerta sicula* which have developed on the Istrian Islands have a maximum age of 9,000 years. The time required for the formation of new subspecies in Holarctic localities seems to lie, in most cases, between 5,000 and 15,000 years, a very short period in terms of geological ages, but a long period in terms of generations of animals. Goldschmidt (1940) may be right in saying that if in all cases such long periods were required for the production of slight subspecies, all geological time would not be sufficient to explain the present diversity of animal and plant life. However, there is little doubt, as we have already said, that speciation proceeds much more rapidly where animal populations are well isolated and removed from such retarding influences as post-Pleistocene population mixing. The cases of the Ipswich Sparrow (*Passerculus princeps*) on Sable Island and of the Red Grouse (*Lagopus scoticus*) in Britain (see p. 164) are positive proof that speciation can proceed rapidly even in the north temperate zone, provided that strict isolation is maintained. Not even a guess is possible, at the present time, concerning the speed of speciation on small, well-isolated tropical islands, or on mountain tops, or in caves. All we can say is that it is certainly much more rapid than speciation on the large temperate-zone continents.

There is considerable difference between various animal groups in regard to the speed of speciation, even when the environmental conditions are comparable. Reinig (1939) states that the bumblebees (*Bombus*) of the islands of Corsica and Sardinia belong without exception to different subspecies from those found on the mainland. Among the birds of these islands only a few have developed endemic races. Among the *Partula* snails of the Society Islands there are some species which break up into numerous races on each island, while other species are found without conspicuous variation in the entire archipelago (Crampton). The fact that we find on certain islands populations that are indistinguishable from mainland species, in addition to endemic races, does not necessarily indicate different speeds of speciation in the different species. It is rather to be attributed to the fact that the unchanged populations are recent arrivals from the mainland. This is obvious from an analysis of the hemiptera of Hawaii (Usinger 1941), of the birds of the Galápagos (Swarth 1934), and of the birds of Rennell and Biak (Mayr 1940a).

Speciation in marine animals moves at a snail's pace, as compared to that of terrestrial animals. The connection between the Atlantic and the Pacific Oceans (at Panama or Nicaragua) was interrupted some two or three million years ago, but some of the species of fish and crustaceans are still the same on both sides of the Isthmus of Panama. Among the crabs (brachyura), 11 species remain identical, while 13 species have split into representative pairs (Finnegan 1931). The paleontology of marine animals indicates the same slow evolution as does the existence of so many bipolar species. The speed of evolution should not be over-rated, even in terrestrial groups. Apparently all the living orders of birds already existed at the beginning of the eocene (sixty million years ago), and even greater antiquity (or slower speed of speciation) seems to characterize insect groups. Many of the insects of the mid-tertiary Baltic amber cannot be separated specifically from living species, and even an amber fauna believed to be cretaceous was found to be remarkably similar to the recent fauna (Carpenter *et al.* 1937).

It would be misleading to draw conclusions as to the speed of speciation entirely from the speed of subspeciation. It must not be forgotten that intraspecific interbreeding, that is, the continuous exchange of genes between neighboring populations, is a retarding process. Species that have become reproductively isolated drift apart much more rapidly than subspecies that still belong to a single interbreeding unit. We may conclude from the evidence presented that geographic variation is not too slow a process to account for the present multitude and diversity of animal life.

EXTINCTION

The world would be overcrowded with animal species if some did not always die out as new ones originate. The paleontologist encounters fewer and fewer of the recent species as he goes back through the geological levels. Some of this change is due to extinction; some of it due to the evolutionary transformation of species. In other words, the species of the paleontologist may be absent from later strata either because they have merely changed beyond recognition or because they have actually become extinct. Extinction is, in a way, the counterpart of speciation, but in spite of its importance it has received much less attention. Fossil evidence indicates that the "life span" (the time between origin and extinction) of some species is very long; for others, it seems short. Few tabulations exist as yet of probable life spans. Simpson (1931) has presented us with a valuable discussion of this problem, on the basis of a comparison of the Pleistocene and the recent mammal faunas of Florida. H. Howard and A. Miller (1939) find that from 33 to 49 percent of the avian specimens in typical Pleistocene Rancho La Brea asphalt pits belong to extinct species. The number of extinct species in these pits is about 15 percent of the total of identified bird species.

Islands play a peculiar role in this extinction process. They permit certain aberrant forms, which unquestionably would be doomed on the mainland, to survive as relics (New Zealand, Madagascar faunas), while, on the other hand, the smaller islands in particular may act as evolutionary traps, since the populations that live on them tend to become so uniform genetically that they are adapted only to the particular set of conditions under which they live. Thus there may be present almost no heterozygous individuals with concealed potentialities for preadaptation to sudden environmental changes, with the result that such forms become exceedingly vulnerable to extermination. About 97 percent of all bird species known to have become extinct within the last 200 years were island birds. All of them lived on rather small or at least well-isolated islands, while not a single species became extinct on large islands such as Borneo or New Guinea. Of the 76 endemic land birds of Hawaii, about 18 are now extinct, while 11 forms have become extinct in the New Zealand group (J. Greenway *in litt.*). Another proof for the extinction-promoting character of small islands is the fact that only rarely do they harbor very distinct species. This is strikingly illustrated by the fauna of some of the old and well-isolated small islands in the New Zealand group.

The history of such extinctions is both fascinating and puzzling. Bond (1940) has reported that 12 forms of birds have become extinct in the West Indies, with 12 additional ones being on the verge of extinction. When the steamer "Makambo" was wrecked on Lord Howe Island (near Australia) in 1918, rats (*Rattus* [*Epimys*] *norvegicus*) escaped to the shore and multiplied. A few years later no less than 5 indigenous and 2 introduced species of land birds of the total of 14 species had become extinct. Several of these had been very common birds prior to the rat invasion, but they were unable to cope with the new enemy (Hindwood 1940). Thrushes of the genus *Turdus* were common in 1910 on Uvea and Lifu, Loyalty Islands. No visible ecological changes have occurred during the last thirty years, but in 1938 the two species had apparently completely disappeared. The case of the thrushes on the Loyalty Islands is rather typical for many of these extinctions (in contradistinction to the Lord Howe Island case), in that there are no visible causes for the sudden disappearance of a form except that the total size of the population was so small and the genetic composition probably so uniform that the most minute change of environmental conditions became fatal. There is little doubt that, as postulated by Sewall Wright on theoretical grounds, well-isolated islands are evolutionary traps, which in due time kill one species after another that settles on them.

PRIMARILY EXTERNAL FACTORS

ISOLATIVE FACTORS AND SPECIES FORMATION

A single mutation does not make a new species except in the case of polyploidy. New species are due to a gradual accumulation and integration of small genetic differences. If there were species in which each individual was equipped with such excellent dispersal faculties that it would have an even chance to mate with any other individual of the species (no matter how far distantly it was borne), we would have complete panmixia (random interbreeding). It is sometimes assumed that panmictic species are excluded from further evolution. This is not the case. A sufficiently high rate of *recurrent* mutation, together with strong selection pressure and accidents of sampling (if the number of individuals is small), can produce rather rapid evolution, even in a panmictic species. However such a species changes as a whole, it is rather uniform in any one given generation and its changes are apparent only to the paleontologist. A panmictic species can never break up into two or more species (except by instantaneous speciation).

All the individuals of a panmictic species form one large interbreeding population. Such species exist in perfect form in theory only, except for the very small populations of certain insular species in which the diameter of the geographic range is no greater than twice the cruising radius of its individuals. All other species, and this includes the overwhelming majority of animal species, are broken up into local populations. These local populations owe their origin to the fact that external and internal factors restrict the random dispersal of individuals in various ways. These factors are reënforced by additional mechanisms which cause or help the isolation of populations and species from others. Excellent discussions of the importance of isolating mechanisms have been given by a number of recent authors: Cuénot (1936), Dobzhansky (1941a),

Huxley (1940), Robson and Richards (1936), Timofeeff-Ressovsky (1940a), and others. All these authors agree that the isolating factors can be classified, broadly speaking, into two large groups, i.e., geographic and reproductive barriers. The latter are frequently referred to as biological or physiological isolating mechanisms. There is a fundamental difference between the two classes of isolating mechanisms, and they are largely complementary. Geographic isolation alone cannot lead to the formation of new species, unless it is accompanied by the development of biological isolating mechanisms which are able to function when the geographic isolation breaks down. On the other hand, biological isolating mechanisms cannot be perfected, in general, unless panmixia is prevented by at least temporary establishment of geographic barriers.

There are certain advantages in a slight modification of this basic classification, which is based not so much on the descriptive qualities of the isolating mechanisms as on the method by which they accomplish this isolation. Isolation, according to this classification, may be accomplished because the potential mates do not meet (*restriction of random dispersal*), or because they do not mate even if they meet (*restriction of random mating*), or because they do not produce their normal quota of offspring even though they mate (*reduction of fertility and related phenomena*). The naturalist and ecologist may prefer this classification, which also has the advantage of permitting a more accurate analysis of incomplete cases of isolation. It is for these reasons that we adopt it in our subsequent discussion.

RESTRICTION OF RANDOM DISPERSAL BY GEOGRAPHIC BARRIERS

The concept of the species as one continuous population is, as we have seen, an abstraction which exists in nature only in exceptional cases. On the contrary, studies of ecologists have proven that the ranges of nearly all species are subdivided by a network of geographic and ecological barriers which break the species up into numerous colonies and local populations. These barriers reduce the flow of individuals from one population to the next, but only a few of them stop it altogether. The effectiveness of these barriers is therefore of great interest, since this factor influences to a considerable extent the speed with which the internal isolating mechanisms may be established. The effectiveness of the barriers is, at the same time, conversely correlated with the powers of dispersal. An unsurmountable barrier to one kind of animal may be no obstacle at all in another kind. Let us now examine the nature and efficiency of some of these barriers.

Water is the most effective barrier for land birds. This is the reason
we have such active speciation in island regions. The various subspecies
and allopatric species of the *Zosterops rendovae* group are separated from
each other by straits that are 1.7, 2, 5, and 6 kilometers wide (Fig. 23).
These birds fly at a minimum speed of about 30 kilometers per hour and
flights of 3.4, 4, 10, and 12 minutes would enable them to overcome the
gaps. Ugi Island, one of the Solomon Islands, is only 7 kilometers distant
from the mainland of San Cristobal, but it has striking endemic races

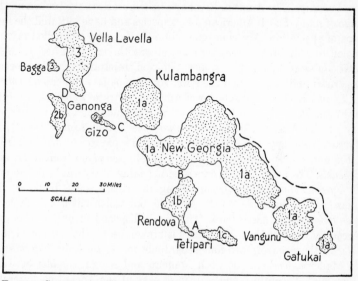

Fig. 23. Superspecies *Zosterops rendovae* in Central Solomon Islands. Extreme localization of related species and subspecies in a tropical archipelago.
1 = *Zosterops rendovae* and subspecies; 2 = *Zosterops luteirostris* and subsp.;
3 = *Zosterops vellalavella*. The shortest distances between the islands are:
A = 1.7 km.; B = 2 km.; C = 6 km.; and D = 5 km. (From Mayr 1940a.)

of at least three species. Of the 265 species of land birds which are known
in that part of New Guinea which is opposite New Britain, only about
80 species have a representative on that island. In other words, the 45-
mile-wide stretch of water which separates the two islands has prevented
the crossing over of 70 percent of the New Guinea species. Even more
striking is the situation in the western Papuan Islands. The strait between the islands of Salawati and Batanta, which is less than two miles
wide, has prevented the crossing of 15 full species of Salawati birds to
Batanta and of 2 species from Batanta to Salawati. Furthermore, a
considerable number of species is represented on the two islands by

different subspecies (Mayr 1941b:198). Among the 47 species of Passerine birds known from the D'Entrecasteaux Islands, which are only 15 kilometers from the coast of New Guinea, no less than 29 (or 62 percent) belong to different subspecies than are found on the New Guinea mainland. Florida and the island of Cuba, which are separated by 125 miles of water, have only a small proportion of identical species of terrestrial animals.

Not only straits of the sea, but also large rivers may form distributional barriers. The Amazon River and its tributaries have broken up the range of many South American forest species and have initiated the first steps of speciation. My colleague, John T. Zimmer, has called my attention to a number of striking cases among the ant thrushes. In *Myrmotherula menetriesii* the upper Amazon separates the subspecies *menetriesii* and *pallida*, and the lower Amazon *omissa* and *cinereiventris;* in *Cercomacra cinerascens* the lower Amazon separates *immaculata* (north bank) and *iterata* (south bank), and the Rio Madeira, a southern tributary of the Amazon, separates *iterata* (east) from *sclateri* (west); in *Myrmotherula longipennis* the upper Amazon separates *longipennis* from *garbei*, and two southern tributaries separate *ochrogyna* from *garbei* and *paraensis*. The most striking case is perhaps that of the ant bird *Phlegopsis nigromaculata*, which occurs along the entire south bank of the Amazon from the Andes to the Atlantic, but which has been unable to cross over to the north bank. This weak dispersal faculty is also evidenced by the fact that this species is broken up by the southern tributaries of the Amazon into four geographic races: *nigromaculata* west of the Madeira, *bowmani* between Madeira and Xingu, *confinis* between Xingu and Tocantins, and *paraensis* east of the Tocantins. Literally dozens of species show similar distributional pictures. The long-stretched lakes of the African rift valleys are sometimes effective subspecies borders, as, for example, Lake Tanganyika for the babbler *Turdoides jardinei*, which occurs in the race *emini* on the east bank and in the race *tanganyikae* on the west bank. Small arboreal or semi-arboreal mammals are even more affected by such water barriers, as shown by their subspeciation on both banks of the Chindwin River in Burma and the Congo in Africa. Dice (1939b) has examined the mouse populations on both banks of the broad and rapid Snake River, in Idaho, and found them to be quite distinct. M. Wagner was apparently the first naturalist to call attention to the importance of rivers as barriers between allopatric species. He pointed out, as early as 1841 (*Reisen in der Regentschaft Algier*), that this was particularly true for animals with reduced mobility, such as flightless beetles (he cites the North African genera *Pimelia*,

Blaps, Adesmia, Erodius, Asida, Tentyria, and so forth) and snails. He confirmed this, in his later writings, for the lower Danube and the large rivers of Asia Minor (Wagner 1889). Even rather small streams can form subspecific barriers, as, for example, the Main River of southern Germany for certain races of the beetles *Carabus monilis* and *C. violaceus* (Buchka 1936).

It might be argued that a river is an ecological and not a geographic barrier. However, this is rather an academic point, since I know of no definition which would permit us to draw a sharp distinction between the two kinds of barriers. This is even more true for other distributional barriers. Just as land animals are stopped by water, so are mountain animals stopped by lowlands. Mountains, as far as their inhabitants are concerned, are distributional islands in a "sea of lowlands." This is why the distributional picture of mountain birds resembles so much that of island birds. The mountain birds of New Guinea illustrate this very well. About 40 or 45 percent of all the land birds of that island do not descend below 600 meters. Most of them are found in the big central chain that runs from the Weyland Mountains to the mountains of southeastern New Guinea, but many of them occur also in some isolated ranges in the northwest (Arfak, Wandammen), north (Cyclops), and northeast (Huon Peninsula) of New Guinea. I have analyzed the Passerine species among these mountain birds in order to determine the influence of the lowland barriers on distribution and speciation (all superspecies were counted as species for the purpose of this analysis and allopatric forms within superspecies as subspecies). There are 119 species, of which 4 are restricted to one of the isolated ranges, 9 to the western part of the central range (2 of them have 2 subspecies each), and 3 to the eastern part (one with 2 subspecies); 14 species are found throughout the central range, but not on one of the isolated ranges, and 13 of these have different subspecies on the eastern and western parts. Of the 12 species which occur in the central ranges and the Arfak, only 3 have not subspeciated; among the 16 species which occur in the central ranges and all outlying ranges, only 3 are monotypic; among the 41 species which occur in the Arfak, Huon, and central mountains, only 9 show no geographic variation. One of the mountain species divides into 10 subspecies, one into 9, five into 7, and four into 6 subspecies. A map (Fig. 24) of the superspecies *Astrapia nigra* (bird of paradise) shows the insular character of the ranges of these mountain species and the extreme variation produced by this type of isolation. In North America the best cases of geographic isolation of mountain birds are presented by some of the species of *Junco* and *Leucosticte*.

Every animal is adapted to specific ecological conditions, and its area
of distribution consists, therefore, of patches of suitable habitat, surrounded by barriers consisting of unsuitable habitats. The distances
between the suitable habitats are, in general, smaller than the normal
dispersal potencies of the "isolated" populations, and in such cases
we speak of continuous ranges, even though this may not be strictly true.
In other cases the belt of unsuitable habitat may be wide enough to
cause effective isolation. This is true for forest animals in a savanna
country, or for animals in an isolated grassland patch in forest country,

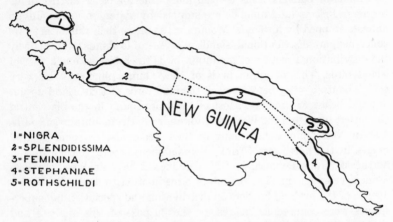

1=NIGRA
2=SPLENDIDISSIMA
3=FEMININA
4=STEPHANIAE
5=ROTHSCHILDI

FIG. 24. Geographical Isolation of mountain species (birds of paradise of the
genus *Astrapia*). Insular ranges and extreme taxonomic divergence of high
altitude birds of a single superspecies. Four of the five species have been considered generically distinct on the basis of purely morphological criteria.

or for inhabitants of an isolated lake or swamp, and so forth. A few
examples will show this more clearly.

The island of New Guinea is mostly forested. Grasslands exist only
in the south, in the southeast, above timber line and in a few other isolated patches. The genus of weaver finches *Lonchura*, which is restricted
to the grasslands (and to grassy swamps), has developed 12 species on
the island. Nine of these (as well as most of the subspecies of the 4
polytypic species) have very limited geographic ranges, some of them
being known only from a single locality. Only 3 species, which are less
specialized ecologically (*trististissima*, *castaneothorax*, and *grandis*), have
a somewhat wider distribution, but all 3 break up into a number of races.

Mutatis mutandis, the same is true for forest birds. There is, for example, an isolated belt of true tropical rain forest along the hills in the

western half of the Indian Peninsula. This forest belt is separated by
about 1,000 kilometers from the forest along the slopes of the Himalayas,
and many separate forms have developed in this forest island. There
probably was a rather recent connection during the last Pleistocene
pluvial period, and in some species of birds no visible differences have
yet developed in the population of the isolated forest. This is true, for
example, of the great Indian Hornbill (*Dichoceros bicornis*) (Fig. 25). A

FIG. 25. The range of the hornbill *Dichoceros bicornis* in India. No subspeciation has yet occurred, although absence of tropical forests on most of the Indian Peninsula has split the species into two widely separated groups of
populations (After Ali 1935).

similar separation of tropical rain forests occurs in Africa (upper and
lower Guinea forest), with the resulting influence on speciation (Chapin
1932). Even more striking are ecological barriers in insects that are restricted to a single food plant. Every area from which this food plant is
absent forms a dispersal barrier.

Even parasites may be affected by the habitat preferences of their
hosts. Jordan (1938) finds that the central European subspecies (*agyrtes*)
of the mouse flea *Ctenophthalmus agyrtes* is restricted in Normandy to
the woods, in a district where it overlaps with the northwestern subspecies *nobilis*, which in this area lives in the open country (hedges and
meadows). It is probable that the two fleas live on two different sibling
species of *Apodemus* (see p. 202).

The degree of isolation afforded by various habitat zones is well illustrated in Table 12.

TABLE 12

ENDEMISM IN PASSERINE BIRDS OF NEW GUINEA IN VARIOUS HABITATS AND ALTITUDINAL LEVELS

PRINCIPAL HABITAT	TOTAL NUMBER OF SPECIES	Endemic Genera		Endemic Species	
		Number	Percentage	Number	Percentage
Open country (second growth, and so forth)	35	0	0	4	11
Grasslands (Savannas, and so forth)	43	1	2	14	33
Lowland forest (Sea level— 400 m.	72	27	38	53	74
Hill forest (400 m.—1,400 m.)	51	21	41	38	75
Lower mountain forest (1,400 m.—2,200 m.)	53	33	62	51	96
High mountain forest (2,200 m.—3,600 m.)	22	11	50	22	100

Geographic barriers are active not only in separating species ranges horizontally but, under certain circumstances, also vertically. On the border of Guiana, Venezuela, and Brazil, there are a number of mountains, the remnants of a vast elevated sandstone plateau which eroded away sufficiently to leave these isolated rocks. Some of these mountains are sheer cliffs which rise up more than a thousand feet above a talus slope. The animals living on top of these cliffs are very effectively isolated from their nearest relatives at the foot of the cliff. This has produced cases of strong subspeciation (Chapman 1931).

In other cases of altitudinal variation the isolating factors are not as clearly developed (Rand 1936, Mayr 1940a, b). A particularly interesting condition prevails on the south slope of the mountains of southeastern New Guinea (Wharton Range). This slope is inhabited by a number of grassland birds which range from sea level up to the highest peaks. However, these grasslands are not continuous through this entire altitudinal scale, but are broken up into three belts, a lowland zone, a mid-mountain zone, and an alpine zone, all three of them completely separated from one another by forest belts. At least two species of birds have developed an endemic subspecies in each one of the three grassland zones (Fig. 26).

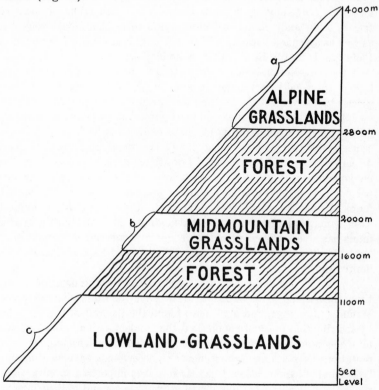

Fig. 26. Each of three altitudinal grassland belts in southeastern New Guinea has its own set of endemic races of certain species of birds. Intervening forest belts cause complete isolation, as shown by this diagram. In the grass warbler *Megalurus timoriensis* the three altitudinal subspecies are: a = *alpinus*, b = "*punctatus*"; and c = *macurus*. In the quail *Synoicus ypsilophorus* the corresponding subspecies are: a = *monticola*; b = *mafulu*; and c = *plumbeus*.

Similar barrier effects of unsuitable habitats have been described for ecologically specialized species of nearly all groups of animals. The well-known blackish races among mammals on the lava flows of the American Southwest could evolve because these rock-loving species are unable to cross the surrounding sandy deserts. Those lava flows that are in broad contact with pale rock formations have failed to develop distinct black races (Dice and Blossom 1937, Hooper 1941). Waterfalls are sometimes important barriers for fresh-water animals. The Murchison Falls of 130 feet or more separate very effectively the fish fauna of Lake Victoria (and Kioga) from that of the Upper Nile. Only 3 species occur in an identical form above and below the falls in a fish fauna of some 50 species below and 120 above (Worthington 1940). Additional examples, as well as a general discussion of the effect of barriers, may be found in Plate (1913) and in Hesse, Allee, Schmidt (1937).

In the sea isolation is rarely complete, and the partially isolated populations are usually very large. It is mainly for this reason that marine species have fewer subspecies than terrestrial species and that the entire evolution in the sea is slower and more conservative. There is much less difference, if we compare the fossils of marine strata from the Cretaceous period with modern faunas, than terrestrial strata show. The great disparity between the numbers of terrestrial and marine species can also be explained on this basis. Of the known species of animals about 93 percent live on land and only about 7 percent in the sea. The marine fauna of mollusks, crustaceans, or annelids of a given locality is, in most cases, infinitely larger than the corresponding land fauna, but the marine fauna has a very wide distribution (sometimes covering all oceans, or at least the entire Pacific), while most of the terrestrial species have a very limited range.

Population size and variability.—Naturalists have known for a long time that island populations tend to have aberrant characteristics. Wright (1931, 1932, and elsewhere) found the theoretical basis for this by showing that in small populations the accidental elimination of genes may be a more successful process than selection. Furthermore, recessive mutations have a much better chance to become homozygous than in a large panmictic population. It is therefore very important to learn something about the actual size of distributional islands and of their populations.

Some of the smallest and most isolated areas are probably caves, and this explains to some extent the very aberrant development of cave animals. Populations that are found on isolated rocks in the sea or in single ponds are probably equally small. Kramer and Mertens (1938a), in their work on the island population of *Lacerta sicula*, found no lizards on islands of much less than 2,000 square meters. The smallest inhabited island measured 57 × 34 meters (1,938 square meters) (see also Kramer and von Medem 1940). Hubbs (1940b) found more than 50 new species and subspecies of fish in isolated desert springs, some of them apparently in habitats of less than 100,000 cubic feet capacity. The areas in the Cyclops and the Wandammen Mountains in New

Guinea that are available to mountain animals are only a few square miles in extent, but they are the home of numerous endemic subspecies. Lack (1942) has made some careful estimates on the size of populations in the Galápagos Islands.

The subspecies of birds which are endemic on Sable Island, on Tucopia (Santa Cruz), on Vatu vara (Fiji), and other islets consist probably of less than 1,000 individuals. Some even smaller populations, the last surviving individuals of these species, are reported by Fleming (1939) from Little Mangare Island, Chatham Islands. The Chatham Islands Robin (*Miro traversi*) survives in 20 to 35 pairs, and Forbes' Parrot (*Cyanorhamphus auriceps forbesi*) in about 100 to 150 individuals, while the Chatham Islands Bell Bird (*Anthornis melanocephala*), which was present in 1906, has since disappeared, possibly a victim of "genetic homogeneity." There are no predators on the island and nothing has changed in the conditions during the last fifty years. Turbott (1940) has made a census of the bird population of Taranga (Hen) Island, 10 miles off the coast of New Zealand, and found about 17 species of land birds on this island of 1,175 acres. The estimated number of pairs of the various species were: *Prosthemadera* 1,150, *Anthornis* 1,100, *Hemiphaga* 440, *Gerygone* 215, *Creadion* 210, *Cyanorhamphus* 210, *Petroica* 185, *Zosterops* 170, *Rhipidura* 120, *Ninox* 50, and the other 7 species less than 50 pairs per species. All these species are also found on the mainland of New Zealand.

Dice (1939a) has worked out the size of the population of the Black Hills deermouse (*Peromyscus maniculatus osgoodi*) and found that this restricted population is comprised of between one and five million individuals. Willis (1940) records many cases of restricted species ranges, mostly among plants, which are very valuable if they are taken without his sweeping conclusions. Dowdeswell, Fisher, and Ford (1940) determined by careful marking methods that the population of the butterfly *Polyommatus icarus* on Tean Island, Scilly Islands, contained about 350 individuals. Apparently no migration took place to neighboring islands, but about 100 individuals emerged between August 26 and September 8.

An exact determination of the size of an isolated population is of importance, in view of Sewall Wright's work on gene loss in small populations. Owing to "accidents of sampling," small populations have a trend toward genetic homogeneity or at least toward a much-reduced variability. This is quite apparent in taxonomic work, although only a few systematists have taken the trouble to make careful measurements and to work out the coefficients of variation. Lack (1940a) found that the 2 most variable species of the Galápagos finches, *"Geospiza magni-*

rostris and *G. fortis,* are significantly less variable in three measured characters on small isolated islands than they are on large or central islands. This relation did not hold in four other less variable species." The reduced variability of isolated populations is sometimes even more conspicuous in qualitative characters (e. g., color variation) than in measurements (see also Kinsey 1937b). On the other hand, the often-made statement that "abundant species are more variable than rare ones" is not necessarily correct. Some very rare polytypic species are much more variable than some common monotypic ones. The decisive point is not the abundance of the species as a whole, but the size of the effective breeding population.

The calculations of Sewall Wright (1931, 1932, and elsewhere) indicate that effective populations have to be rather small, in the order of several hundred individuals or less, before they can be expected to approach genetic homogeneity due to accidental gene loss. If the population size is larger (thousands to tens of thousands of individuals), there still may be rapid evolution owing to mutation pressure (in the absence of appreciable selection), but the population will remain much more variable. If the size of the effective breeding population is still greater, approaching panmixia in varying degrees, evolution will be slowed down considerably. The consequence of this consideration is that evolution should proceed more rapidly in small populations than in large ones, and this is exactly what we find. The genera that are found in the West Indies, in the Solomon Islands, in the Galápagos Islands, and on Hawaii break up into numerous subspecies and species. The species of the same genera may not even be divided into subspecies on equivalent continental areas. Kinsey (1936, 1937b) demonstrates this influence of population size on the degree of (sub-)speciation existing in the gall wasps of the genus *Cynips,* and Reinig (1939) on the bumblebees of the genus *Bombus* (examine, for example, his map of *B. agrorum*). The kingfisher *Tanysiptera galatea* (Fig. 15) has only 3 poorly defined subspecies in the large area of the mainland of New Guinea, but it has developed 6 very distinct forms (most of them regarded as species) on the small islands where it also occurs. The potentiality for rapid divergent evolution in small populations explains also why we have on islands so many dwarf or giant races, or races with peculiar color characters (albinism, melanism), or with peculiar structures (long bills in birds), or other peculiar characters (loss of special male plumage in birds). Mertens (1931, 1934) lists aberrant characters that are found among island reptiles. They are probably also found among invertebrates, but I know of no recent summary on the subject, except those concerning loss of flight among island insects and blindness among cave animals.

The reduced variability of small populations is not always due to accidental gene loss, but sometimes to the fact that the entire population was started by a single pair or by a single fertilized female. These "founders" of the population carried with them only a very small proportion of the variability of the parent population. This "founder" principle sometimes explains even the uniformity of rather large populations, particularly if they are well isolated and near the borders of the range of the species. The reef heron (*Demigretta sacra*) occurs in two color phases over most of its range, a gray one and a white one, of which the white comprises about 10 to 30 percent of the individuals. On the Marquesas Islands and in New Zealand, two outposts of the range, only gray birds occur, while the white birds comprise 50 percent on the Tuamotu Islands, another marginal population (Mayr and Amadon 1941). The differences in the composition of these populations is very likely due to the genetic composition of the original founders. The same explanation probably covers most of the cases in which isolated populations of polymorphic species have a much-reduced variability.

Fluctuating population size.—The number of individuals in every population of animals is subject to regular annual and irregular cyclic changes. The number of individuals of a *Drosophila* species at the height of the breeding season may be many thousand times as high as during the pessimum period of their annual cycle, and similar changes occur in most animals. The difference between the number of individuals at the beginning of the breeding season (adults only) and at the end of the breeding season (adults and young) is rather small in birds. In the Song Sparrow (*Melospiza melodia*) M. M. Nice (1937) found that 100 birds (50 pairs) could potentially increase to 900 birds by raising 4 successful broods, but that owing to high losses of nests, eggs, and young, as well as to mortality among the adults, the maximum population size probably did not exceed 300 or 350. The normal population at the beginning of the new breeding season is estimated to be composed of about 60 percent old birds and 40 percent one-year-old birds. The corresponding figures in the House Wren (*Troglodytes aedon*) are, according to information kindly furnished by Dr. Kendeigh, as follows: 100 adults may raise potentially 410 young during one breeding season (510 total), but the maximum population probably does not exceed 360. The population at the beginning of the breeding season is composed of about 28 percent old and 72 percent one-year-old birds. The nesting success among sea birds (gulls, terns, and so forth) is apparently still lower, and there is a correspondingly lower annual fluctuation and turnover.

Of greater importance than the seasonal changes, at least in a few species, are the cyclic changes such as have been described in some arctic animals (Elton 1930). These population fluctuations are, as Sewall Wright (1940 a, b) and others have shown, of great importance in speeding up changes in the genetic make-up of a population. The effective population size of such a fluctuating species is much closer to the smaller than to the larger number. "Thus if the breeding population in an isolated region increases ten-fold in each of six generations during the summer (N_0 to 10^6 N_0) but falls at the end of the winter to the same value N_0, the effective size of population ($N = 6.3$ N_0) is relatively small" Wright (1940b:242). It is obvious that the survival of only one N_0 out of one million N_0's must have a considerable effect on the genetic composition of the respective population, and this is true no matter whether accident or superior survival value accounts for the survival of the remaining few.

It would lead too far afield to examine, in this connection, the factors that are responsible for the fluctuations or which prevent species from becoming too abundant. The textbooks of ecology contain much interesting material on the question of the "balance of nature," a good deal of which has an obvious bearing on the problem of speciation.

Restriction of Random Dispersal by Internal Factors

External barriers are relative factors. An absolute barrier to a salamander or to a fresh-water fish may not be a barrier at all to a bird or to a flying beetle or to a fly. And an insurmountable barrier to a bird may not be a barrier to a tardigrade or a rotifer. The faculty to overcome barriers, the ability to colonize new territories, and to become adapted to new ecological conditions depends on internal factors about which we are still very ignorant. The zoögeographer is continuously impressed by the differences that exist even between closely related species. Such differences in the dispersal faculties have a considerable effect on the population structure of the various species. This becomes particularly obvious when the dispersal faculty of a species undergoes a sudden change.

The biogeographer encounters not infrequently the phenomenon that a species, after a long period of stagnation, suddenly enters upon a phase of aggressive range expansion. The best-analyzed case of this sort is probably that of the Serin Finch (*Serinus canaria serinus*), which during a period of 150 years populated most of western and central Europe

(Mayr 1926). Other cases have been listed by Timofeeff-Ressovsky (1940a:115–121). The Australian White-Eye (*Zosterops lateralis*) invaded the New Zealand group in 1856 and has now settled on most of the islands. It had to jump an ocean gap of 2,000 kilometers. Several species of the bug genus *Nysius* on Hawaii are rather recent arrivals from the American mainland (Usinger 1941). Such rapid expansions are the best explanation for the taxonomic uniformity of some species over wide ranges. The distribution maps of many species indicate that periods of stagnation and periods of great range expansion alternate. During the "aggressive" period such species may be able to jump geographic barriers that would normally stop them. The mountain wagtail of Europe (*Motacilla cinerea*) had such an expansive phase during the last century and the early part of this century. During this period it descended from the mountains and hills of central Europe and colonized the great plains of northern Germany and Denmark, finally reaching mountainous Scandinavia, where it multiplied very rapidly. It is quite conceivable that the species will eventually die out in the marginal habitats of the plains, after it has passed this expansive stage. The Scandinavian and the central European populations would then be completely isolated. There is much evidence that this type of phenomenon happens frequently. Ripley and Birckhead (unpublished) have made it appear probable that the fruit doves of the *Ptilinopus purpuratus* group colonized Polynesia in two large "waves." The majority of the forms of the older wave have, in the meantime, developed into allopatric species, while all the members of the second wave (except the very isolated *richardsi*) may still be considered subspecies. The distribution of the thrushes of the *Turdus javanicus-poliocephalus* group in the Indonesian islands (Fig. 8) and other similar distribution pictures can be explained only if we assume that these species have had aggressive colonizing periods, during which they were able to jump barriers which are normally insurmountable to them. However, this does not imply that all range expansions are due to a change of internal factors.

Climatic events, such as the deterioration of the climate during the Pleistocene glaciation, or the drying up of parts of the tropical continental shelves during the height of the glaciation, or the opening up of vast continental areas behind the retreating ice during the post-Pleistocene era, have all contributed toward the shifting of populations. As far as the process of speciation is concerned, these periods of range expansions have primarily two effects. First, they lead to an expansion of the restricted ranges of isolated species, a process often accompanied by the jumping of minor geographic barriers, and set the stage for the beginning of the process of diversification, which is the beginning of all speciation. Secondly, they produce an overlap of ranges among numbers of closely allied and formerly strictly allopatric species. In other words, they complete the process of speciation. Range expansions are thus of vital importance, in connection with both the beginning and the conclusion of the speciation process.

Internal factors, affecting dispersal, play an important role, even when no visible external barriers are involved. That the random dispersal of individuals is impeded to a greater or lesser extent by such internal factors may be concluded from the fact that most species are subdivided, to some extent, into different and diverging populations, even in the absence of distributional obstacles. If every animal would stay, for its entire life, exactly on the spot where it was born, animal populations would be extremely localized. Actually, however, every animal moves a certain distance away from its place of birth before it reproduces. How far the offspring of a pair of animals might scatter and what controls these movements was entirely unknown some twenty-five years ago. The exact methods of tracing the movements of marked individuals have been applied to this problem during recent years, and facts are beginning to accumulate.

The results of this work indicate that very small animals are subject to much involuntary dispersal, but that most larger animals are amazingly sedentary throughout their lives and make very little use of their potential dispersal powers. This is, in general, also true for birds. Birds are potentially good fliers, and it seems peculiar that they should not scatter all over the face of the earth. Actually they seem to use their power of flight rather to return to their "home" in cases of involuntary dispersal (storms, seasonal adversities) than for active range expansion. Even insignificant natural barriers frequently stop the interchange of individuals between neighboring populations (Mayr 1941b).

Individuals of both sedentary and migratory species tend to stay in the same area (or to return to it) for reproduction year after year. This has been proven by so many recent studies that it would be unfair to single out a particular one. This field is reviewed regularly in the journals *Bird-Banding* and *Vogelzug*, both devoted to reports on banding activities. However, we still lack a really good summary of the field. An equally pronounced faithfulness toward a once-chosen locality seems to be possessed by many mammals, as has been shown in the case of mice, bats, rabbits, and game animals. Many fresh-water fishes are apparently also sedentary:

The results of three summers' work at Douglas Lake, Michigan, quite definitely indicate that there is little movement of the native game fish from one part of the lake to another. Of all the fish marked at several locations in Douglas Lake and released at the point of capture none were retaken in distant parts of the lake. Recaptures were made only in the near vicinity of original capture and release [Rodeheffer 1941].

The same has been shown for many species of marine fish (see, for example, Hart, Tester, and McHugh 1941). In lizards the work of Noble (1934) and Fitch (1940b) has proven that individuals are extremely localized in their movements and may live their entire lives within a radius of a few hundred feet. In many species of birds, lizards, fish, and so forth, the males (and sometimes also the females) defend a more or less strictly defined territory during the breeding season, another factor favoring localization (Nice 1941).

Homing.—Many animals possess the ability to return to a certain locality after they have been absent voluntarily or involuntarily. The same individual of many migratory bird species tends to return to nest in the same garden or even the same tree after having spent the winter in the tropics or in the southern hemisphere. Experiments have proven the most extraordinary homing faculty of many bird species, although nothing definite is yet known about the sensory basis of this faculty. Homing has also been shown to exist in a number of other vertebrates (mammals, fish), but, so far as I know, there is no conclusive proof for its existence among invertebrates, although bees and other insects are capable of orientation by visual cues. Sedentary birds, such as the house sparrow (*Passer domesticus*), have very little homing ability. Fitch (1940b) also found that western fence lizards (*Sceloporus occidentalis*) were unable to find their way back to their home territories after having been removed a short distance. (But see Noble 1934.)

Not all birds that are capable of accurate homing will necessarily breed near their birthplace. A mallard female returned from its winter quarters to the same nest box at Antioch, Nebraska, for at least seven consecutive seasons (1927–1933), which, together with other evidence, proves the excellent potential homing faculty of this species (Lincoln 1933). But it is also known that many individuals of this and related species will breed far from their place of birth, which is apparently due to the fact that pair formation in many migratory ducks takes place in the winter quarters. A drake that was bred in Maine may meet, at the Florida Gulf coast, a North Dakota duck and follow her to her breeding area in North Dakota. The result is almost complete panmixia and much-reduced subspeciation. Many of the Holarctic ducks, such as the gadwall (*Anas strepera*), shoveller (*Spatula clypeata*), and so forth, have no subspecies, or only one or two very slight ones, in spite of their wide circumpolar distribution.

Pair formation in the geese (*Anser, Branta,* and related genera) takes place under different circumstances, and the result is an entirely different species structure. Geese are among the very few birds in which the family does not break up at the end of the breeding season, but parents and young stay together for nearly a year. They migrate together to the winter quarters, they spend the entire winter together, and they do not separate until after the return to their nesting area. This closeness of the family system, together with their colonial or semi-colonial breeding habits, guarantees the closest kind of inbreeding. No other arctic or subarctic bird breaks up into so many pronounced races as the geese. The Canada geese of the genus *Branta* have some 6 to 9 geographic races in North America, some of which are so different that some authors propose to put them in 3 or 4 different species. On Southampton Island, Sutton (1932) found at least 2 forms: a larger one (*leucopareia*) inland on streams, and a smaller one (*hutchinsi*) on islands in the shallow coastal lakes. The inland form arrives earlier in the spring and builds a large moundlike nest; the coastal species starts nesting later in the season and lays its eggs in a depression of the ground. The two forms are exceedingly similar, except for the small difference in size, but habits have produced a degree of reproductive isolation which may be of specific rank. The very peculiar taxonomic conditions of these geese, e. g., the geographic proximity of strikingly different forms in the absence of geographic barriers or of intergrading populations, can be explained only on the basis of internal factors. These factors consist, as stated, in the social habits, colonial nesting, and the long continuance of the family unit, as demonstrated by Heinroth (1911) for *Anser* and confirmed for *Branta* by J. Moffitt (*in litt.*).

Another puzzling situation of bird taxonomy has been largely solved through the discovery of the social and reproductive habits of the geese. There are two geese in arctic North America, the Lesser Snow Goose (*Chen h. hyperborea*) and the Blue Goose (*Chen caerulescens*), which seem to differ in only one character, namely coloration (see plate IV, *Journal für Ornithologie, LXXIV,* [1926]). The white bird is the common bird, while the blue one is restricted to several large breeding grounds on Baffins Land, Southampton Island, and the Bear River Region. The blue birds nest sometimes in pure colonies, more often, however, in mixed colonies with the white form, and it is in such locations that mixed pairs and heterozygotes are found. The latter are similar to the blue form, but the belly is more or less white. Breeding experiments by aviculturists and zoölogical gardens indicate that the difference between the two color phases may be due to a single pigment gene, which shows normal Mendelian segregation, and biologists have therefore not hesitated to proclaim the blue and the white forms as color phases of a single species. Some field naturalists, however, have rejected this solution, because the clannishness of the two forms, both on the breeding grounds and in the winter quarters, indicates to them that two species are involved. The solution is to be sought in a thorough study of a mixed colony, but such has not yet been undertaken. An Eskimo who observed the colonies of western Southampton Island (Cape Kendall) estimated that there were about 900 pairs of *Chen*, of which one-third were blue. On the basis of random mating, one would expect 100 pairs of blue geese, 400 mixed pairs, and 400 pairs of snow geese, but there were only 20 mixed pairs, according to the reports of this Eskimo (Sutton 1931). This figure, if correct, would indicate selective mating and thus favor the assumption of the specific distinctness of the two forms, but there are many objections. To begin with, the breeding area certainly contained many separate breeding colonies, so that no condition of random mating existed; furthermore, the evidence of the Eskimo as to the number of mixed pairs is very doubtful. The fact that most breeding colonies consist of either pure snow or blue geese is probably due to the above-mentioned structure of the goose family. Since they are single interbreeding units, they will be of one color type, if they have been founded by birds of the same color phase (see *Demigretta*, p. 237, for a similar situation).

Dispersal restricting factors and geographic variation.—The comparison of the far-ranging ducks (*Anas*) with the extremely localized geese (*Branta*) brought out clearly the importance of the internal factors that control dispersal. Even though the geographic ranges (and hence the geographic barriers) were nearly identical in both cases, the species are very uniform in the case of the ducks and break up into numerous well-defined races in the case of the geese. The evidence for differences in dispersal faculty is not available in other cases, and we are forced to infer its value indirectly by analyzing intraspecific variability. Measurements of two coexisting species of snails showed that one species (*Clausilia cravenensis*) was more uniform (less variable) at any given collecting station than the other species (*Cl. rugosa*), but that on a comparison of the material of nineteen collecting stations the differences between the *cravenensis* populations were greater than between the *rugosa* populations (Alkins 1928). This probably indicates that *cravenensis* is less subject to dispersal and therefore tends more to the formation of local forms.

The formation of local races in the absence of distributional barriers will occur whenever the combined effects of recurrent local mutations and of selection pressure outweigh the effect of the interchange of individuals between local populations. The taxonomist encounters such cases continuously; one example will illustrate them sufficiently.

There is no definite physical or climatic barrier to interbreeding between the desert plain mammals of the Tucson and Yuma districts in southern Arizona, yet a number of species (about 7) are represented by different subspecies in the two districts. Undoubtedly, many or all of the subspecies of the Yuma district are continually interbreeding at the borders of their ranges with their relations in the Tucson district [Dice and Blossom 1937].

The taxonomist likes to speak of "subspeciation by distance" in such cases. No serious effort has yet been made to determine the effective rate of exchange of individuals between one local population and the next (factor m of Sewall Wright 1931, 1940a, b), but some rough calculations have been made which give us indirectly an indication of how various species may differ in regard to this factor. There are two ways of approaching this problem. One method consists in determining the amount of "swamping" in incompletely isolated populations. The deer mouse of the Nebraska sand hills (*Peromyscus maniculatus nebrascensis*) is a small, incompletely isolated population which is being swamped continuously by individuals from the surrounding darker races. The sand-hill populations and also those plain populations from near the sand hills are consequently much more variable than the populations of the same species living many miles removed from the influence of the sand-colored populations. The higher variability in pelage color of the sand-hill stocks "is well illustrated by the standard deviations of the tint-photometer readings. They are: 4.28, 4.13, 2.98, 2.98, 2.97 and 2.94 for the sand-hill stocks. They are: 3.64, 3.25, 2.82 and 1.72 for the stations near the sand hills, and are below 2 for all the stations away from the sand hills" (Dice 1941). Exactly parallel conditions have been observed in regard to the endemic races of rock-inhabiting mammals that occur on the lava flows of the arid American Southwest. Well-defined blackish races have evolved only on those rocky lava flows that are completely isolated by sandy or otherwise rockless areas.

Raven Butte [for example] is not completely isolated from the immediately adjacent Tinajas Atlas Mountains, and rock inhabiting mammals are able to pass freely back and forth between the black lava of the butte and the pale granites and gneisses of the mountains. The area of the butte is so much less than that of the mountains that it is not surprising that the color of the mammals on the butte is similar to the color of those taken on the lighter colored rocks of the mountains [Dice and Blossom 1937].

The correlation between swamping and completeness of isolation was determined more accurately for the lava flows (malpais) of Valencia County, New Mexico (Hooper 1941). There are 8 species of mammals that occur on the lava flows and in other rocky locations, but are absent from the adjoining sandy desert plains. In not one of these species are all the individuals from the lavas darker than the individuals outside. In 4 species there is no difference whatsoever, in 4 others the malpais populations average darker. No species reaches the extremes of increased pigmentation attained by the corresponding species in the Tularosa basin. The reason for this difference is that the Tularosa malpais are almost completely (at least for 29/30 of their circumference) isolated in the sandy desert, while the Valencia malpais are in broad contact (1/10 to 3/5 of their margin) with adjoining rocky areas. Sumner showed the same for the beach-sand-inhabiting races of *Peromyscus polionotus*. *P. p. leucocephalus*, which lives on isolated sandy islands, is very much paler than *P. p. albifrons*, which lives on the sands of the mainland beach, but is continuously swamped by the dark *P. p. polionotus* from the dark soils of the interior. The break between the dark and the pale races does not coincide in this case with the break between the pale sands and the dark soils.

Often not enough credit is given to the dispersal faculties of certain species, and the swamping factor is consequently underestimated. Kramer and Mertens (1938a) have analyzed the races of the lizard *Lacerta sicula* on the islands off the coast of western Istria. They find that the distinctness of the island populations depends primarily on two factors, the size of the island and the time of separation from the mainland. However, they completely overlook a third factor, namely, chance dispersal across the water, a method of distribution well established in lizards. Many puzzling situations in regard to these island races become clear, if we allow for swamping. For example, Rivera Island, which according to size and time of separation should have a population about as distinct as that of Polari Island, has a much more differentiated population because it is more than twice as far away from the mainland. Galiner Island, which on the basis of size and age should have a population similar to Galopan, differs markedly, but is rather close to the mainland in race and distance.

A second method for determining swamping makes use of the degree of subspeciation. Rensch (1933) bases his analysis on the fact that the more sedentary an animal is (and the smaller the factor m), the more it will tend to break up into geographic races. This is reflected not only in the number of races per polytypic species, but also in the proportion of monotypic species (species without geographic variation) among all species. Insectivores (mammals), for example, have on an average 50 percent more races per polytypic species than bats of similar size. There are 20 percent more species of bats without geographic variation than among the insectivores (moles, shrews, and so forth). Six families of more or less sedentary Palearctic birds had 100 percent more races per polytypic species than 9 families of migratory birds. Among the 115 species of the sedentary families only 34 (or 29.6 percent) were monotypic, while among the 288 species of the migratory families 115 species (40.0 percent) were monotypic. This indicates, as might be expected, that migration produces greater dispersal (increased m) and hence decreased subspeciation.

Habitat selection as an isolating factor.—The dispersal of a species is obviously determined not only by its mobility, by its homing faculty, and by its ability to overcome geographic obstacles, but also by its ecological plasticity, that is, by its ability to settle in different habitats. A species which is restricted in its occurrence to one single very narrow ecological niche, is likely to be subjected to identical selective forces throughout its range and is likely to show little geographic variation, unless the localities of its occurrence are insular. On the other hand, a species which is equally at home in a number of different sets of environmental conditions and which is at the same time either sedentary or strongly homing, should break up into a maximum of geographic races. The song sparrow (*Melospiza melodia*), with about 28 subspecies on the North American continent, is a good example of such a species.

Naturalists have always marveled at the unfailing accuracy with which animals can find the right ecological niche to which their species is adapted. This "habitat selection" (Elton 1930) is an important factor in species formation, as pointed out by several recent authors (Grinnell 1928, Lack 1940b, Miller 1942). It is generally impossible to determine accurately what the factors are that determine this habitat preference, but often it seems to be rather the "general aspect" of the environment than a specific physical or chemical constant (Bates 1941b, Lack 1940b). Habitat selection is unquestionably involved also in the development of the bird races that are adapted to specific soil colors. Such birds seem to seek definitely soils which agree with their own color, in contrast to ground mammals whose preference for a certain soil is more likely to be determined by the consistency of the soil (rocky, gravelly, sandy) than by its visual aspect. Niethammer (1940), who experimented with the color preference of South African larks, writes as follows:

It is very striking in southwest Africa that reddish larks are found only on red soil, and dark ones on dark soil, even where two completely different types of soil meet, as at Waltersdorf, for example, where the dark soil, rich in humus, comes in contact with the red Kalahari sand. *Mirafra sabota hoeschi* stayed entirely on the dark soil, in spite of the fact that the area of the red sand began only a few hundred meters from its territories. On the other hand, I met *Mirafra africanoides* on the red sand up to its very edge but never on the dark soil, which was inhabited exclusively by *Mirafra sabota hoeschi*. Similar conditions prevailed at the Farm "Spatzenfeld" with the exception that the red sands here border light lime pans, where *Spizocorys starki* lives. I tried to chase little groups of *Spizocorys starki* to the red sands, but in vain—they turned before the beginning of the red soil and flew back directly, as if they knew, to their accustomed light lime soil. The red *Mirafra fasciolata deserti* which in Spatzenfeld inhabits the red sands did not go astray either in the lime pans. The reverse experiment I made in Lidfontein. I tried to chase the red *Mirafra africanoides gobabisensis* from a red dune to the light lime soil—again in vain. I do not believe that the experiment will ever have a different result because it is obvious that the birds are conscious of the color of the soil that corresponds to their own coloration.

RESTRICTION OF RANDOM MATING (BIOLOGICAL ISOLATING MECHANISMS)

The inability of the potential mates to meet each other was the reason for isolation in the situations discussed to this point. Such isolation by external barriers (frequently assisted by internal factors) will lead to a break-up of a formerly uniform species into distinct populations and subspecies, but such geographic isolation will not be sufficient to complete the speciation process. A species is defined by us as a reproductively isolated group of populations, and it is obvious from this definition that species must possess isolating mechanism which safeguard this reproductive isolation. Geographic isolation without the development of biological isolating factors cannot lead to species formation, because if two species meet, which up to that moment have been geographically isolated populations, they will interbreed freely, unless a new set of barriers begins to operate, thus replacing the former geographic barriers. The question is: What are these biological barriers and how do they originate?

Some rather elaborate classifications of the biological (physiological) isolating mechanisms have been proposed in recent years, but we can reduce these to four simple steps:

1. Mating does not take place because *ecological factors* prevent the meeting of the potential mates, at least while they are in reproductive condition.

2. Mating does not take place because there is an ethological incompatibility (*ethological factors*).

3. Copulation is prevented through the physical inconformity of the copulatory organs (*mechanical factors*).

4. Mating takes place, but is more or less unsuccessful, owing to varying degrees of sterility or hybrid inviability ("*genetic*" and *physiological factors*).

Reproductive isolation between most related species is accomplished by a combination of several of these factors. Diver (1939) illustrates this in a suggestive case:

I have observed an interesting attempt at a cross between two species now placed in different genera, *Helix aspersa* and *Cepaea hortensis*. There is no marked spatial isolation between these two species, since their geographical distributions overlap widely and they are not uncommonly found together in the same habitat. . . . The facts of this observation were that a single *hortensis*, which had been isolated in a cage containing two *aspersa*, was found to be in courtship with one of them. When this courtship had been in progress for a little time, the other *aspersa* became sexually active and attempted to intervene, but much to my surprise without any success. The original pair continued for many hours making innumerable futile attempts to mate before they finally gave up the struggle. Though in this case the "psychological" barrier failed to hold, the mechanical barrier did and the genetic barrier was never tested.

The relative importance of the various isolating mechanisms is different in different groups of animals. It seems, however, as if there was always one primary factor. In birds, with their songs, territories, and complicated courtships, it seems as if behavior patterns were paramount, and we know of many cases of good sympatric species or even genera which are not separated by a sterility barrier (certain ducks, pheasants, and pigeons). In the moth genus *Platysamia*, on the other hand, Sweadner (1937) reports partial or complete sterility between forms which seem to have no ethological isolating mechanisms or only very weak ones. Different means accomplish the same end in both cases: the effective biological isolation of two closely related sympatric species.

ECOLOGICAL ISOLATING FACTORS

Habitat differences.—Closely related sympatric species are often characterized by differences in their habitat requirements. One species may live in the forest, the other in open fields, or if they are fresh-water organisms one may live in shallow water, the other in deep water, and so forth. We have already come to the conclusion in our discussion on sympatric speciation (Chapter VIII) that such ecological differences develop during geographic isolation. Lack (1940b), who at one time thought that habitat segregation might lead to sympatric speciation, admits now that this is exceedingly unlikely. He postulates, and I agree with him, that most habitat differences are "historical accidents." "This seems the only way to account for differences in the habitat distribution of closely related species, differences which are often slight and [at least in birds] apparently unrelated to any adaptations, but yet are characteristic for each species." That the ecological differences between species might have originated through geographic variation of habitat requirements is indicated by the very conspicuous differences which we have found to exist between different populations of the same species (*Turdus poliocephalus*, p. 57; *Corvus corax*, p. 57). Where two well-defined subspecies of one species occur at the same locality, but in different habitats, it is evident in most cases that these differences first originated in geographically isolated populations which formed overlapping ranges by secondary expansion. Dice (1940a) suggests that this is true in the case of the overlapping races of *Peromyscus* and this seems also the best interpretation of the ecological races of the Song Sparrow (*Melospiza melodia*) in the San Francisco Bay region of California (Mayr 1940a). The same is true for those altitudinal races that are not connected by intergrading populations.

Of particular interest are cases in which differences in habitat requirements distinguish subspecies which are in geographic contact and contribute toward keeping them isolated. This occurs, for example, among two species of aquatic or semiaquatic reptiles of Florida (Carr 1940). Both species, the turtle *Pseudemys floridana* and the snake *Natrix sipedon*, are found in two kinds of habitats, in inland waters (lakes, ditches, creeks) and in coastal waters (seashore, coastal rivers, and so forth). The turtle has a northern (*floridana*) and a southern (*peninsularis*) race among its inland populations and a northern (*mobiliensis*) and a southern (*suwanniensis*) race among its coastal populations. The fact that the inland and the coastal subspecies completely exclude each other in the northern part of the range is not explained by the geography of the country. Farther south

both *peninsularis* and *suwanniensis* occur in Citrus Co., the former being found only in the lakes and ditches, and the latter only in the rivers, and this relationship apparently holds in all the gulf counties from here to Pensacola. South of Citrus Co. *peninsularis* gradually replaces *suwanniensis*. . . . In Lake Panasoffkee . . . the two forms meet and intergrade. In *Natrix sipedon* we find virtually the same situation.

Two closely related species of dragon flies now overlap in north-central

Florida, the isolating barriers having broken down in late Pleistocene. The northern species *Progomphus obscurus* is, in the zone of overlap, restricted to rivers and streams, the southern species *P. alachuensis* inhabits lakes (Byers 1940). Numerous similar cases have been quoted in the literature, for example those concerning warblers (*Phylloscopus*) and mice (*Peromyscus*).

Altitudinal races are often quoted as sympatric ecological races, but this is not quite correct since the two forms do not occur exactly at the same localities. We have already treated altitudinal races in an earlier chapter (p. 196), but it may be mentioned here that altitude preference is a very real isolating mechanism, not only for races but also for closely related species. This has a bearing on the question as to the ecological relationship of related species. The older taxonomic and ecological literature contains some rather verbose discussions on the question: "Whether the areas occupied by allied species are in general identical, overlapping, or totally distinct?" We know now that all three types of distribution occur. Many of the allopatric species of former days are nowadays considered subspecies, and the rule that the next relative of any given species is some allopatric species is not necessarily correct in groups, which employ the polytypic species concept consistently. Closely related species have in continental districts usually broadly overlapping ranges (for example, in the bird genera *Dendroica* in North America, *Parus* in the Palearctic, *Pachycephala* in New Guinea, and so forth). Stresemann (1939) has, however, listed a number of examples in which two related species are almost completely allopatric, but do not hybridize in the narrow zone of overlap. He suggests, and the facts seem to support his thesis, that reproductive isolation has preceded ecological divergence in these cases. The two species are still so similar in their requirements that, as competitors for the same habitats, they do not succeed in entering each others' ranges. On the other hand, Diver's work has shown (see p. 203) that several closely related species can share each others' ranges, even though their ecological requirements are seemingly identical. The same has been found by the bird ecologist (Lack 1940c).

The situation is somewhat different on islands. To begin with, many related species with insular ranges (islands or mountains) are strictly allopatric, because they are, in fact, nothing but "glorified subspecies." On the other hand, mere geographic representation does not always prove very close relationship. The number of ecological niches on small islands is generally much reduced and the competition correspondingly sharpened. If there are several competing species, the one that arrives first will be the successful colonist and will prevent the landing of later arrivals (Mayr 1933:322, Stresemann 1939:361). Ecological competitors need not be very closely related, as the history of extinctions proves. All these facts have been quoted merely to indicate how complicated the ecological balance of nature is and how difficult it is to arrive at valid generalizations concerning ecological isolating mechanisms.

It is obvious from this discussion, as we might add parenthetically, that no such rule exists as "No two species of the same genus occur in the same locality." This rule is supported by certain unscrupulous pseudotaxonomists, who use it as a thinly veiled excuse for the most reckless generic splitting. Rather the opposite is true; we find that the majority of the species of a genus have partly overlapping ranges.

Seasonal isolation.—A much more effective method of ecological isolation than by habitat specialization is given by the development of different breeding seasons. This occurs most commonly in forms with short breeding seasons, as is often the case with invertebrates. The breeding season of birds covers several weeks or months and is usually identical or broadly overlapping in closely related sympatric species. The exception to this rule is presented by certain sea birds whose breeding season is sometimes correlated with water temperatures. Junge (1934) has suggested that the fact that the gull *Larus argentatus* starts nesting about two weeks earlier than *Larus fuscus* prevents the establishment of more than a very few mixed pairs in the joint colonies of these two closely related European species (see also Richter 1938).

Fleming (1941) has recently shown that the understanding of speciation in the whale bird genus *Pachyptila* is much facilitated if ecological isolating factors are taken into consideration. The genus contains six species whose breeding ranges in the southern waters are arranged in concentric circumpolar rings. Each species may be identified closely with specific water temperatures and conditions, as illustrated in Table 13.

It is obvious from this table that the 4 species of the closely related *desolata* and *vittata* groups are strictly geographically representative, but overlap broadly with the two allopatric species of the very different and frequently generically separated *turtur* group. Geographic isolation, as such, has little significance as an isolating mechanism in these wide-ranging oceanic birds, and it is probable that an interchange of individuals between insular populations occurs. Only thus could identical races of *P. vittata* be found, for example, on Tristan da Cunha in the South Atlantic and on the Chatham Islands (near New Zealand), localities separated by half the earth's circumference. Different sub-

TABLE 13

WATER ZONES AND BREEDING RANGES IN *Pachyptila*

(According to Fleming 1941)

SUBGENERIC GROUP	SPECIES	ANTARCTIC ZONE	SUBANTARCTIC ZONE	SUBTROPICAL ZONE
turtur	crassirostris		Mid-Nov.	
	turtur			Mid-Oct.
desolata	desolata	End Dec.		
	belcheri		Mid-Nov.	
	salvini		? Mid-Nov.	
vittata	vittata			Early Sept.

⟷ = Latitudinal distribution.

The date represents the beginning of egg laying.

species of the same species in this genus are always found at the same latitudes, or, more exactly, in the same hydrological zones. But once a population becomes adapted to a new zone of ocean water, it adopts a new mode of life, including a different breeding season, and becomes permanently separated. Different species in the same species group never breed together, but they may breed in close geographic proximity on islands lying near the common boundary of two hydrological zones. The species of the *turtur* group overlap in several places with those of the *desolata-vittata* groups. Where *turtur* comes in contact with *vittata* (Chatham and Stewart Islands), and where *crassirostris* breeds in company with *desolata* (Heard Island and Kerguelen), there is strong seasonal isolation, but *crassirostris* and *belcheri* breed on the Kerguelen at the same season and there is valid evidence that additional biological isolating mechanisms keep the species apart. The main point is that the isolating factors between closely related species of these ecologically highly specialized water birds are ecological factors (strengthened by ethological factors), and not mere geographic isolation.

The Australian roller *Eurystomus orientalis pacificus* winters in large numbers in the tropical islands from Celebes to New Guinea. In these islands there live a number of closely related and fairly similar resident races of the same species, for example *Eurystomus orientalis waigeuensis*, and it is not rare that one can find individuals of both races at the same time at the same location. However, the Australian bird never comes into breeding condition in its Papuan winter quarters and crossing of the two races is thereby prevented. The same is true, *mutatis mutandis*, for many migrant races of birds that winter in the range of resident races (Blanchard 1941).

Water temperatures, being more stable than air temperatures, are apparently often the factor which controls the difference in the breeding season in related species of aquatic animals. Mertens (1928a) lists this as the principal isolating factor between *Rana ridibunda* and *Rana esculenta* and between the toads *Bombina variegata* and *bombina*. Blair (1941) finds an incomplete, but still rather effective separation of breeding seasons between several species of American toads of the genus *Bufo*. The deep- and the shallow-water forms of many lake fishes differ in their breeding season, and the same factor is an effective barrier between the herring races of the North Sea (Schnakenbeck 1931) and between the races of the cuttlefish (*Sepia officinalis*), according to Cuénot (1933), although it is not certain in the latter case that the form *filliouxi* does not represent the nonbreeding first-year population.

It is a moot question whether or not such seasonally separated forms would interbreed in nature if this barrier were to break down. There is a pair of well-separated species of moths *"Eupithecia innotata* Hufn., which feeds on *Artemisia*, and *E. unedonata* Mab. which emerges much earlier on *Arbutus*. By cooling the pupae of the *Arbutus* species, Dietze (1913) delayed emergence and produced fertile hybrids with the *Artemisia* species" (Hogben 1940:278). This evidence does not necessarily prove that the difference in the breeding season is the only or even the principal isolating mechanism between the two species. Ethological barriers, which may not operate under captivity conditions, may exist in nature as an additional safeguard.

ETHOLOGICAL ISOLATING FACTORS

Recent studies by the students of animal behavior, as well as the revised interpretation of many earlier observations, indicate that behavior differences are among animals the most important factor in restricting random mating between closely related forms. Such *ethological*[1] factors refer primarily to the various courtship patterns that precede pair formation or copulation, including the display or production of special colors, scents, sounds (and songs), and movements. The exact interpretation of the phenomena belonging to this field is rather difficult, since many of these characters have a double or even triple function: They may serve (1) as warning or threatening characters to deter competing individuals of the species, (2) as recognition marks to guarantee the mating of conspecific individuals, (3) as stimulators to raise the physiological readiness for copulation or to synchronize cyclic phenomena (see Huxley 1938a, b, c, Richards 1927).

But there are many difficulties, even when these characters have only a single function. For example, it is now realized that many phenomena that have been recorded in the past as furthering intraspecific sexual selection are actually specific recognition marks. Their primary function seems to be to facilitate the meeting and recognition of conspecific individuals and to prevent hybridization between different species. To give even the merest outline of the isolating function of such ethological factors would require considerably more space than is available in the present treatise. The literature on animal behavior contains much information on differences in behavior patterns of closely related species which should be examined by those who are interested in this problem. A few examples must suffice. Every bird student knows that the species

---

[1] From the Greek τὸ ἔθος, the custom, the habit, the "behavior pattern." A popular and convenient term in European behavior literature.

of the North American flycatcher genus *Empidonax* and of the Old World warbler genus *Phylloscopus*, which are almost indistinguishable to the eye, can be recognized easily by the mating calls or territorial songs. Petersen (1903) observed no less than 37 species of the butterfly genus *Lycaena* in a single valley of the Elburs Mountains, in Persia, without any evidence of interspecific mating. He believes that the correct species recognition is guaranteed by the specific scents of each species and that the visual characters which separate closely related species in this genus are due to accidents of evolution and not due to selection. J. Crane (1941) found in a study of the Central American fiddler crabs of the genus *Uca* that the males of each species had a definite courtship display "which varies so greatly with the species that individuals can be recognized at a distance by their characteristic motions." The important points in regard to these crabs are: (1) that 12 to 15 species may occur within the same restricted area, for example on a mud flat of 600 square feet, without sufficient differences in habitat preference to serve as isolating mechanism; (2) that all these species, although closely related and belonging to the same genus, were clearly defined (separated by bridgeless gaps), indicating that some isolating mechanism existed to prevent swamping; (3) that the recognition marks (of color pattern and courtship dances) were strictly specific; and (4) that pair formation was a long-drawn-out process, sometimes consuming many days, thus guaranteeing the avoidance of hasty "mésalliances" of individuals belonging to different species.

In many species of birds there is a more or less lengthy time interval, a so-called "engagement period," between the day of pair formation and the first copulation. This period may last from three or four days to two weeks or even several months. The engagement is likely to be "broken" if the behavior patterns of the two mates do not fit exactly. This is the reason wild hybrids are rare in bird species with definite pair formation and engagement periods, but fairly common, as we shall see presently (p. 260), in genera and families without pair formation.

These ethological factors are fairly effective, even where the differences are rather minute, as noted by Diver (1939) for *Cepaea* and by Herter (1934) for the hedgehog. In mammals and other primarily olfactory animals special scents are probably very important, as are the rhythm and pitch of wing vibrations and similar features in *Drosophila*. Dice (1940b) makes the important point, which is fully corroborated by the ornithological evidence, that the establishment of reproductive isolation through ethological factors precedes in mammals, in general, the development of intersterility. The divergence of the separated forms will accelerate, once the interspecific gap has developed, until it finally reaches the level of intersterility.

We have mentioned in an earlier chapter that the local song races in birds were probably not due to inherited song patterns, but rather to the conditioning of the young birds to the songs of their fathers and the neighboring males. The experimental study of behavior patterns has not yet reached a point where we can say which patterns are inherited and which are due to conditioning. The fact that Whitman, Heinroth, Lorenz, and other students of bird behavior have found that birds sometimes prefer to mate with individuals of that species with which they have been reared as foster children, rather than with mates of their own species, warns us to be cautious (Cushing 1941). Such conditioning is likely to play a more important role among vertebrates, with their highly developed nervous systems, than with invertebrates (Elton 1930:84). It may help in promoting local "fads," which may serve as a contributory isolating mechanism if they occur in isolated populations. The importance of such nongenetic habits should not be overrated, even in vertebrates. Cowbirds mate with cowbirds, and cuckoos with cuckoos, even though these parasitic species are reared in the nests of foster species. Also in all the species in which the female has the entire care of the young, such as birds of paradise, humming birds, and so forth, the young will not know anything of the display behavior of their fathers. It must be entirely innate, at least in the solitary species, if it is to be specific.

Mechanical Isolating Factors

We unite under this heading all those factors which prevent successful copulation because of the incompatibility of the sexual organs. This is a field about which we know next to nothing and which probably plays only a very subordinated role. The differences in the sexual armatures which exist between related species of insects are, in most cases, not sufficiently strong to prevent successful copulation, as has been pointed out by Goldschmidt (1940) and Dobzhansky (1941a). Other observations that were interpreted in the past as being due to such mechanical factors have recently been unmasked as ethological, that is, as being due to incompatibilities of the very complicated epigamic behavior that precedes copulation in many animal species.

Reduction of Mating Success

Nature has one last trump card, when all the other isolating mechanisms fail, and that is lowered fertility (reproductivity). This comprises a whole scale of phenomena, but they all belong to one of two classes: (1) Nonproduction of viable (F_1) hybrids, either because fertilization is prevented (inability of the spermatozoa to reach or to penetrate the eggs) or because, after fertilization, there are cytogenetic disturbances, chromosomal incompatibilities, abnormalities in various growth and organ-forming processes, and so forth; or (2) sterility (of varying degrees) in the (F_1) hybrid. A full treatment of the subject has been given by Dobzhansky (1941a), and we do not need to add anything to his excellent analysis. This field is the domain of the cytologist, geneticist, and embryologist; the taxonomist, with his specific methods, cannot work in it. Isolation through sterility is most important in those groups of organisms in which ethological isolating mechanisms are not highly developed, and this, in turn, is correlated with the method of reproduction, as we shall see.

ISOLATING MECHANISMS AND THE METHOD OF REPRODUCTION

Mammals, birds, butterflies, snails, and most of the other animals whose biological isolating mechanisms we have been discussing have two characteristics in common. First, the sexually active individuals have a certain "cruising radius" and actively seek each other, and secondly, fertilization is internal (mammals, insects, and so forth) or at least individual (amphibia, and so forth). Individual fertilization is the exclusive method of reproduction of all land animals. Among sea animals individual (mostly internal) fertilization is typical for the marine mammals, for many fish (e.g., most nest-building species), for most arthropods (except cirripedia), and for certain vermes (most platyhelminthes, nematodes, oligochaetes, and so forth). Most other marine organisms and particularly all sessile species depend on mass fertilization. This is the usual method of sexual propagation in sponges, coelenterates (free-swimming and sessile), most polychaetes, bryozoa, bivalves, echinodermes, tunicates, and many marine fish, to mention merely the major groups. What usually happens in animals belonging to these groups is that all the members of a colony or of a free-swimming swarm discharge their eggs and sperm simultaneously, in response to definite external stimuli. These stimuli must be highly specific; otherwise all the related sympatric species might spawn together, thus exposing themselves to the danger of considerable hybridization. Not much is known yet about the mechanisms that provide for the synchronous reproduction of conspecific individuals, but it seems as if two essential steps were involved. First, there is a purely environmental stimulus, consisting apparently of a rather complex combination of factors relating to temperature, light, salinity, oxygen concentration, pH level, mineral contents, and so forth. If all these factors are right, a physiological readiness for reproduction is attained. One of the individuals will finally reach such a high degree of sexual readiness that it produces a "sex stuff," an organic substance the release of which into the water will result in the spawning of all other conspecific individuals in the vicinity. It is conceivable that selection could build up such an exact response to the particular sex stuff of every species that this would act as an isolating mechanism, at least in conjunction with the inorganic environmental stimuli. There is no reason why these various stimuli should not act as isolating mechanisms with the same high efficiency as courtship patterns in birds and specific scents in moths. In fresh water the prevailing reproductive methods are again different, with internal or at least individual fertilization fairly common and with the reduction of free-swimming larvae. If there is an expulsion of the sex products into the water, it usually is limited to the sperm, while the eggs develop in brood pouches, and so forth of the female. Again the emphasis is placed on a different set of isolating mechanisms.

It is probable that ecological factors ("niche characteristics") play a bigger role than ethological factors in all those animals that are restricted to a narrow ecological niche. This will be true for a sea animal that is associated with a distinct level of salinity, or for a river animal that can exist and reproduce only under very specific water conditions, or for a soil-inhabiting animal that can live only in a specific type of soil (not to mention host-specific animals). A vast amount of work remains to be done before the relative importance of the various isolating mechanisms in animals living under different ecological conditions and utilizing different reproductive methods can be stated accurately.

THE BREAKDOWN OF ISOLATING MECHANISMS
AND ITS CONSEQUENCES

Isolating mechanisms are not infallible, and, when they fail, forms will cross that had more or less diverged in their genetic make-up and taxonomic relationship. Such interbreeding is called hybridization. It is very difficult to define this term, or at least to delimit it against various forms of intraspecific interbreeding. The use of the term hybridization is undoubtedly justified if individuals of different families, genera, or good species interbreed. But to what extent can the interbreeding of individuals of different subspecies or merely of distinct populations of the same species be called hybridization? If we were to accept a species definition as narrow as that of Lotsy (see p. 118), almost any cross-mating of genetically distinct individuals (different biotypes) might be called a case of hybridization, and Lotsy, in fact, did not hesitate to go to this extreme. We shall presently examine whether or not it is possible to delimit hybridization against geographic intergradation, but we must first study some other aspects of the hybridization problem.

Where and when does hybridization occur? The most common hybrids are those between subspecies; species hybrids are rarer, generic hybrids are still rarer, and hybrids between members of still higher systematic categories are quite exceptional. Hybridization, therefore, indicates relationship, but it should be stated emphatically that the degree of sterility observed in the hybrids does not indicate the degree of relationship. In some orders of animals even intergeneric crosses are fertile, while in others, as for example in *Drosophila*, crossings are partly sterile between some of the subspecies or between species that are hardly distinguishable. The cytogenetic reasons for this are manifold and still rather obscure (Hertwig 1936, Dobzhansky 1941a). In birds, the families Anatidae (ducks), Columbidae (pigeons), and Phasianidae (pheasants) are noted for the relatively high fertility of interspecific crosses. Such different-looking (though closely related) species as the Golden and the Amherst Pheasant (*Chrysolophus pictus* and *amherstiae*) seem to be perfectly fertile in their F_2, F_3, and so forth. The same seems to be true for the various species of the genus *Canis* (dogs, wolves, jackals, coyotes). They are good species and several of them have overlapping ranges; still, hybrids between them are very rare in nature. It is therefore not admissible to use sterility as a species criterion in animals.

All the cases of hybridization in animals may be classified, from the viewpoint of the systematist, into those that are caused by a breakdown of the mechanisms that prevent (1) random mating and (2) random dispersal. To the first class, which we might also call "sympatric hybridization," belong all those cases in which an occasional hybrid is produced between two good species that coexist over wide parts of their ranges without mixing. The second class, which we might call "allopatric hybridization," includes primarily the hybrid swarms which occur where the ranges of two incompletely separated species meet in a border zone, owing to the premature breakdown of a geographic barrier. These two types of hybridization involve two rather different types of biological phenomena, even though the geneticist may not see any difference between the hybrids that are produced.

OCCASIONAL HYBRIDS BETWEEN SYMPATRIC SPECIES

We have seen that four kinds of factors (ecological, ethological, mechanical, and genetic) participate in preventing the production of hybrid individuals between sympatric species. The mere fact that such hybrids occur indicates that some of the isolating mechanisms may break down occasionally, and it may be interesting to find out under what circumstances this takes place. In birds, we have a fair amount of information, since some collectors, sensing their scarcity value, have specialized in the collecting of hybrids, and amateur observers have always been fascinated by them. We can state, on the basis of the data collected by these naturalists, that sympatric hybrids are found primarily in genera in which copulation is not preceded by pair formation and an "engagement period." In most species of birds of paradise (Paradisaeidae), for example, one or several males perform on a display ground and the female appears there merely when she is ready for fertilization. After this has been accomplished, she alone builds the nest, incubates the eggs, and raises the young. It apparently happens, on rare occasions, that a female is attracted to the display ground of the wrong species and is fertilized. There are now some two or three dozens of such hybrids known, which is, indeed, a small number, considering that more than 100,000 skins of birds of paradise were exported from New Guinea between 1870 and 1924. Such hybrids are known between ten genera (Fig. 27) (Mayr 1941a). Two of these genera (*Astrapia*, *Cicinnurus*) have crossed with only one other genus, 3 genera (*Epimachus*, *Parotia*, *Seleucides*) with 2 other genera, 4 genera (*Paradigalla*, *Craspedophora*, *Paradisaea*, *Diphyllodes*) with 3 other genera, and one genus (*Lophorina*) with 4 other genera. No hybrids are known from the 7 other New Guinea genera, which is primarily due to the fact that the species of these genera are very rare. The only exception is the genus *Manucodia*, with 3 distinct species, which is quite common but from which no hybrids are known. The puzzle as to why this genus is not involved in intergeneric (or interspecific) crosses has recently been solved by Rand (1938), who found that the birds of this genus form pairs and the males take part in the raising of the young. This is in contrast to all other birds of paradise, with the apparent exception of the closely related genera *Phonygammus* and *Macgregoria*. These 3 genera have failed to develop conspicuous sexual dimorphism. Sympatric hybrids (many of them intergeneric) have also been described from all the other families of birds in which pair formation is absent (at least in certain genera), for example, humming birds (*Trochilidae*), Grouse (*Tetraonidae*) and

Manakins (*Pipridae*). The only common hybrid of this type among European birds is that between the capercaillie (*Tetrao urogallus*) and the Black Cock (*Lyrurus tetrix*), more than 200 hybrid individuals being known. The two species are, to a considerable extent, ecologically separated, which may help to uphold the distinctness between them, since back crosses between the F_1 ♂ and the *Tetrao* ♀ are occasionally fertile (Bergmann 1940).

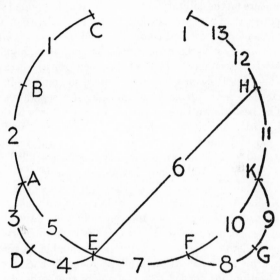

FIG. 27. Diagram of intergeneric hybridization among birds of paradise. The letters refer to the parental species. A = *Paradigalla;* B = *Epimachus;* C = *Astrapia;* D = *Parotia;* E = *Lophorina;* F = *Craspedophora;* G = *Seleucides;* H = *Diphyllodes;* I = *Cicinnurus;* K = *Paradisaea.* The numbers refer to the specific names that were applied to these hybrids, as listed by Mayr 1941a.

It is not accidental that we find in the above-mentioned families not only the highest development of sexual dimorphism, but also the greatest difference between the males of closely related species. These differences are so striking that even the geographic races are so different in many species as to be considered to be generically distinct by earlier authors. There is necessity for highly specific recognition marks in those species in which copulation is not preceded by pair formation or lengthy engagement periods. On the other hand, sexual dimorphism tends to deteriorate on small islands on which selective species recognition is unnecessary, since no other species of the genus is present (p. 49). This may shed added light on many situations which have been described in the past under the heading, sexual selection.

Hybrids occur much more rarely among pair-forming species of birds. In such cases the male and female have committed not only an original "mistake," but have apparently not "corrected" it afterwards by abandoning the brood. Suchetet (1896) has given a full summary of the earlier literature on the subject, and Meise (1936b) has added some additional recent cases. There are now known, for example, 10 or 11 hybrids between *Hirundo rustica* (barn swallow) and *Delichon urbica* (house martin) and 16 hybrids between *Carduelis carduelis* (goldfinch) and *Chloris chloris* (greenfinch). Hybrids between *Parus caeruleus* (blue titmouse) and *Parus cyanus* (lazure tit) were so common in a part of Russia that they were, at one time, considered a separate species (*P. pleskei*). The best-known case in North American birds is that of two species of North American warblers, the blue-winged warbler (*Vermivora pinus*) and the golden-winged warbler (*V. chrysoptera*), which form occasional hybrids of two distinct types, the so-called Brewster's warbler (*V. leucobronchialis*) and Lawrence's warbler (*V. lawrencei*). The two parental species differ in at least five obvious characters, but are fairly similar in song and habitat requirements, although the golden-wing is the more northerly species and generally prefers the higher parts of slopes in the localities where the two species overlap (Forbush 1929). There is no modern analysis of the situation available, but it is known that the hybrids are fertile (they produce young in back crosses) and that hybridization has not led to a blurring of the border between the two species. The two species do not live in the climax forest, but rather in clearings, at the edge of the forest, and in abandoned fields, and it is probable that the hybridization is of recent date and caused by man-made habitat disturbances. Hybrids form only a very minute percentage of the individuals in all the species mentioned, and I know of no case in which the occurrence of hybrids has resulted in a blurring of the border line between these species. We are dealing here with cases of exceptional breakdowns of the isolation between well-defined sympatric species. A breakdown of the isolation between good sympatric species, owing to human interference, is more frequent in groups that live in narrower ecological niches than birds do. The undeniable blurring of the border between some of the *Bufo* species (p. 267) may find its explanation in this manner (Blair 1941), and it seems plausible that this may also be the explanation for the occasional occurrence of hybrid populations between Californian species of garter snakes (*Thamnophis*) (Fitch 1940a) (see

p. 133). It will not be possible to state how widespread this phenomenon is among insects until the polytypic species concept has found a wider acceptance in entomology.

HYBRID POPULATIONS OR HYBRID ZONES

If a geographic isolating barrier, which had separated two diverging populations, is lifted, any of four processes may occur: (1) The two populations have, during the isolation, developed to full species, which are reproductively isolated and sufficiently distinct in their ecological requirements not to be close competitors. The lifting of the barrier will generally lead to a broad mutual overlapping of the ranges. (2) The two populations have developed to full species, which are reproductively isolated, but are closely competitive owing to nondevelopment of sufficent differences in the ecological requirements. The result is a narrow overlap in a border zone, such as found between *Cepaea nemoralis* and *vindobonensis*, *Luscinia luscinia* and *megarhynchus*, and other cases described in our discussion of overlaps (p. 176). (3) The two populations have acquired different habitat preferences during their isolation, but not reproductive isolation. This results in a curious interlacing of ranges, with hybridization at the borders of habitats. (4) The two populations have not perfected either different habitat preferences or biological isolating mechanisms that would guarantee reproductive isolation and consequently will hybridize freely on coming into contact. In this case a more or less extensive hybrid population, a zone of secondary intergradation, will be formed in the area of contact.

We have already called attention (p. 99) to the difficulty of distinguishing such zones of hybridization from ordinary zones of primary intergradation. Most taxonomists speak of intergradation when two subspecies gradually merge with each other. They find that there is, inserted between the two subspecies, a series of intermediate populations which connect the two extremes perfectly and which are no more variable than other neighboring populations. In a hybrid zone, on the other hand, we find that the change from one character combination (subspecies *a*) to the other combination (subspecies *b*) is very abrupt and that in the area of the break a population occurs which is exceedingly variable. In such hybrid populations, individuals may be found that are indistinguishable from subspecies *a*, others that are like *b*, while the majority are intermediate (in various character combinations).

Central Europe has witnessed, within the last 50,000 years, one of the most spectacular liftings of a major geographic barrier, an event that has left a deep mark on many species. At the height of the Pleistocene ice age not only most of northern Europe was covered with ice, but another area of glaciation formed in the Alps. The Alpine and the Scandinavian ice caps approached to within 300 miles of each other in central Germany. There was a cold steppe between the two ice margins, uninhabitable to all but a few arctic animals. The fauna that had been living in Europe up to the ice age was forced to retreat either to the west of the Alps (southern France, Spain) or to the southeast (Balkans) (Stresemann 1919, Meise 1928a, b, Reinig 1937). Nearly all European species of animals lived in these two more-or-less completely isolated refuges for a considerable part of the Pleistocene—and diverged considerably during this isolation. When the ice began to retreat northward, the species expanded their eastern and western ranges and finally met in central Europe. The result was either a hybrid zone, such as is found in *Corvus* (Meise 1928a), *Sitta* (Sachtleben, Løppenthin), and *Aegithalos* (Stresemann), indicating that speciation had not been completed; or overlap (see p. 176), indicating the completion of speciation. The facts are so striking and so clear that they do not seem to permit of any other interpretation.

The same barrier and its breakdown has, of course, affected all animals, not birds alone. We have already discussed its effect in the genera *Rana* and *Triton* It is unquestionably also of importance among insects, but only a few examples have so far been described. The hybrid zones in the Alps, described by Pictet (1935), may have the same origin (see also Bateson 1913).

A series of hybrid zones in eastern Europe and Asia (Meise 1928a, b) also owe their existence to a breakdown of some former barriers. Dementiev (1938) lists 36 Russian species of birds that form such hybrid zones, most of them coinciding in a few regions which form distinct belts, such as are found in western Siberia, between the Caspian and Aral Lakes, and north of the Caucasus. A well-known "contact zone" is located in the province of Astarabad (northeastern Persia), from which hybrid flocks have been described, for example, between the shrikes *Lanius collurio kobylini* and *L. c. phoenicuroides* and between the goldfinches *Carduelis carduelis subcaniceps* and *L. c. loudoni*. Paludan (1940) illustrates, in a colored plate, the merging which takes place in the Astarabad district between two superficially very distinct but allopatric "species" of buntings, *Emberiza melanocephala* and *icterica*. In a single flock individuals may be found that are almost typical of either species, as well as every imaginable intermediate stage.

In North America similar hybrid zones have been described in a number of species. The western bronze grackle (*Quiscalus quiscula aeneus*) and the eastern purple grackle (*Qu. qu. quiscula* and *stonei*) meet in a hybrid zone which extends from Louisiana to New England (Chapman 1936). In a single nesting colony in this belt, 10 males were collected of which 4 were *stonei*, 2 were *aeneus*, and 4 showed various stages of intermediacy; in another colony, among 10 males, one was *stonei*, 3 intermediate, and 6 more or less typical *aeneus*. The hybrid zone between the eastern yellow-shafted flicker (*Colaptes auratus*) and the western red-shafted flicker (*Colaptes cafer*) runs from British Columbia to Texas, and the infiltration of genes of one species into the range of the other is noticeable for a zone more than 1,000 kilometers in width and more than 3,000 kilometers long (Allen 1892). Hybrid zones between less wide-spread species or subspecies are shorter, as may be seen by Miller's (1941) maps of the allopatric *Junco* species and by the map of the races of the wild sheep (*Ovis*) in North America (Cowan 1940).

I know of no case among North American birds in which a hybrid zone was derived from more than two sources. Among the insects of the upper Mississippi Valley, a few cases of hybrid populations are known in which an eastern, a western and a northern component are distinguishable (Kinsey 1936, Spieth 1941). In all these cases there is apparently no reproductive or ecological isolation, and rather broad areas of intergradation could therefore develop. Post-Pleistocene range expansions have produced 6 contact zones in the moth genus *Platysamia* between previously isolated populations. In 3 instances a zone of complete secondary intergradation has developed, in 2 cases (*nokomis* x *cecropia*, *columbia* x *cecropia*) there is no intergradation, but occasional hybridization, while the sixth contact (between *gloveri* and *cecropia*) is too recent to have had much effect (Sweadner 1937). It seems, on the basis of these data, as though *P. cecropia* had reached specific status, while all the other forms are still actually or potentially interbreeding.

Similar hybrid zones are found on all continents (Meise 1928b). A celebrated case is that of the pheasant genus *Gennaeus* (Silver Pheasants) where a number of hybrid populations have developed in upper Burma between the strikingly different though allopatric species *lathami* (= *horsfieldi*) and *nycthemerus*. Some 20 names have been applied to individuals, showing the various recombinations of the characters of the 2 parental species (Ghigi 1907, Ticehurst 1939). A number of hybrid zones are also known in New Guinea (Meise 1928b), including one between the Yellow and the Red Birds of Paradise (Fig. 13), but a more detailed discussion of these cases would not yield any new principles.

The most striking aspect of many of these hybrid zones is their relative stability. The width in the case of *Corvus* is from 75 to 100 kilometers, and there is no evidence that it has broadened materially within the last 5,000 years. Even assuming that adult birds nest year after year in the same tree and that the young settle down no farther than 500 meters from the place of birth (which is well within the probable minimum), the hybrid zone should now cover the whole width of Europe. Meise suggested that hybrids might have a lowered viability, and this explanation has been accepted by Huxley (1939, 1940) and Dobzhansky (1940), since no alternative seems possible. So far there is no evidence that this assumption is correct; as a matter of fact, nests in the hybrid zone which were examined contained the normal number of young. There is also the possibility of selective mating, but again there is no positive evidence. Collecting of crows has proven that there are no "pure" specimens in the hybrid zone. Even birds that seemed in the field to be either *cornix* or *corone* showed their hybrid nature on closer examination in the laboratory. This fact more or less invalidates the sample counts of pure and mixed pairs by field naturalists. Meise (1928a:76) lists for one locality, among 103 *corone* and 25 *cornix*, 13 percent of mixed pairs, instead of the expected 32 percent; in another locality, among 7 *corone* and 31 *cornix*, 20 percent of mixed pairs, instead of 30 percent; and at a third locality, among 3 *corone* and 11 *cornix*, 33 percent of mixed pairs, as expected. The samples are too small and the visual evidence too unsatisfactory to be conclusive or to justify statistical treatment.

Dobzhansky (1941a) considers that "the zones of intergradation are narrower where the duration of the contact has been longest, and broader where the contact is more recent. This is expected if isolating mechanisms are in process of formation where these incipient species hybridize." To me, this interpretation does not seem to correspond to the facts. According to Meise, the width of the hybrid zone in the case of *Corvus* is determined by local ecological factors. Narrow stretches occur in the most "recent" part of the zone (Schleswig) and in the oldest (the Alps). The zone at the southern foot of the Alps is narrow, because *cornix* is a bird of the plains and *corone* inhabits the higher levels. In the case of the grackle (*Quiscalus*) the zone is narrow in the south not only because wide uninhabited stretches of prairie (western Louisiana) and mountains (Tennessee) separate the ranges of *aeneus* and *stonei* over much of the territory and because there is a habitat difference between the two forms in Louisiana (Chapman 1936), but also because the southern birds are sedentary, while the northern birds are migratory and are thus more likely to scatter into each others' breeding ranges. This evidence may be summarized by stating that no sufficient reason has yet been found for the narrowness of many hybrid zones of long standing, except possibly a lowered viability of the hybrid. All the cases described hitherto have one feature in common, namely, that between two rather distinct and homogeneous allopatric forms a zone is inserted in which both types are found (in a small minority), as well as every possible type of intergrade or recombination. Such hybrid zones are apparently true "melting pots" between the parental forms.

A special type of hybridization is encountered, if the two hybridizing populations had developed different habitat preferences during their isolation, a situation referred to by us under process (3) on page 263. The meeting of such populations is limited by their habitat preferences, and, instead of developing a well-defined hybrid zone, such populations will show a curious interlacing of ranges, with hybridization wherever the two respective habitats meet. The distribution of the various sub-species in the snake genus *Rhinocheilus* can probably be explained on this basis (Klauber 1941b).

There is, however, still another kind of allopatric hybrid zone. We find occasionally, although these cases are in the minority, that random mating is cut down in the zone of contact and that the number of hybrids is small. The western (*europaeus*) and the eastern (*roumanicus*) species of the European hedgehog (*Erinaceus*), which are apparently another product of the Pleistocene isolation, overlap now in two narrow zones, one in northern Germany from the Baltic to Silesia, and the other along the eastern foot of the Alps. Herter (1934) found that of 82 individuals caught near Berlin, 66 belonged to *europaeus*, 10 to *roumanicus*, while only 6 showed a combination of the characters of the two species. There is no ecological isolation between the two species, and crosses in captivity are apparently completely fertile. A similar situation for North American toads (*Bufo*) has been reported by Blair (1941). Extensive collecting data indicate that wherever two or more members of the *americanus-terrestris-fowleri-woodhousii* complex occur together, some intermediates are to be expected. A very careful analysis was made of a mixed *americanus-fowleri* population, and it was found that at least three isolating mechanisms between the species were operating, i.e., breeding season, habitat preference, and mating call. None of these, however, was absolute, and a heterogeneous mid-season population was found. The fact that only a few individuals revealed hybrid origin indicated that the hybridization was of rather recent date and possibly due to habitat disturbance caused by man. Nevertheless, the possibility of a reduction of the viability or fertility of the hybrids cannot be ruled out altogether, even though no evidence for it could be found in the breeding experiments.

There is a difference of appearance, but not of kind, between continental hybrid zones, such as we have just described, and hybrid island populations. It happens occasionally that an insular habitat is colonized from two different sources by populations (subspecies, and so forth) of a species which had diverged morphologically, but had not yet developed reproductive isolation. I have described several such cases from the South Sea Islands, for example, for *Pachycephala* on Whitney Island (hybrid population between *Pachycephala pectoralis dahli* and *bougainvillei*) (Mayr 1932c) and for *Megapodius* on Dampier Island (hybrid population between *Megapodius freycinet affinis* and *eremita*) (Mayr 1938b). Lack (1940a, 1942) found that two of the *Geospiza* populations in the Galápagos Island gave every indication of hybrid origin:

On Culpepper Island in the extreme north occurs the highly variable *Geospiza conirostris darwini*, which shares characters of *G. magnirostris* (widespread on other islands) and *G. conirostris propinqua* (on Tower Island) and is probably of hybrid origin between these two. On the tiny islets of Daphne and Crossman (which are not near each other) occurs a highly variable *Geospiza* species intermediate in characters between *G. fortis* and *fuliginosa*, and overlapping with both. Presumably it is of hybrid origin; if so, here is the unusual case of the two species which occur together over most of their range without interbreeding, but which interbreed in two small isolated localities.

Three highly variable insular populations of gall wasps (Cynipidae) which Kinsey (1937b) describes from Colorado and Utah are probably also of hybrid origin. The hybrid populations of fish and other freshwater organisms (see, for example, Hubbs 1940b, Hubbs and Bailey 1940) which are found in certain stream systems are apparently also due to the colonization of one habitat by immigrants derived from two different sources.

One of the striking phenomena of recently formed hybrid populations is their tremendous variation. Both parental types, as well as all the possible recombinations of the parental characters, may be found in the same effective breeding population. Where the influx of the parental types continues, as in the continental hybrid zones and on certain islands, the variability will remain constantly high. Meise (1936b) has called attention to the fact that the variability may become much reduced where the continuous influx of the parental types is stopped. In western Algeria two sparrows occur, the house sparrow (*Passer domesticus*) near human habitations, and the willow sparrow (*P. hispaniolensis*) in various types of habitats away from human settlements. The two species are uniform and constant in their characters. In central

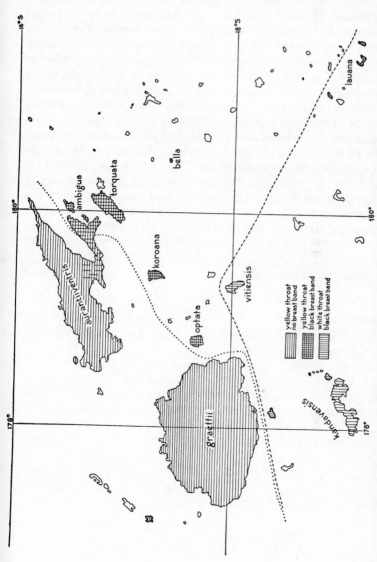

FIG. 28. Geographic variation of *Pachycephala pectoralis* in the Fiji Islands. The vertical and the horizontal shading illustrate the distribution of the two main groups of subspecies. The cross hatching indicates the presence of intermediates which can be interpreted as more or less stabilized hybrid populations.

and eastern Algeria the two species form an exceedingly variable hybrid population, including both parental types and a variable intermediate type "*flückigeri*." What makes this case exceptional is that in several isolated oases of southern Algeria and in southwestern Tunisia only *flückigeri* is found, which has become quite stabilized at these localities. A similar stabilization has occurred in several *Passer italiae* populations which Meise (1936a) also explains as products of a *P. domesticus* x *hispaniolensis* cross. He interprets in like manner the lack of variability in *Pachycephala pectoralis koroana*, which is intermediate in location and characters (throat yellow, breastband black) between the *vitiensis* group (throat white, black breastband present) and the *aurantiiventris* group (throat yellow, breastband absent) (Mayr 1932d) (Fig. 28). Much additional evidence makes it apparent that Koro Island was originally occupied by the *aurantiiventris* group and was colonized a second time by the *vitiensis* group. A particularly well-analyzed case of a stabilized hybrid population is that of *Junco hiemalis cismontanus* Dwight (Miller 1941:329–343). Hybridization has resulted in all these cases in an increase of variability of the affected populations and in exceptional cases in the formation of new intraspecific units, but it has led in no case to the formation of new species.

Speciation through Hybridization

In all the listed cases hybridization was caused by the breaking down of an isolating mechanism, usually by the lifting of a geographic barrier. The result was that two populations, or two subspecies, or two representative species, which up to that time had remained distinct and well-separated units, began to mix and to eliminate the gap that had previously existed between them. Instead of furthering speciation, that is the establishment of discontinuities, hybridization has, in all these cases, accomplished just the opposite. Lowe's (1936) claim to the contrary has been refuted effectively by Stresemann (1936) and by Lack (1940a). Patterson (1942) believes that *Drosophila americana* is of hybrid origin, but it is by no means certain that this species does not show the original variability of this species group and that *texana* and *novomexicana* are not merely specialized offshoots of an earlier, more variable stock.

SELECTIVE FACTORS AND SPECIES FORMATION

The important role in evolution that is played by selection has already been treated by us in an earlier chapter (p. 85). In this chapter we are merely concerned with the question of how selective factors influence the establishment of discontinuities and what selective factors tend to enlarge the gaps between incipient species. Competition and predation are generally listed as the two most important factors to be considered in this connection. A survey of this field indicates, unfortunately, that our knowledge of the actual influence of these factors on the speciation process is still very slight. In fact, it is surprising how badly ecologists have neglected these questions. To give an exhaustive treatment of this subject, as we have done for the isolating factors, is quite impossible. All we can attempt, at the present time, is an analysis of the fundamental problems, on the basis of a few concrete cases.

Competition.—That strong competition is a retarding factor in evolution has never been seriously questioned. The rapidity and the degree of divergent evolution of the Drepanididae and other families on Hawaii is due to the fact that so many empty ecological niches were available. Exactly the same applies to the evolution of the Geospizidae in the Galápagos Islands. The absence of competitors, to use Sewall Wright's language, apparently facilitates the crossing of valleys between one adaptive peak and another. In nearly every East African lake there is one small species of plankton-eating fish which is very abundant, forming an important source of food for the larger fishes. A number of subspecies and allopatric species of the Cyprinid genus *Engraulicypris* fill this niche. In Lake Edward, however, this pelagic genus is absent, and the same niche is filled by a Cyprinodont, *Haplochilichthys pelagicus*, which has forsaken the usual Cyprinodont habitat of shores and swamps to live a truly pelagic existence (Worthington 1940). It is not clear whether *H. pelagicus* was able to develop in Lake Edward because *Engraulicypris* was not present or whether the latter could not colonize this lake because the habitat was already occupied by the Cyprinodont species, but this is not of great consequence. The important lesson here is, rather, that competition had a very decided influence on speciation in Lake Edward. Lack (1940a) calls attention to the fact that even the absence of competition will not lead to a multiplication of species, if it is not combined with geographic isolation. The rich development of Geospizid species in the Galápagos Archipelago contrasts strikingly with the situation on isolated Cocos Island, where only a single species of these finches was able to develop, in spite of the number of available ecological niches. Potential colonizers on continents will generally be unsuccessful, because most of the suitable habitats are already occupied to capacity. Competition is also strong on very small islands, where the habitat is poor (see above, p. 250). Competition is a factor that is very difficult to analyze, because its importance becomes obvious only when it is either lacking or reduced to a minimum (Buxton 1938, Usinger 1941).

Predation.—The role of predation is even more difficult to evaluate. Some recent authors have claimed that predation impedes seriously the multiplication of species, but it is not certain that these claims are based on sound arguments. The absence of predators on oceanic islands has nowhere led to the production of high numbers of species, although it has permitted the development of aberrant types, such as flightless birds (Madagascar, New Zealand, and so forth) and giant tortoises. Predators have an a posteriori effect; they can exterminate aberrant types by entering their range after they have developed. They are also a conservative factor by preventing superspecializations, but it is not apparent how they could possibly affect the establishment of discontinuities. Worthington (1937, 1940), supported by Huxley (1941), tries to prove that the reason for the differences in the numbers of endemic species of fish between various East African Lakes "lies in the presence or absence of large predators." He illustrates this by the Cichlidae, the family with the highest number of endemic species.

TABLE 14
THE CICHLID FAUNA OF THE EAST AFRICAN LAKES

LAKE	AGE	SIZE (SQUARE KILO-METERS)	GREATEST DEPTH (METERS)	PREDATORS PRESENT	NUMBER OF ENDEMIC CICHLID SPECIES
Rudolf	10,000 B.C.	9,000 to 10,000	75	+	3
Albert	} Second Pluvial	5,350	48	+	4
Edward		2,120	122	−	18
Victoria		68,800	80	−	58
Tanganyika	} Early Cenozoic	31,900	1,275	+	Ca. 90
Nyasa		30,800	730	(+)	171

Table 14 shows at a glance that the size and the age of the lakes are vastly more important than the presence of predators. It is probable that the rather recent arrival of the predators *Lates* and *Hydrocyon* has led to the extermination of certain Cichlid species in Lake Tanganyika and Lake Albert, but I cannot see that these predators retarded in any way the speed of speciation or interfered with the formation of discontinuities. Worthington's thesis is based on the hypothesis of sympatric speciation in fresh-water lakes, but this type of speciation is highly improbable, as we have shown in an earlier chapter (p. 214). The small number of species in Lake Rudolf is not surprising, since this lake has not been in contact with any other river system than that of the Nile, and its large population size prevents rapid changes. Furthermore, some of its endemic species may have died out as the water became progressively more alkaline (it is now twenty times more alkaline than most waters flowing into the Nile). That Lake Albert has no more endemics than it has is not surprising either, since it is broadly connected with the Nile. Lake Edward (small) and Lake Victoria (large), being well isolated, have large numbers of endemic species, even though they are not very old lakes. That Lake Nyasa has more endemics than Lake Tanganyika is probably due to the fact that in its past history it was connected with a greater number of river systems.

It is obvious from this discussion that the case in favor of predators as inhibitors of speciation (multiplication of species) is very weak.

DIFFERENCES IN THE SPECIATION OF PLANTS AND ANIMALS

We have demonstrated in the preceding discussion that there is a great variety of factors which influence the speciation process; we have also seen that certain factors are more important in some groups of animals, other factors in other groups. But even if we take all these differences into consideration, animals as a whole seem to differ considerably from plants as a whole. Even if we omit from consideration the apomictic species and speciation by polyploidy, which have no exact parallel among animals (spontaneous sympatric speciation by polyploidy is unproven in animals, see p. 191), and study only "ordinary" plants, we find some very striking differences. Plants are tied for their entire life span to the spot where the seed germinates, and the transport of the pollen which leads to fertilization is accomplished by external agencies, such as wind and insects. To prevent mistakes and all-too-frequent hybridization, plants require different isolating mechanisms (cytogenetic factors, habitat preference, flowering season, and so forth) from animals, at least different from those of freely moving animals with individual fertilization. In regard to dispersal, there is also decided disparity between the two groups. The individual animal has a smaller or larger cruising radius, within which it is exposed to a number of environmental conditions. Its offspring, on the other hand (except in the group of "cosmopolitan" species, see p. 211), tends to stay near its place of birth. In plants the individual is tied to one spot and subjected to the highly specific conditions of its environment. Its offspring, however, as seeds or spores, are subject to very wide dispersal, but will survive only if they can germinate in a similar ecological niche.

These are broad generalizations, with many exceptions of which I am fully aware. The important point is that the unquestionable difference in the relative importance of the various factors that promote or impede speciation must have an influence on the nature of the "species" in the two respective groups. The great dispersal power of the light, wind-borne seeds of many plant genera led to more or less panmictic populations and favored the establishment of speciation processes that are independent of geographic variation. We shall not be able to obtain a real insight into the different speciation processes and their distribution and relative importance in the various groups of plants and animals until the ecological factors (dispersal, various specializations) and the ethological factors (courtship patterns, mate preferences and aversions, and the like) have been correlated with the taxonomic facts (degree and speed of subspeciation, and so forth) and with the cytological and genetic findings (sterility, and so forth). The time has come for the naturalist to organize these data and to present us with a better-balanced picture of species formation than can be given by the specialist in only one of the experimental or laboratory sciences.

CHAPTER X

THE HIGHER CATEGORIES
AND EVOLUTION

THERE ARE MORE than one million species of living animals in existence. It is an obvious practical necessity for the taxonomist to "classify" these species in order to facilitate their cataloguing, arranging in the collection, and identification. Many principles of classification are possible. The species could, for example, be arranged according to the alphabetical sequence of the scientific species names, or according to size, or according to the habitat and the climatic zone in which they live. Such classifications are logical and defensible, if we are interested merely in the practical aspect of classification. However, all these systems have one or another serious weakness.

MACROTAXONOMY

Aristotle, almost 2,300 years ago, was the first to realize that the most practical system of organisms is based on the degree of similarity of their morphological or anatomical characters. This has eventually become known as the "natural" system. Applying this principle, it was found that numbers of species could be united into groups which were identifiable by a certain combination of characters, and that such units could again be combined into higher categories, until all species were arranged into a hierarchy of systematic categories. Starting from the bottom, this arrangement included species, genus, family, order, class, and phylum, as well as a number of intermediate stages, such as section, tribe, and the sub- and super-stages of the other categories. The important point of this classification is that the assignment of a species to a definite category characterizes it immediately as possessing a very definite combination of structures and biological attributes. So perfect, indeed, is this agreement of taxonomic position and structural characteristics that it became a source of considerable amazement and speculation among the naturalists. Some of the natural philosophers in the first half of the nineteenth century attempted to construct systems on the basis of logical categories, rather similar to the modern system of the chemical elements, but none of these systems of horizontal and vertical columns or of concentric circles was very successful.

The theory of evolution solved the puzzle of the high degree of perfection of the natural system in a manner that was as simple as it was satisfactory: The organisms of a "natural" systematic category agree with one another in so many characteristics because they are descendants of one common ancestor! The natural system became a "phylogenetic" system. The natural system is based on similarity, the phylogenetic system on the degree of relationship. It seems probable that a complete change of the classification is necessitated by changing the criterium on which the system is based.

Fortunately, the difficulty just stated is more abstract than real. The fact is that the classification of organisms that existed before the advent of evolutionary theories has undergone surprisingly little change in the times following it, and such changes as have been made have depended only to a trifling extent on the elucidation of the actual phylogenetic relationships through paleontological evidence. The phylogenetic interpretation has been simply superimposed on the existing classification; a rejection of the former fails to do any violence to the latter. The subdivisions of the animal and plant kingdoms established by Linnaeus are, with few exceptions, retained in the modern classification, and this despite the enormous number of new forms discovered since then. The new forms were either included in the Linnaean groups, or new groups have been created to accommodate them. There has been no necessity for a basic change in the classification. This fact is taken for granted by most systematists, and frequently overlooked by the representatives of other biological disciplines. Its connotations are worth considering. For the only inference that can be drawn from it is that the classification now adopted is not an arbitrary but a natural one, reflecting the objective state of things [Dobzhansky 1941a:364].

Are the Higher Categories Phylogenetic Units?

It is the aim of the systematist, who believes in evolution, to recognize higher categories which contain only the descendants of a common ancestor. Every taxonomic category should thus, ideally, be monophyletic. Such a phylogenetic system has two advantages: first, it is the only system that has a sound theoretical basis (something the natural philosophers of the early nineteenth century looked for in vain), and secondly, it has the practical advantage of combining forms (and there are only a few exceptions to this) that have the greatest number of characters in common. Besides these advantages, a natural system encounters also two kinds of difficulties. One is temporary and superficial; it consists in the insufficient knowledge of the phylogenetically important characters of many groups. The other difficulty lies in the necessity of presenting phylogenies in a linear sequence of species, genera, families, and so forth, while the phylogenetic tree (the closest analogue we have to evolutionary interrelationships) has the additional dimensions of space and time. No system of the taxonomist could, for this reason, be an exact representation of the phylogeny, even if all the facts were known. The relation between taxonomic systems and phylogeny may consequently be expressed as follows: It is one of the aims of taxonomy to establish and recognize only such categories of classification as are based on phylogenetic relationship. Existing classifications will fall short of this ideal, to a lesser or greater degree, partly for lack of data and partly on account of the impossibility of presenting a phylogenetic tree in a linear sequence. These difficulties seem to be of such magnitude in some groups that a few authors have seriously proposed giving up the phylogenetic system altogether and replacing it by a "practical" classification, that is, by one which would permit the most rapid identification of the members of these groups. That botanists are more apt to consider such "practical" classifications is probably due to the fact that the morphology of plants is vastly simpler and less varied than that of all but the simplest animals.

Special adaptations, for example for living in deserts, in the sea, in mud, for flying, and so forth, produce ecological types which are suitable for a classification based not on relationship, but on the superficial similarity of adaptive structures. That such a classification is universally rejected by the taxonomist is not so much due to philosophical considerations, as being more "artificial," less "natural," but simply because such ecological adaptations generally affect only one or a few characters and encounter, therefore, many more practical difficulties than the phylogenetic systems. It is interesting in this connection to study the systems of animals that were proposed from the end of the Middle Ages to the time of Darwin. We can see how systematic units that were based on superficial, adaptive characters were eliminated, one after another, and were replaced by new units, containing organisms that share a greater number of characters. Even without the knowledge of evolution, a system would eventually have been reached by this process, which would have been essentially identical with our present one.

It must not be forgotten, however, that classification does not and cannot express phylogeny; it is merely based on phylogeny. It is possible to propose a number of different classifications, even in cases where there is no doubt about the phylogeny. This is due not only to the fact that the phylogenetic tree is not linear, but also because it is a living tree, which is continually growing. The growth is infinitely faster in some branches than in others, and species that belong to the same "branch" may be farther apart (both actually and figuratively) than species belonging to different branches. This dynamic aspect of evolution makes it seem probable that many of our "phylogenetic classifications" are oversimplified, but it does not detract from the fundamental soundness of the phylogenetic principle of classification.

The establishment of phylogenetic units encounters the greatest difficulties in the groups in which the most striking structures have degenerated for various reasons and in which, in consequence, the socalled loss convergences occur. I want to illustrate this with a few examples. The living birds have been classified for more than one hundred years (since Merrem 1816) into 2 major groups, the Ratites (or ostrichlike, flightless birds) and the Carinates (or true flying birds). Comparative anatomical research has, however, proven that the Ratites are a polyphyletic group, containing secondarily flightless birds, descendants of probably 5 different flying groups. Modern bird systematists therefore discard the term "Ratites" and arrange the flightless birds in 5 orders, equivalent to the orders of flying birds. They know that the many striking similarities between these 5 orders are secondary isomorphisms, developed in connection with the loss of flight.

Another excellent example has recently been related by Richards (1938):

Among the bees there is a number of cuckoo genera of which the larvae live as parasites in the nests of industrious species. These cuckoo bees have evolved from industrious species and in favorable examples the resemblance is still so close that the ancestral genus is pretty certain. Yet some of the genera no longer closely resemble any industrious genus. Moreover, there is a very definite "parasitic facies" dependent not only on the loss of pollen-collecting apparatus, but on the presence of bright, sometimes wasp-like colors, etc.; most parasitic bees can be recognized as such without observation of their habits. For these reasons two different classifications have grown up. One endeavors to place each parasitic genus next to its supposed ancestor. This is the phylogenetic scheme and, in general, I believe the best one, but it has the disadvantage that a number of genera are hard to place. The other scheme places all the parasitic bees together in one group which, at least in the female sex, is easily defined by the absence of pollen-collecting apparatus. Sub-groups within this assemblage roughly correspond to the various lines of ancestry. Although artificial this scheme has certain advantages in classifying the bees of, say, Africa which are very imperfectly known.

Grütte (1935) showed that there was very little evolution among these parasitic genera and that nearly every one of them had developed from a normal bee genus. Parasitism apparently reduces the evolutionary potentialities. In most cases these social parasites are host specific, but the genus *Sphecodes* (which derived from *Halictus*) now victimizes *Halictus*, *Andrena*, and *Colletes*. A careful analysis of this situation enabled Grütte to establish the true relationships of nearly all these bees. This is not possible in the case of many true ecto- and endoparasites, which have lost most of their distinguishing features during the long history of their parasitism. The taxonomy of parasites is therefore a particularly difficult field. Roberts (1941) in a study of loss convergences in grasshoppers comes to the conclusion

that the loss or suppression of a structure is a relatively frequent and simple occurrence in contrast to the development of a new type or form of structure. Thus, the presence of a structure may be quite significant, but its absence should be treated entirely negatively. . . . The outer distal spine of the hind tibiae appears not to be influenced by any particular type of environment. In as much as it is present in the more primitive subfamilies, its absence in other subfamilies may be accounted for by the loss of the structure rather than it never having been present in the phylogeny of the group . . . its loss has occurred independently in several different lines of evolutionary development.

The paleontologist is confronted by still another difficulty. He frequently finds on closer analysis that one of his genera is composed of certain stages of three or four different lineages and is thus obviously polyphyletic. Schindewolf (1936), Arkell and Moy-Thomas (1940:397–405), and others have cited numerous such situations, nearly all of them involving invertebrates. Two classifications are possible in such cases, a horizontal and a vertical one. Although the vertical one seems to be theoretically the better, the horizontal classification is frequently more practical. The student of recent organisms is less likely to encounter such difficulties, because there is available to him a much greater number of characters than persist in fossil material. This is particularly true for fossil invertebrates, of which usually only the shell is preserved, which is more subject to modification than the features of internal anatomy. However, there is no doubt that even among recent animals the number of polyphyletic categories which the taxonomist has not yet been able to eliminate is considerable. Among song birds we have the notorious family Timaliidae (babblers), which is nothing but a convenient catchall for all those genera of Old World song birds which do not seem to fit into other families. The family Muscicapidae (Old World flycatchers) contains a large number of broad-billed genera which seem to have developed independently from various narrow-billed groups ("warblers"). The true grouping of the genera in the "family" Muscicapidae will not be learned until other characters besides the bill have been examined.

The term "monophyletic" is frequently interpreted as meaning descendants of a single individual. This is, in bisexual animals, obviously an impossibility. We employ the term monophyletic as meaning descendants of a single interbreeding group of populations, in other words, descendants of a single species. A clear understanding of this situation makes it apparent that, as far as animals are concerned, the possibility of "reticulate" evolution (as against divergent or convergent evolution) may be largely disregarded. Reticulate evolution is possible only where different species, genera, and families can hybridize successfully, and this occurs only exceptionally in animals, as we have seen in the preceding chapter.

Summarizing this evidence, we may say that the "natural system" of the modern taxonomist is based on phylogeny and that the higher categories are monophyletic units. Shortcomings, in striving for this ideal, are due to insufficient knowledge, and the only intrinsic difficulty of a phylogenetic system consists in the impossibility of representing a "phylogenetic tree" in linear sequence. The phylogenetic system of the higher categories is not only the inevitable consequence of the acceptance of the theory of evolution, but it also guarantees a greater number of joint characteristics to the members of the various higher units than any other principle of classification that has so far been proposed.

The Nature of the Higher Categories

It is important for the practical purposes of the working taxonomist, as well as necessary for a real understanding of organic evolution, that we devote some thought to the meaning of the higher categories. How did they develop in nature? What is their position relative to one another? Do they possess objective reality, or are they artificial units created by the taxonomist for his convenience? If we want to discuss these questions we must limit ourselves, for practical reasons, to one of these categories and test our conclusions eventually on the others. It is most convenient to base our discussion on the genus, since it is the lowest and most tangible of the true higher categories.

"Lumpers" and "Splitters."—We have repeatedly emphasized the fact that there is extremely little disagreement in well-worked taxonomic groups as to the limit of the species. Nearly all authors will agree as to what is a species and what is not, except for the border-line cases among the allopatric species. Such agreement is utterly lacking as regards the

higher categories, and this is the reason they have also been called the "subjective" categories. The bird genus as defined by Mathews, Roberts, and Oberholser has little in common with that of Stresemann, Peters, and Mayr, to quote some contemporary ornithologists. The same disagreement is apparent in regard to the families, orders, classes, and so forth. What is the principal reason for this utterly confusing divergence of opinion? It seems to me that it is largely due to the fact that the taxonomists themselves may be classified as idealists or as realists (see p. 289, for additional reasons). The idealist believes that quantity and quality of taxonomic differences reflect rather accurately the degree of relationship, and that this, in turn, could and should be reflected in the nomenclature. He therefore creates a highly refined hierarchy of taxonomic units and terms. The realist, on the other hand, sees that no system of nomenclature can adequately express the complicated intergrading degrees of relationship, and he therefore finds the higher categories primarily a convenient help for the badly overburdened memory of the taxonomic worker. This, generally, makes him a "lumper," as it is called in the professional jargon of the taxonomist, that is, a person who prefers larger units to smaller ones, if there is a choice.

The lumper and the "splitter" do not disagree on the question of whether or not the higher category should be a monophyletic group; they both answer this question affirmatively. They also agree on the fact that the genus has a certain degree of reality. Nobody will seriously deny that in a well-worked group it will be possible to list a number of criteria which will only apply, let us say, to 6 species but to no others. This group of 6 species is thus an objective unit. The disagreement begins when we ask: Are the joint characters of these 6 species generic criteria or not? The question is thus not whether or not the genus, as such, has reality, but rather *whether or not the borders of the genera are real!* We have seen (Chapter VII) that species are real and objective units, because the delimitation of each species is definite and not open to argument except in the border-line cases. If we again accept the definiteness of delimitation as a criterion, we come to the conclusion that the genus lacks the objective reality of the species, because the greater majority of genera are not separated from other genera by big, clear-cut gaps. Most monotypic genera could be united with some other genus, and most polytypic genera could equally well be subdivided into smaller genera. Where the border of the genus should be drawn is left to the subjective judgment of the individual worker.

The situation can, perhaps, best be illustrated by a diagram showing a section of a phylogenetic tree with 12 species (Fig. 29).

A branch, A, separated from branch B somewhere in the phylogeny of the family to which the 12 species belong. Branch A later divided into twigs 1, 2, 3, and 4, and twigs 2 and 4 subsequently subdivided again into 6, viz., 4 twiglets producing a total of 12 final tips of the phylogenetic branch equaling the 12 species. If a splitter and a lumper were to look at this situation, they would have no ground for argument as far as the phylogeny is concerned and both would agree that the twigs

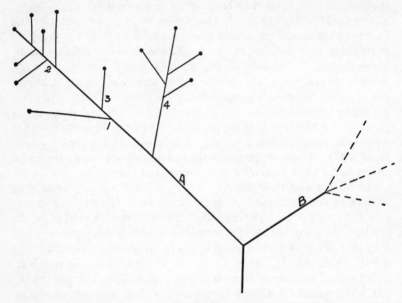

F<small>IG</small>. 29. Diagram of part of a phylogenetic tree. The twelve tips of the twigs and twiglets of branch A represent twelve species. The "lumper" will arrange these in one genus with four species groups, the "splitter" will divide them into four genera.

1, 2, 3, and 4 belong to branch A, and that branch A has no other twigs. Both would also agree that 4 species come out of twig 2 and 6 species out of twig 4. The only difference between the lumper and the splitter would be that the lumper would consider the 12 species of branch A a convenient unit which is widely separated from branch B and is not so unwieldy as to require subdivision; while the splitter would consider the little gaps which admittedly exist between the species groups (twigs) 1, 2, 3, and 4 to be of sufficient importance to be expressed by 4 different genera, 2 of them monotypic. This diagram, with minor variations, illustrates well the situation which nearly always exists when there is some disagreement concerning generic limits.

The definition of the genus.—It is not surprising to find how few authors have dared to define the genus. A definition like that of Greenman (1940:372): "The species of a genus must conform in all essential morphological characters to those of the type species of the genus under consideration," has all the weaknesses of the long-abandoned "morphological" species definitions. It is useless for practical purposes, since no two authors are likely to agree as to what the "essential" characters are.

The degree of variability of the identifying characters of a taxonomic category is very important for its delimitation. Related species differ by certain characters which are their specific characters, but they have other characters in common which are their generic, family, or other common characters. In other words, the higher categories are characterized by the less-variable characters. The degree of difference between two species is not necessarily a generic criterion, because species are more distinct to the taxonomist in some families than genera are in other families. On the whole, we may say that genera tend to be separated by greater and by more differences than species.

The best definition of a genus seems to be one based on the honest admission of the subjective nature of this unit, and it may not be possible to say much more than that "the genus, to be a convenient category in taxonomy, must in general be neither too large nor too small" (Thorpe 1940:357). A tentative definition might be: "A genus is a systematic unit including one species or a group of species of presumably common phylogenetic origin, separated by a decided gap from other similar groups. It is to be postulated for practical reasons, that the size of the gap shall be in inverse ratio to the size of the group." The second sentence of this definition requires an explanation. We have groups, as has been stated repeatedly, that are exceedingly variable and others that are very uniform. If the same standards of difference were applied, we might have to put every species of one family into monotypic genera and all the species of another family into a single genus. Genera with 500, 1,000, or even 2,000 species are very inconvenient, and any excuse for breaking them up into smaller units should be good enough. In birds of paradise, on the other hand, morphological differences between the species are so well developed that not only all the superspecies, with two exceptions (*Manucodia*), have been put into different genera, but that even representative species in the genera *Manucodia*, *Diphyllodes*, *Astrapia*, *Paradisaea*, and so forth have been separated generically on what seems superficially very good reasons. The genus would become completely synonymous with the species and would lose its function as category of convenience, if we were to recognize genera that are based merely on certain morphological differences.

It is obvious from this discussion that the delimitation of the genus is, to a considerable extent, a matter of judgment, and that this judgment in turn depends on wide experience and on some intangibles. It has happened frequently that some older taxonomist has divided a family into let us say eight genera, using what seemed entirely superficial characters. When the complete anatomy and life history of the species became known, it turned out that the original generic arrangement was quite correct. For example, Hinton (1940) was the first author to study the internal anatomy of the Mexican water beetles of the family Elmidae. The characters he found nearly always supported the previously created genera, based on features of external anatomy. In two cases new genera had to be erected on characters of the internal anatomy, but external characters were found subsequently which supported this division. But difficulties remain, even when all the facts are known. This is particularly true in cases in which the fossil record permits a reconstruction of the phylogeny. We find, for example, cases in which we can follow the transformation of one genus into another, from stratum to stratum. In other cases we find that certain lines have developed much faster than others and that we now have among a set of "phylogenetic brothers" some species that are still congeneric and others that are considered separate genera. Cases among recent birds that must be interpreted in this manner are illustrated in the diagrams on page 285.

In all these genera we have a number of species or species groups which, although separated from one another by clear gaps, are not distinct enough to be regarded as separate genera. But in each genus one or two species have developed an offshoot, which clearly descended from one of these species and which is now (rightly or wrongly) considered a separate genus. The origin of these genera is entirely clear in the case of *Serresius*, *Todirhamphus*, *Thyliphaps*, *Oedirhinus*, and *Dicranostephes*, because the species of these genera are still allopatric to the species from which they arose. They are obviously only populations that during their isolation developed highly peculiar characters. In the case of *Chrysophaps* and *Tanysiptera*, the relationship is not quite as clear, but even these genera are more closely related to *one* of the species of the ancestral genus than the various species of the ancestral genus to one another. How shall the taxonomist treat such cases? Shall he lump together all the derived genera? Shall he give special rank to the species that are ancestral to these genera (or at least very close to the ancestral

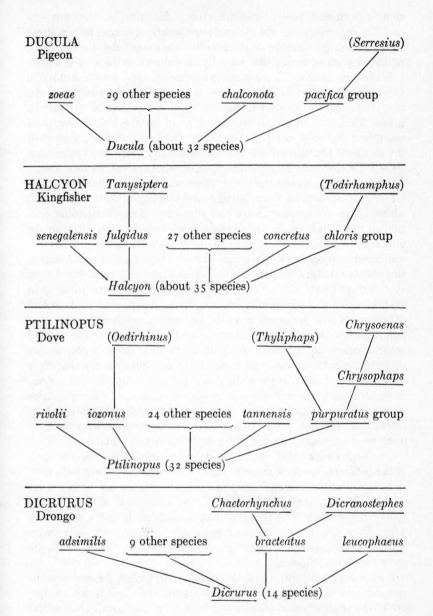

stock)? Such cases present great practical difficulties, but they are very useful in demonstrating what the paleontologists, of course, fully realized a long time ago, namely, that "generic characters" can develop very rapidly—in other words, that some living genera may be very young.

Monotypic genera.—The genus concept has a very definite history in every group of animals. The original genus of Linnæus was very wide; it corresponds much better to the family of today than to our current genus. This, incidentally, is additional proof for the lack of reality of the genus limits, as compared to those of the species, because most of the species of Linnæus are still the species of the present-day systematist (except for the inclusion of additional geographic races). As new species were discovered all over the world, there was not only the necessity of creating new genera for them, but also that of subdividing the old genera, which began to get very large and unwieldy. This subdividing continued, unfortunately, in the better-known groups, even after no (or only few) new species were left to be discovered. The generic "splitters" compared every species of a genus with the type species and found in this manner that most of these species had slight structural differences, even though they consisted only in the presence of an extra bristle or in slightly different body proportions. Applying a strictly morphological definition of the genus as a yardstick, they considered these often infinitesimal differences as sufficient excuse for the creation of additional generic names. No attention was paid by these authors to practical or biological considerations, and it happened not infrequently that they placed different races of the same polytypic species in different genera. Sharpe and Ridgway were the leaders of this school among the ornithologists, and their splitting efforts have been "successfully" continued by Oberholser, Mathews, and Roberts. The result is that we now have more than 10,000 generic names for 8,500 species of birds!

The beginning of this "supersplitting" era coincided with the birth of the polytypic species concept. It thus happened that new genera were created on purely morphological grounds simultaneously with the reducing of all "morphological species" to subspecies of larger units (polytypic species). The result is that A. Roberts includes 865 South African species of birds in 620 genera, Mathews places nearly every Australian species in a different genus, and Oberholser tends to do the same for North America.

Fortunately for ornithology, this purely morphological genus concept was not accepted by the majority of workers, and there is not a single one of the younger ornithologists who believes in such small genera. The latest estimate is that at the present time 2,600 genera of birds are recognized, with 8,500 species (i.e., 3.27 species per genus) and with 27,000 subspecies (more than 10 subspecies per genus). Even accepting these somewhat more conservative figures, it is admitted that birds are oversplit generically. An average of 5 species per genus (or 1,700 genera) would be definitely preferable to the present ratio. North American birds are particularly badly oversplit. Among genera recognized in the fourth edition of the official Checklist of the American Ornithologists' Union (1931), the following, at least, could be dispensed with and will probably disappear eventually from later editions:

Thalassogeron (= *Diomedea*), *Thyellodroma* (= *Puffinus*), *Moris* (= *Sula*), *Casmerodius* (= *Egretta*), *Sthenelides* (= *Cygnus*), *Chaulelasmus* (= *Anas*), *Mareca* (= *Anas*), *Dafila* (= *Anas*), *Eunetta* (= *Anas*), *Nettion* (= *Anas*), *Querquedula* (= *Anas*), *Charitonetta* (= *Glaucionetta*), *Arctonetta* (= *Somateria*), *Melanitta* (= *Oidemia*), *Lophodytes* (= *Mergus*), *Astur* (= *Accipiter*), *Parabuteo* (= *Buteo*), *Asturina* (= *Buteo*), *Thallasoaëtus* (= *Haliaeëtus*), *Pagolla* (= *Charadrius*), *Eupoda* (= *Charadrius*), *Oxyechus* (= *Charadrius*), *Squatarola* (= *Pluvialis*), *Phaeopus* (= *Numenius*), *Rhyacophilus* (= *Tringa*), *Totanus* (= *Tringa*), *Arquatella* (= *Erolia*), *Pisobia* (= *Erolia*), *Pelidna* (= *Erolia*), *Steganapus* (= *Phalaropus*), *Lobipes* (= *Phalaropus*), *Endomychura* (= *Brachyrhamphus*), *Scotiaptex* (= *Strix*), *Nannus* (= *Troglodytes*), *Cistothorus* (= *Telmatodytes*), *Arceuthornis* (= *Turdus*), *Corthylio* (= *Regulus*), *Compsothlypis* (= *Dendroica*), *Chamaeothlypis* (= *Geothlypis*), *Passerherbulus* (= *Ammodramus*), *Melospiza* (= *Passerella*), and *Rhynchophanes* (= *Calcarius*).

A student of North American birds could probably add additional names from the families Phasianidae, Alcidae, Trochilidae, Tyrannidae, and Parulidae. There are thus at least 42 unnecessary names among the 400 genera under which the 800 species of North American birds are classified.

The number of monotypic genera, that is genera containing a single species, is very high in birds. Some of them are based on really isolated species and are therefore justified. Many others are based on species which, in all their characters, fit very well in a genus with other species, except that they have "gone crazy" in regard to a single character. The adherent to a purely morphological genus concept will see in the single aberrant character justification for generic separation. The "new systematist," who believes in the group concept of the genus, will look at such species "as a whole" and will include them in the same genus with all the other species which do not differ in the one peculiar character. The fourth edition of the *A. O. U. Check-List* (1931) contains 53 (or 42 percent) monotypic[1] genera among the 127 genera of Passerine birds.

[1] Including genera that contain a single superspecies.

My *List of New Guinea Birds* (1941a) contains 50 (or 38 percent) monotypic genera among a total of 131 genera; if birds of paradise are omitted (with 13 monotypic genera), there are 37 (or 32 percent) monotypic genera among 114 Passerine genera, a figure which still seems unnecessarily high.

The high number of monotypic genera has been rather puzzling to the thinking taxonomist. The reasons for it are manifold and not yet fully understood. Sometimes such genera are due to the aberrant development of a single character, but, biologically speaking, they are not separated by a greater gap than the species of some related genus. Sometimes a genus is monotypic because its type species is the last remnant of an otherwise extinct stock. A third reason is usually overlooked. We can have much divergent evolution without the origin of new species and considerable speciation without much evolutionary divergence. This sounds rather paradoxical, but there is convincing evidence that it occurs. There are, for example, species that are changing continuously, but are not breaking up into new species because they are restricted to an island or have low dispersal faculties, and so forth. On the other hand, we have cases such as the sibling species, in which speciation (the establishment of reproductive isolation) has occurred without a corresponding degree of evolutionary divergence in the taxonomic characters. Willis (1940 and earlier papers) has established a special rule, the rule of the hollow curve, to describe the regularities in the number of species per genus in the larger families. If we plot the number of genera against the number of contained species, we get a very characteristic hollow curve, which indicates that many genera have only one or two species, while a few genera have large numbers of species, with all other genera intermediate. S. Wright (1941b) finds that this shape of curve is to be expected on the basis of mere chance, if in a large family the total number of species remains constant and the process of duplication of species is balanced by extinction. The question of monotypic genera is quite complicated and depends not only on taxonomic and genetic factors, but also on paleogeographic and ecological conditions.

What is true for the genus is even truer for the categories above the genus. Wetmore (1940) recognizes 27 orders of recent birds, Stresemann (1927–1934) no less than 48 orders, while some students of fossil reptiles suggest, not without justification, that all orders of birds should be reduced to family rank, since the entire "class" of birds was nothing but one of the orders of reptiles. Rensch (1934:96–100) gives a particularly lucid discussion of these problems, supported by many instructive examples.

The reaction against the excessive splitting of the higher categories has set in not only in ornithology, but in paleontology as well (Arkell and Moy-Thomas 1940) and among students of invertebrates. Hand-lirsch (1929) warns against the chaos produced by excessive splitting and quotes as examples:

In the family of the praying mantis Giglio-Tos (1927) arranges the known 1500 species in 30 subfamilies and 500 genera. There is thus an average of only 3 species per genus. Among the genera no less than 150 were made by Giglio-Tos himself; 175 are monotypic, 74 have two species. Roewer (1923) puts the 1700 species of opiliones in 500 genera, of which more than half (300) contain only 1 or 2 species. The order of Strepsiptera with 150 species has been split by Pierce into 5 super-families, 20 families, subfamilies or tribes, and 45 genera or subgenera, of which 29 are monotypical.

We cannot blame the nontaxonomist for developing a rather low opinion of the taxonomist when he comes across such type of work!

The reasons for this splitting are manifold. Sometimes it is due to the vanity of authors who want to "survive" with as many names as possible; sometimes it is due to a too-great reliance on single characters, as Hennig (1936a), for example, points out for certain genera and families of diptera. The eclipse of the purely morphological genus concept is being assisted by a "deflation" of the value of "key characters." In former days, when a species was discovered that did not "key out" in the accepted generic key of a family, it was at once described as a new genus. The workers who did this forgot that the genus, as delimited by their own key characters, was a man-made unit, and not one of nature. It would have been much better, in most cases, to revise the generic key so as to admit the aberrant species, instead of making a new genus. Occasionally, however, the splitting is perpetrated by authors who are not only first-rate taxonomists but who also base every one of their divisions on the most careful morphological and anatomical analysis. The revision of the family Goodeidae by Hubbs and Turner (1939) is a good example for this. Every one of the 18 species or superspecies of this family is characterized by very distinct characters, which leads the authors to separate them into 18 genera (11 created by Hubbs), in 4 subfamilies. There is no question that the authors make an excellent case for subdividing this family into 4 major and 18 lesser groups of species, but is it advisable to overburden the memory of the taxonomist by calling all of them genera? This work has been singled out because it is an exceptionally fine piece of anatomical-morphological research and because I agree with all of the conclusions of the authors, except with their nomenclature. The genus, if it is to remain useful, has to retain its character as a collective category.

The species group as a subgeneric unit.—There have been a number of recent attempts to combine in the genus two simultaneous functions: (1) To give it back its character of a broad collective category, (2) to convey some information concerning the subdivisions (smaller gaps) between the species of the genus. The oldest compromise is the *subgenus*, but this category has never been particularly popular. After all, if it is used in combination with genus, species, and subspecies names, it amounts practically to a quadrinomial nomenclature, quite aside from the fact that it burdens the memory just as much as if it were a generic name. If it is not used, I cannot see why it should be recognized at all. In ornithology the subgenus is nearly always used in one of two situations: either when an author would like to make a new genus, but does not quite have the courage to do so, in the face of the growing opposition against new genera; or, just the opposite, when an author wants to sink a genus as unnecessary, but does not quite dare to do so because it is particularly old or well-known. The subgenus is a temporary stage in either case. Several modern authors have therefore proposed to do away with the subgenus altogether and to use the "species group" instead to signify subdivisions within the genus. Ramme (1933) has applied this principle to various grasshopper genera, and Knipper (1939) arranges the 53 monotypic and 18 polytypic species of the snail genus *Helicigona* in 25 species groups (to mention only two of many similar works). Some large genera of birds are: *Accipiter* (hawk) with 45 species, *Cisticola* (warbler) with 45 species, *Columba* (pigeon) with 52 species, *Ploceus* (weaver bird) with 55 species, and *Zosterops* (white-eye) with 67 species. Much larger genera, with 500, 1,000, or even 2,000 species, are found among invertebrates and especially among insects. There is every reason to believe that these giant genera will eventually be broken up into a number of smaller ones. The temporary use of subgenera may facilitate such a future subdivision. The breaking up of a large genus should be done through cleavage. If this is impossible, it is by far preferable to retain the genus in its entirety than to try to chip off a few monotypic genera.

It is obvious from this discussion that the question as to whether the genus is a natural unit must be answered as follows: The genus is based on the fact that the species are not evenly distinct from one another, but are arranged in smaller or larger groups, separated by smaller or larger gaps. The genus is therefore based on a natural phenomenon. How many of such groups are to be included in one genus and how the genus should be delimited from other genera are matters of convenience, to be left to the judgment of the individual systematist. The genus of the systematist is his own artificial creation, and not a natural unit. The same is true for the higher categories above the genus (family, order, and so forth); the groups on which they are based may be natural, but their terminologies and comparative values are not.

MACROEVOLUTION

We have devoted the first part of this chapter to a discussion of supraspecific evolution from the viewpoint of the taxonomist (macrotaxonomy). But the higher categories and their evolution have a much broader significance. In recent years an attempt has been made by several authors to distinguish between micro- and macroevolution. Under the term microevolution such evolutionary processes are understood as occur within short spaces of time and in lower systematic categories, in general within the species (hence also, intraspecific evolution). By the term macroevolution we understand the development of major evolutionary trends, the origin of higher categories, the development of new organic systems—in short, evolutionary processes that require long periods of time and concern the higher systematic categories (supraspecific evolution). There is only a difference of degree, not one of kind, between the two classes of phenomena. They gradually merge into each other and it is only for practical reasons that they are kept separate.

The study of phylogenetic trees, of orthogenetic series, and of evolutionary trends comprise a field which was the happy hunting ground of the speculative-minded taxonomist of bygone days. The development of the "new systematics" has opened up a field which is far more accessible to accurate research and which is more apt to produce tangible and immediate results. It is therefore not surprising that taxonomists have rather neglected the study of macroevolution during recent years. It would be an interesting task to discuss and analyze in detail what is known about evolution in the higher groups, but this would lead us too far afield in this treatise, which is devoted primarily to a presentation of the contribution of the taxonomist to the problems of the origin of species. We can therefore offer only a very cursory survey of macroevolution.

Geneticists and most taxonomists have devoted most of their attention to microevolution, and the field of macroevolution was left more or less to the paleontologist and the anatomist. This has led to difficulties and misunderstandings, since paleontologists, taxonomists, and geneticists talk three different languages, and all three of them have certain mistaken ideas about the basic facts and axioms of their sister disciplines.

To state that orthogenesis proves that evolution proceeds without selection would be just as erroneous as to state that orthogenetic series do not exist. And even if some of the generalizations and interpretations of the paleontologist and the taxonomist are wrong or expressed in unfortunate (for example Lamarckian) terms, this does not invalidate the facts on which these interpretations are based, and nothing is gained by ignoring them. Organic evolution shows many very interesting regularities, and we must be grateful to the paleontologists and the anatomists who have attempted to establish some general laws. Those who are interested in this field should consult the recent publications of de Beer (1940b), Beurlen (1937), Böker (1935 = 1937), Franz (1935), Gregory (1936a, b), Griggs (1939), Rensch (1939a), Schindewolf (1936), Sewertzoff (1931), and others.

MACROEVOLUTIONARY FACTORS

A number of recent authors have attempted to show that it is feasible to interpret the findings and generalizations of the macroevolutionists on the basis of the known genetic facts (random mutation) without recourse to any other intrinsic factors. We have indicated in Chapter IV that the last word on these questions has not yet been said and will not be said until we know a great deal more about geno-physiology. However, as Dobzhansky (1941a), Rensch (1939a), and many others have pointed out, there are already many genetic phenomena known which deprive the macroevolutionary processes of much of their former mysteriousness. I shall try to give a short review of these factors, but must leave their more-detailed substantiation to the genetic literature.

1. *The smallness and frequency of mutations:* The study of laboratory stocks, as well as the analysis of natural populations, indicates a high frequency of small genetic changes. Mutations are very rarely major upheavals of the genotype (see Chapter IV; also Dobzhansky 1941a, Muller 1940, Timofeeff-Ressovsky 1940a).

2. *The multiple (pleiotropic) effect of genes:* Many, perhaps most genes affect simultaneously several organs, viz., physiological processes in the body. The selective advantage of a single one of these effects may lead to a spread of the gene and the correlated "neutral" characters. This may explain the rapid spread of many characters without conceivable selective advantage.

3. *The multiple genic basis of a single trait:* Work on domestic animals has shown that selection will continue to produce results generation after generation, if applied to characters that are affected by a number of different genes. Furthermore, crossing over will permit the accumula-

tion of favorable genes in a single chromosome and thus prevent the flattening out of the selective effect (Mather 1941).

4. *Many mutations reversible:* This fact permits a drifting back (within limits) to a former condition, if, for example, the mutative advantage of a gene is eliminated or reversed (Muller 1939).

5. *The growth of individual organs and structures often a function of the growth of the whole organism:* The work of D'Arcy Thomson (1917), Huxley (1932), and others has shown that individual structures may grow relatively faster or slower than the organism as a whole (allometry). The final size of the structure depends, in such cases, on the final size of the organism.

6. *The speed of evolution a matter as much or more of extrinsic as of intrinsic factors:* The influence of isolation, swamping, population size, accidents of sampling, and the like has been discussed in the previous chapter.

7. *Selection a powerful evolutionary factor:* Even genes with a small selective advantage will eventually spread over entire populations (Fisher 1930), particularly in a fluctuating population, when during a pessimum period only the best-adapted individuals survive.

8. *The evolutionary specialization of one organ system compensated for by the reduction of others:* This is possible, owing to processes of competitive growth during embryonic growth (Huxley 1932, Teissier 1934, Rensch 1939a, 1940). This compensation is complex; it may be entirely phenotypical in the beginning, but it tends to be enforced by mutational processes.

MACROEVOLUTIONARY PRINCIPLES

The above are only some of the known genetic and evolutionary factors which help to explain macroevolutionary "laws" and phenomena, such as the following:

The principle of orthogenesis.—Certain organs seem to undergo (within a phylogenetic series) a steady process of progressive evolution. This has been interpreted by some paleontologists as indicating the presence of intrinsic factors which control the continuous "improvement" of these organs. It is now known that the process of orthogenesis itself (in a purely descriptive sense) has many exceptions, as, for example, that many lineages split into three or four, of which only one continues the orthogenetic trend, or that a trend is suddenly halted or even reversed, and so forth. Typical orthogenetic phenomena may be interpreted on the basis of the first, third, fifth, and seventh of the factors listed above.

The principle of size increase in phylogenetic lines.—This principle, which was established by Cope and Dépèret, is, strictly speaking, only a special manifestation of the principle of orthogenesis. It is now known that it has many exceptions, since in many lines large forms have been succeeded by smaller descendants. Furthermore, an increase in size has a definite selective advantage, not only in periods of a cooling climate (see Bergmann's rule, p. 90), but even under steady external conditions (Castle 1932). The first, third, and seventh factors listed above are sufficient for an interpretation.

The principle of convergent evolution.—The same parallel specializations are frequently acquired in independent lines. This is sometimes due to a basic relationship, since it has become quite apparent that related animals tend to have homologous chromosomes and genes (see above, p. 74 [herons] and Sturtevant and Novitski 1941). In other cases such parallelism is due to convergence, based on the fact that some of the fundamental structures of animals can change only in very few directions. The canine tooth of mammals can grow bigger or smaller, or lengthen to the sabre-tooth shape. It is thus not surprising that this latter type has evolved independently in the carnivores (Machairodontidae) and in the marsupials (Thylacosmilus). This is but one of thousands of similar examples. In other cases convergent evolution is not accidental, but is due to selection by similar environmental factors or to the parallel loss of a function (Ratites, among the birds).

The principle of specialization.—According to this tenet, every phylogenetic sequence leads from generalized "primitive" forms through more and more specialized forms, until it finally ends in overspecialization and extinction. This principle also is true only to a limited degree. In most major groups there are some primitive forms left, whereas others are proceeding toward specialization. Specialization is not necessarily an advantage. Which one of two insect species is better adapted, the one which spends its entire life cycle on one species of plant, or the other which can feed on a hundred? On the other hand, wherever there is strong competition, specialization undoubtedly gives an advantage, and there is always the possibility that such specialization will lead to a new "adaptive plateau," with unsuspected evolutionary possibilities, such as were discovered by the mammalian and avian branches of reptiles while most of other reptilian lines came to an end owing to overspecialization along a less-promising line. There is no difficulty in explaining specialization on the basis of the known genetic phenomena. Neither is it particularly difficult to visualize the vulnerability of highly specialized forms to extinction. They are adapted for one specific set of environmental conditions and are much less capable of adjusting themselves to sudden or drastic changes of environment than are unspecialized forms. This is the reason unspecialized lines often outlive their specialized offshoots or descendants.

The principle of irreversibility.—It has been stated that if an organ has once been lost in evolution it cannot be redeveloped, or if it has changed its function it cannot regain its old function; in fact, that no evolutionary trend can ever be reversed (the so-called "Dollo's Law"). Dollo himself never made such exaggerated claims, and the law which is named after him has innumerable exceptions. It can be accepted only as a very broad generalization. Phylogenetic lines are known which first increased in size and later decreased. Every organ is determined by so many genetic factors that it is against all probability that it would be reconstructed in the same manner, once it has been lost. Still, it is remarkable how superficially similar the structures are, which, after having been lost in the phylogenetic past, have been acquired again for the same function. Whales (and relatives) are aquatic mammals which, through reptiles and amphibia, had developed from fishes. Many of the structures of the whale (general shape, fins, and so forth) are remarkably similar to fish structures, lost long previously. The question of reversibility from the genetic viewpoint has been treated in detail by Muller (1939), and from the phylogenetic viewpoint by Gregory (1936a).

The principle of harmonious organic reconstruction. Every major transformation of an organ is, in general, correlated with a greater or lesser change of the entire organism. The acquisition of flight in birds, to mention a drastic case, involved a rebuilding of the entire skeleton, eventual loss of teeth, change of metabolism, change of the sense organs, of the brain, of most of the behavior patterns, and so forth. The organism seems to change as a harmonious entity, and not by random mutation of its parts. This objection to the conventional interpretation of evolution by the geneticists (random mutation and selection) has been made again recently, in a particularly impressive manner, by Böker (1935, 1936). As Rensch (1939a) points out, however, harmonious reconstruction is feasible on the basis of the known genetic facts (the first, fifth, seventh, and eighth factors listed above). It must not be forgotten in this connection that the genotype of an organism is not merely a summation of its genes, but an integrated whole (p. 69).

Whether function precedes a structure, or vice versa, gives rise to eternal argument. Did finches develop heavy bills because they ate seeds, or are finches able to eat hard-shelled seeds because they had developed heavy bills? The answer is, of course, that neither is correct. Warblers did not wake up one morning with heavy bills ("we are now finches!'') and have to eat seeds thereafter, nor did they develop heavy bills in a Lamarckian fashion because they saw some nice big seeds and said to themselves: "Let's develop a good heavy bill so we can crack these seeds." The development of the heavy bill was a slow process, probably involving dozens of small mutational steps, each one surviving only if proving its usefulness in the actual test of selection. It must be admitted, however, that it is a considerable strain on one's credulity to assume that finely balanced systems such as certain sense organs (the eye of vertebrates, or the bird's feather) could be improved by random mutations. This is even more true for some of the ecological chain relationships (the famous yucca moth case, and so forth). However, the objectors to random mutations have so far been unable to advance any alternative explanation that was supported by substantial evidence.

The principle of conservative characters.—Characters are usually lost rather quickly as soon as they are no longer needed, as demonstrated by the loss of eyes in cave animals, and so forth. This may be due partly to the pressure of reversible mutations (Muller 1939) or because the genes that control these characters have a multiple effect and, some of the "secondary" effects being deleterious, they are being selected against, after the primary effect has lost its selective advantage (S. Wright 1929, Emerson 1938). More difficult to explain is the survival of conservative characters long after they have lost their apparent usefulness. Lorenz (1937), Heinroth, and others have shown that this is particularly true for reflexes and behavior patterns. The flightless birds still possess all the stabilizing reflexes needed for flight (Krumbiegel 1938). Most birds still scratch themselves with the posterior extremity (leg) "behind" the wing, as if the anterior extremity was resting on the ground, which it has not done since birds became flying animals (more than one hundred million years ago). Just why such characters are retained is not obvious. An even-greater puzzle is the question as to why in certain groups entire "blocks of characters" are retained without change, characters that are the family, order, or class characters.

The principle of the instantaneous origin of new types.—It has been claimed by Schindewolf (1936) that all or nearly all the major types of animals have appeared on the earth in a more or less finished form, with the links to the presumable ancestors missing. This is, so far as I can judge, exaggerated or untrue. If we examine the reptiles, for example, we find that such forms as *Seymouria*, *Romeria*, and the primitive mammals possess character combinations, just as we would expect them from ancestral forms. They are the "crotches" of the branching phylogenetic tree. And *Archaeopteryx* is as perfect a missing link between reptiles and birds as one could possibly hope for. No special evolutionary processes need to be postulated, even in groups where such missing links have not yet been found and where the primitive roots of the various stems always seem to be missing. Aberrant types can be produced only in effective isolation and in rather small distributional areas. The number of individuals in such populations is small and the probability that they will leave a fossil record is very small, since the known fossils represent only a fraction of the former animal life. Furthermore, the early forms of most lines are of small size and therefore fragile and not easily preserved. There is also some reason to believe that many of the primitive forms were inhabitants of the tropical forests, of which we have a particularly poor fossil record. The fact that there are many gaps in our knowledge of the phylogenetic lines does not indicate, as has been claimed by some authors, that evolution of the higher categories proceeds by big steps, by veritable leaps. On the surface, it appears as if the ideas of Schindewolf were the same as those of Goldschmidt, who postulates the occurrence of "systemic mutations" to account for the origin of new species and even of higher categories. The resemblance, however, is not complete, since Schindewolf would not cite the origin of a new species as a case of "step evolution." Paleontologists have too many examples of perfect evolutionary series, leading without obvious breaks from species to species in subsequent horizons, to believe in the instantaneous creation of species.

Another puzzle of the paleontologist is beginning to be cleared up, namely the different rates of evolution in different groups or in different periods of the same group. This may be due to changes in the mutation rate, but there is no certain evidence as yet. But, as we have seen in an earlier chapter (p. 243), it may also be due to ecological factors or to the small-population principle (p. 236). An animal group that is searching for a new "adaptive peak" may undergo rapid evolution, but as soon as this peak has been reached evolution may begin to stagnate. This corresponds to the development of man-made machines. The first forty years of the motor car showed a tremendous evolution; it is a safe wager that the changes of the next forty years will be less drastic. When "proavis" began to fly, it evolved very rapidly, but as soon as "the bird" was evolved, only minor changes were made on the basic patent. Birds multiplied during the Tertiary age, but their basic structure has changed but very little during the last sixty million years.

It is sometimes stated that macrotaxonomic characters, the characters of the higher categories, develop in a different way from the differences between individuals, subspecies, and species. The previous discussion has already uncovered the invalidity of this thesis, but we might add one or two statements. To begin with, what are "macrotaxonomic" characters? We can determine this only a posteriori. They are the attributes of higher categories. But it would be impossible to look at contemporary genera and to state which of them would become the ancestors of important families and orders of the dim future. The value of a character is determined primarily by the size of the group which exhibits it. The same is true for categorical rank. If the pterosaurs were still alive today and were as numerous and as rich in species as the birds, they would very likely be considered a separate class and not one of the reptilian orders. If, on the other hand, birds had become extinct at the *Archaeopteryx* stage, it is very probable that *Archaeopteryx* would be listed merely as an aberrant order of feathered reptiles.

In conclusion we may say that all the available evidence indicates that the origin of the higher categories is a process which is nothing but an extrapolation of speciation. All the processes and phenomena of macroevolution and of the origin of the higher categories can be traced back to intraspecific variation, even though the first steps of such processes are usually very minute.

LITERATURE

Adensamer, W. 1937. Ein Beitrag zu Art- und Rassenstudien an mitteleuropäischen Muscheln. Zool. Jahrb., Abt. Syst., 70:227–242.

Ali, S. 1935. The ornithology of Travancore and Cochin. J. Bombay Nat. Hist. Soc., 37:823, fig. 3.

Alkins, W. E. 1928. The conchometric relationship of *Clausilia rugosa* and *Clausilia cravenensis*. Proc. Malac. Soc., 18:50–69.

Allen, J. A. 1892. The North American species of the genus *Colaptes*, etc. Bull. Amer. Mus. Nat. Hist., 4:21–44.

Alpatov, W. W. 1929. Biometrical studies on variation and races of the honey-bee (*Apis mellifera*). Quart. Rev. Biol, 4:1–58.

American Ornithologists' Union Committee. 1931. Check-List of North American Birds. 4th ed. Lancaster, Pa.

Anderson, E. 1939. Recombination in species crosses. Genetics, 24:668–698.

Arkell, W. J., and J. A. Moy-Thomas. 1940. Palaeontology and the taxonomic problem. In: Huxley, J., The New Systematics: 395–410.

Baily, J. L., Jr. 1939. Physiological group differentiation in *Lymnaea columella*. Amer. Journ. Hyg., Monogr. Ser., No. 14:1–133.

Banta, A. M., and T. R. Wood. 1927. A thermal race of Cladocera originating by mutation. Verh. V. Int. Kongr. Vererb., Berlin, 1:397–398.

Bates, M. 1940. The nomenclature and taxonomic status of the mosquitoes of the *Anopheles maculipennis* complex. Ann. Ent. Soc. America, 33:343–356.

—— 1941a. Laboratory observations on the sexual behavior of anopheline mosquitoes. J. Exp. Zool., 86:153–173.

—— 1941b. Field studies of the anopheline mosquitoes of Albania. Proc. Ent. Soc. Washington, 43:37–58.

Bateson, W. 1913. Problems of Genetics. Yale Univ. Press, New Haven.

Bather, F. A. 1927. Biological classification: Past and future. Quart. J. geol. Soc., 83:LXII–CIV.

Baur, E. 1932. Artumgrenzung und Artbildung in der Gattung Antirrhinum, etc. Zeitschr. ind. Abst. Vererb., 63:256–302, map, p. 287.

Beebe, W. 1907. Geographic variation in birds, with especial reference to the effects of humidity. Zoologica N. Y. Zool. Soc., 1:1–41.

Beer, G. R. de. 1940a. Embryology and taxonomy. In: Huxley, J., The New Systematics: 365–393.

—— 1940b. Embryos and ancestors. Clarendon Press, Oxford.

Benson, S. B. 1933. Concealing coloration among some desert rodents of the southwestern United States. Univ. Cal. Publ. Zool., 40:1–70, 2 pls., 8 figs.

Bergmann, St. 1940. Über eine Kreuzung zwischen Rackelhahn und Auerhenne. Ark. Zool., 32B, No. 7:1–7.

Bernard, H. M. 1896. Cat. Madrep. Corals, 2:20. Brit. Mus., London.

Beurlen, K. 1937. Die stammesgeschichtlichen Grundlagen der Abstammungslehre. G. Fischer, Jena.

Bischoff, H. 1934. Der ökologische Rassenkreis der *Chrysis ignita* L. Ent. Beihefte Berlin-Dahlem, 1:72–75.

Blair, A. P. 1941. Variation, isolating mechanisms, and hybridization in certain toads. Genetics, 26:398–417.

Blanchard, B. D. 1941. The white-crowned sparrows (*Zonotrichia leucophrys*) of the Pacific seaboard: Environment and annual cycle. Univ. Calif. Publ. Zool., 46:1–178.

Böker, H. 1935–1937. Einführung in die vergleichende biologische Anatomie der Wirbeltiere, 1 (1935), 2 (1937). G. Fischer, Jena.

—— 1936. Was ist Ganzheitsdenken in der Morphologie? Zeitschr. ges. Naturw., 2:253–276.

Bond, J. 1940. Check-list of birds of the West Indies. Acad. Nat. Sci., Philadelphia.

Bovey, P. 1941. Contribution à l'étude génétique et biogéographique de *Zygaena ephialtes* L. Rev. Suisse Zool., 48:1–90.

Boycott, A. E. 1938. Experiments on the artificial breeding of *Limnaea involuta*, *L. burnetti* and other forms of *L. peregra*. Proc. Malac. Soc. London, 23:101–108, pls. 8–13.

Bragg, A. N., and C. C. Smith. 1941. The ecological distribution of toads of the genus *Bufo* in Oklahoma. Anat. Rec., 81 Suppl.: 70–71.

Buch, L. von. 1825. Physicalische Beschreibung der Canarischen Inseln: 132–133. Kgl. Akad. Wiss., Berlin.

Buchka, E. 1936. Strom trennt Carabus Rassen. Ent. Zeitschr., 49:38–40, 44–47.

Buxton, P. A. 1938. The formation of species among insects in Samoa and other oceanic islands. Proc. Linn. Soc. London, 150th Sess.: 264–267.

Byers, C. F. 1940. A study of the dragon-flies of the genus *Progomphus*, etc. Proc. Florida Acad. Sci., 4:19–86.

Carpenter, F. M., *et al.* 1937. Insects and arachnids from Canadian amber. Univ. Toronto Studies, Geol. Ser., No. 40:7–62.

Carr, A. F. 1940. A contribution to the herpetology of Florida. Univ. Florida Publ., Biol. Sci. Ser., 3:1–118.

Castle, W. E. 1932. Body size and body proportions in relation to growth and natural selection. Science, 76:365–366.

Chamberlin, R. V., and W. Ivie. 1940. Agelenid spiders of the genus Cicurina. Bull. Univ. Utah, 30, No. 13 (Biol. Ser., 5, No. 9): 1–108.

Chapin, J. P. 1932. The birds of the Belgian Congo. Bull. Amer. Mus. Nat. Hist., 65:270.

Chapman, F. M. 1924. Criteria for the determination of subspecies in systematic ornithology. Auk, 41:17–29.

—— 1931. The upper zonal bird-life of Mts. Roraima and Duida. Bull. Amer. Mus. Nat. Hist., 63:1–135.

—— 1936. Further remarks on *Quiscalus*, etc. Auk, 53:405–417.

—— 1940. The post-glacial history of *Zonotrichia capensis*. Bull. Amer. Mus. Nat. Hist., 77:381–438.

Chasen, F. N. 1935. Handlist Malaysian birds. Bull. Raffles Mus. Singapore, 11:1–389.

Clark, F. H. 1941. Correlation and body proportions in mature mice of the genus *Peromyscus*. Genetics, 26:283–300.

Cochran, D. M. 1941. The Herpetology of Hispaniola. U. S. Nat. Mus., Bull., 177:1–398.

Coker, R. E. 1939. The problem of cyclomorphosis in Daphnia. Quart. Rev. Biol., 14:137–148.

Cole, A. C. 1938. Suggestions concerning taxonomic nomenclature of the hymenopterous family Formicidae, etc. Amer. Midl. Nat., 19:236–241.

Colman, J. 1932. A statistical test of the species concept in *Littorina*. Biol. Bull., 62:223–243.

Cowan, I. McT. 1938. Geographic distribution of color phases of the Red Fox and Black Bear in the Pacific Northwest. J. Mammal., 19:202–206.

—— 1940. Distribution and variation in the native sheep of North America. Amer. Midl. Nat., 24:505–580.

Craig, F. W. 1940. The periodical cicada in West Virginia. W. Virginia Univ. Bull. (=Proc. W. Va. Ac. Sci.), 14:39–43.

Crampton, H. E. 1916. Studies on the variation, distribution, and evolution of the genus *Partula*. The species inhabiting Tahiti. Carnegie Inst. Washington, Publ. 228:1–311.

—— 1932. Studies on the variation, distribution, and evolution of the genus Partula. The species inhabiting Moorea. Carnegie Inst. Washington, Publ. 410: 1–335.

Crane, J. 1941. Crabs of the genus Uca from the west coast of Central America. Zoologica: N. Y. Zool. Soc., 26:145–208.

Cuénot, L. 1933. La Seiche commune de la Méditerranée. Étude sur la naissance d'une espèce. Arch. zool. exp. gén., 75:319–330.

—— 1936. L'Espèce. Doin and Co., Paris.

Cushing, J. E. 1941. Non-genetic mating preference as a factor in evolution. Condor, 43:233–236.

Dale, F. H. 1940. Geographic variation in the meadow mouse, etc. J. Mammal., 21:332–340.

Dall, W. H. 1898. Contributions to the tertiary fauna of Florida. Trans. Wagner Free Inst. Sci. Philad., 3:675–676.

Darwin, Ch. 1859. On the origin of species by means of natural selection, or the preservation of favored races in the struggle for life. John Murray, London.

Davenport, D. 1941. The butterflies of the Satyrid genus *Coenonympha*. Bull. Mus. Comp. Zoöl., 87:215–349, 10 pls.

Davis, W. B. 1938. Relation of size of pocket gophers to soil and altitude. J. Mammal., 19:338–342.

De Buck, A., E. Schoute, and N. H. Swellengrebel. 1934. Cross-breeding experiments with Dutch and foreign races of *Anopheles maculipennis*. Riv. Malariol., 13:237–263.

Degerbøl, M. 1940. Mammalia. In: Zoology Faeroes, 65:1–132.

Degner, E. 1936. Zur näheren Kenntnis von *Ambigua fuscolabiata* Rssm. (Gastr. pulm.) im nordwestlichen Unteritalien. Mitt. Zool. Staatsinst. Mus. Hamburg, 46:19–114.

Delacour, J. 1931. Note sur les *Copsychus* malgaches. Oiseau, 1:618–623, map.

Delkeskamp, K. 1933. Die Arten der Gattung *Encaustes* (Col., Erot.). Mitt. Zool. Mus. Berlin, 19:188–198.

Dementiev, G. P. 1938. Sur la distribution géographique de certaines oiseaux paléarctiques, etc. Proc. Eighth Int. Orn. Congr. Oxford (1934): 243–259.

Dice, L. R. 1939a. An estimate of the population of deer mice in the Black Hills of South Dakota and Wyoming. Contr. Lab. Vert. Genet. Univ. Mich., 10:1–5.

—— 1939b. Variations in the deer-mouse (*Peromyscus maniculatus*) in the Columbia Basin of southeastern Washington and adjacent Idaho and Oregon. Contr. Lab. Vert. Genet. Univ. Mich., 12:1–22.

—— 1940a. Ecologic and genetic variability within species of Peromyscus. Amer. Nat., 74:212–221.

—— 1940b. Speciation in Peromyscus. Amer. Nat., 74:289–298.

—— 1940c. Intergradation between two subspecies of deer-mouse (*Peromyscus maniculatus*) across North Dakota. Contr. Lab. Vert. Genet. Univ. Mich., 13:1–14.

—— 1941. Variation of the deer-mouse (*Peromyscus maniculatus*) on the sand hills of Nebraska and adjacent areas. Contr. Lab. Vert. Genet. Univ. Mich., 15:1–19.

Dice, L. R., and P. M. Blossom. 1937. Studies of mammalian ecology in southwestern North America, etc. Carnegie Inst. Washington, Publ. 485:1–129.

Diver, C. 1929. Fossil records of Mendelian mutants. Nature, 124:183.
—— 1939. Aspects of the study of variation in snails. J. Conch., 21:91–141.
—— 1940. The problem of closely related species living in the same area. In: Huxley, J., The New Systematics: 303–328.
Dobzhansky, Th. 1933. Geographical variation in lady-beetles. Amer. Nat., 67:97–126.
—— 1937. What is a species? Scientia: 280–286.
—— 1940. Speciation as a stage in evolutionary divergence. Amer. Nat., 74:312–321.
—— 1941a. Genetics and the origin of species. Revised edition. Columbia Univ. Press, New York.
—— 1941b. On the genetic structure of natural populations of *Drosophila*. Proc. VIII. Int. Genet. Congr. Edinburgh (1939): 104.
Dobzhansky, Th., and S. Wright. 1941. Genetics of natural populations. V. Relations between mutation rate and accumulation of lethals in populations of Drosophila pseudoobscura. Genetics, 26:23–51.
Doederlein, L. 1902. Über die Beziehungen nahe verwandter "Thierformen" zu einander. Zeitschr. Morphol. Anthrop., 4:394–442.
Dowdeswell, W. H., R. A. Fisher, and E. B. Ford. 1940. The quantitative study of populations in the lepidoptera. I. *Polyommatus icarus*. Ann. Eugenics, 10:123–136.
Dunn, E. R. 1934. Systematic procedure in herpetology. Copeia, 1934:167–172.
—— 1940. The races of Ambystoma tigrinum. Copeia, 1940:154–162.
Du Rietz, G. E. 1930. The fundamental units of biological taxonomy. Svensk. Bot. Tidskrift, 24:333–428.
Eiselt, J. 1940. Der Rassenkreis Eumeces schneideri. Zool. Anz., 131:209–228.
Eller, K. 1936. Die Rassen von Papilio machaon. Abh. bayer. Akad. Wiss., N.F., H. 36:1–96.
Elton, C. S. 1930. Animal ecology and evolution. Clarendon Press, Oxford.
Emerson, A. E. 1935. Termitophile distribution and quantitative characters of physiological speciation in Brit. Guiana, Termites (Isoptera). Ann. Ent. Soc. Amer., 28:369–395.
—— 1938. Termite nests. A study of the phylogeny of behavior. Ecol. Monogr., 8:247–284.
Endrödi, S. von. 1938. Die paläarktischen Rassenkreise des Genus *Oryctes*. Arch. Naturg., N.F., 7:53–96.
Engel, H. 1936. Ueber westindische Aplysiidae und Verwandte anderer Gebiete. Capita Zoologica, 8:1–76.
Ewing, H. E. 1926. A revision of the American lice of the genus *Pediculus*, etc. Proc. U. S. Nat. Mus., 68, Art. 19:1–30.
Ferris, G. F. 1928. The principles of systematic entomology. Stanford Univ. Publ., Univ. Ser., Biol. Sci., 5:101–269.
Fiedler, K. 1940. Monograph of the South American Weevils of the genus Conotrachelus. Brit. Mus., London.
Finnegan, S. 1931. Report on the Brachyura collected in Central America, the Gorgona and Galapagos Islands, etc. J. Linn. Soc. London, Zool., 37:656 (607–673).
Fisher, R. A. 1930. The genetical theory of natural selection. Clarendon Press, Oxford.
Fitch, H. S. 1940a. A biogeographical study of the ordinoides Artenkreis of garter snakes (genus Thamnophis). Univ. Calif. Publ. Zool., 44:1–150.
—— 1940b. A field study of the growth and behavior of the fence lizard. Univ. Calif. Publ. Zool., 44:151–172.
Fleming, C. A. 1939. Birds of the Chatham Islands. Emu, 38:380–413, 492–509.
—— 1941. The phylogeny of the prions. Emu, 41:134–155.

Forbes, Grace S., and H. E. Crampton. 1942. The differentiation of geographical groups in *Lymnaea palustris*. Biol. Bull., 82:26–46.

Forbes, W. T. M. 1928. Variation in *Junonia lavinia* (Lep., Nymphalidae). J. N. Y. Ent. Soc., 36:306.

Forbush, E. H. 1929. Birds of Massachusetts, 3:205–218.

Ford, E. B. 1940. Polymorphism and taxonomy. In: Huxley, J., The New Systematics: 493–513.

Frank, F. 1938. Pigmentanalytische Untersuchungen am Rassenkreis *Parus atricapillus* L. C. R. IX$_e$ Congr. Ornith. Int. Rouen: 161–175.

Franz, V. 1935. Der biologische Fortschritt. Die Theorie der organismischen Vervollkommnung. G. Fischer, Jena.

Fuchs, A., and F. Käufel. 1936. Anatomische und systematische Untersuchungen an Land- und Süsswasserschnecken aus Griechenland und von den Inseln des Ägäischen Meeres. Arch. Naturg., N.F., 5:541–661.

Gause, G. F., N. P. Smaragdova, and W. W. Alpatov. 1942. Geographic variation in Paramecium and the role of stabilizing selection in the origin of geographic differences. Amer. Nat., 76:63–74.

Gerhardt, U. 1939. Neue biologische Untersuchungen an Limaciden. Zeitschr. Morph. Ökol., 35:183–202.

Gerould, J. H. 1941. Genetics of butterflies (Colias). Genetics, 26:152.

Ghigi, A. 1907. Ricerche di sistematica sperimentale sul genera *Gennaeus* Wagler. Mem. R. Acc. Sci. Inst. Bologna (6), 6:133–174.

Gislén, T. 1940. The number of animal species in Sweden, etc. Lunds Univ. Arsskrift, N.F., 36, No. 2:3–23.

Gloyd, H. K. 1940. The rattlesnakes, genera Sistrurus and Crotalus. Chicago Acad. Sci., Spec. Publ., No. 4:1–270.

Goin, C. J., and M. G. Netting. 1940. A new gopher frog from the gulf coast, etc. Ann. Carneg. Mus., 28:137–168.

Goldschmidt, R. 1934. Lymantria. Bibl. Genet., 11:1–180.

—— 1937. Cynips and Lymantria. Amer. Nat., 71:508–514.

—— 1940. The material basis of evolution. Yale Univ. Press, New Haven.

Goodey, T. 1931. Biological races in nematodes and their significance in evolution. Ann. Appl. Biol., 18:414–419.

Gordon, M. 1941. [Individual variants in Platypoecilus]. Genetics, 26:153.

Gordon, M., and A. C. Fraser. 1931. Pattern genes in the platyfish. J. Hered., 22:168–185.

Greenman, J. M. 1940. Genera from the standpoint of morphology. In: Symposium on: The concept of the genus. Bull. Torrey Bot. Club, 67:349–389.

Gregory, W. K. 1936a. On the meaning and limits of irreversibility of evolution. Amer. Nat., 70:517–528.

—— 1936b. The transformation of organic designs. A review of the origin and development of the earlier vertebrates. Biol. Rev., 11:311–74.

Griggs, R. F. 1939. The course of evolution. J. Wash. Acad. Sci., 29:118–137.

Grinnell, J. 1928. A distributional summation of the ornithology of Lower California. Univ. Calif. Publ. Zool., 32:13–18.

—— 1929. A new race of humming-bird from southern California. Condor, 31: 226–227.

Grobman, A. B. 1941. Contribution to the knowledge of variation in *Opheodrys vernalis*. Misc. Publ. Mus. Zool. Univ. Mich., No. 5:1–38.

Grütte, E. 1935. Zur Abstammung der Kuckucksbienen. Arch. Naturg., N.F., 4:448–534.

Haas, F. 1940. A tentative classification of the Palearctic Unionids. Zool. Ser. Field Mus. Nat. Hist., 24:115–141.

Hall, E. R., and D. F. Hoffmeister. 1942. Geographic variation in the canyon mouse, *Peromyscus crinitus*. J. Mamm., 23:51–65.

Handlirsch, A. 1929. Gegen die übermässige Zersplitterung der systematischen Gruppen. Zool. Anz., 84:85–90.

Hart, J. L., A. L. Tester, and J. L. McHugh. 1941. The tagging of herring (*Clupea pallasii*) in British Columbia, etc., 1940–1941. Report Brit. Col. Fish. Dept., 1940:J47–J74.

Hartert, E. 1903–1938. Vögel der paläarkt. Fauna. Friedländer and Co., Berlin.

Hasebroek, K. 1934. Industrie und Grosstadt als Ursache des neuzeitlichen vererblichen Melanismus der Schmetterlinge in England und Deutschland. Zool. Jahrb. (Abt. Zool. Physiol.), 53:411–460.

Heikertinger, F. 1935. Die Zukunft der Tiernamen. Zool. Anz., 111:53–59.

Heinroth, O. 1911. Beiträge zur Biologie, namentlich Ethologie und Psychologie der Anatiden. Verh. V. Int. Ornith.-Kongr. Berlin, 1910:589–702.

Hellmayr, C. E. 1929. On heterogynism in Formicarian birds. J. Ornith., Ergbd., 2:41–70.

Helmcke, J.-G. 1940. Die Brachiopoden der Deutschen Tiefsee-Expedition. Wiss. Erg. Tiefsee-Exped. Valdivia, 24:215–316.

Hennig, W. 1936a. Beziehungen zwischen geographischer Verbreitung und systematischer Gliederung bei einigen Dipterenfamilien, etc. Zool. Anz., 116: 161–175.

—— 1936b. Über einige Gesetzmässigkeiten der geographischen Variation in der Reptiliengattung *Draco* L., etc. Biol. Zentralbl., 56:549–559.

Herald, E. S. 1941. A systematic analysis of variation in the western American pipefish, *Syngnathus californiensis*. Stanford Ichthyol. Bull., 2:49–73.

Hering, M. 1935. Dualspecies und Unterart-Entstehung. Deutsch. Ent. Zeitschr.: 207.

—— 1936. Subspecies in statu nascendi. Zool. Anz., 114:266–271.

Herre, A. W. C. T. 1933. The fishes of Lake Lanao: A problem in evolution. Amer. Nat., 67:154–162.

Herre, W. 1936. Über Rasse und Artbildung. Studien an Salamandriden. Abh. Ber. Mus. Naturk. Magdeburg, 6:193–221.

Herter, K. 1934. Studien zur Verbreitung der europäischen Igel. Arch. Naturg., N.F., 3:313–382.

—— 1941. Die Vorzugstemperaturen bei Landtieren. Naturwissenschaften, 29: 155–164.

Hertwig, P. 1936. Artbastarde bei Tieren. Handb. Vererb.-wiss., II B13, Lief. 21:1–140.

Hesse, R., with W. C. Allee and K. P. Schmidt. 1937. Ecological Animal Geography. J. Wiley and Sons, New York.

Hickey, J. 1942. Eastern population of the Duck Hawk. Auk, 59:176–204.

Hiesey, W. M., J. Clausen, and D. D. Keck. 1942. Relations between climate and intraspecific variation in plants. Amer. Nat., 76:5–22.

Hile, R. 1937. Morphometry of the cisco, *Leucichthys artedi* (Le Sueur), in the lakes of the northeastern highlands, Wisconsin. Int. Rev. ges. Hydrol. Hydrog., 36:57–130.

Hile, R., and Ch. Juday. 1941. Bathymetric distribution of fish in lakes of the northeastern highlands, Wisconsin. Trans. Wisc. Acad. Sci. Arts Lett., 33:147–187.

Hindwood, K. A. 1940. Birds of Lord Howe Island. Emu, 40:1–86.

Hinton, H. E. 1940. A monographic revision of the Mexican waterbeetles of the family Elmidae. Novit. Zool., 42:217–396.

Hogben, L. 1940. Problems of the origins of species. In: Huxley, J., The New Systematics: 269–286.

Hooper, E. T. 1941. Mammals of the lavafields and adjoining areas in Valencia County, New Mexico. Misc. Publ. Mus. Zool., Univ. Mich., No. 51:1–47.

Hovanitz, W. 1940. Ecological color variation in a butterfly and the problem of protective coloration. Ecology, 21:371–380.

—— 1941a. Parallel ecogenotypical color variation in butterflies. Ecology, 1941: 259–284.

—— 1941b. The selective value of aestivation and hibernation in a California butterfly. Bull. Brooklyn Ent. Soc., 36:133–136.

Howard, H., and A. H. Miller. 1939. The avifauna associated with human remains at Rancho La Brea, California. Carnegie Inst. Wash., Publ. 514 (1940):39–48.

Hubbel, Th. H. 1936. A Monographic Revision of the Genus Ceuthophilus (Orthoptera). Univ. Florida Publ., II, No. 1, 551 pp., 38 pls.

Hubbs, C. L. 1934. Racial and individual variation in animals, especially fishes. Amer. Nat., 68:115–128.

—— 1940a. Speciation of fishes. Amer. Nat., 74:198–211.

—— 1940b. Fishes of the desert. The Biologist, 22:61–69.

—— 1941. [Review of Goldschmidt's 'Material Basis of Evolution']. Amer. Nat., 75:272–277.

Hubbs, C. L., and R. M. Bailey. 1940. A revision of the black basses (Micropterus and Huro), etc. Misc. Publ. Mus. Zool., Univ. Mich., No. 48.

Hubbs, C. L., and C. L. Turner. 1939. A revision of the Goodeidae (Cyprinodontes). Misc. Publ. Mus. Zool., Univ. Mich., No. 42: 1–80, 5 pls.

Husted, L., and T. K. Ruebush. 1940. A comparative cytological and morphological study of Mesostoma ehrenbergii ehrenbergii and Mesostoma ehrenbergii wardi. J. Morph., 67:387–410.

Huxley, J. S. 1932. Problems of Relative Growth. Methuen and Co., London.

—— 1938a. Darwin's theory of sexual selection, etc. Amer. Nat., 72:416–433.

—— 1938b. Threat and warning coloration in birds. Proc. Eighth Int. Orn. Congr. Oxford (1934): 430–455.

—— 1938c. The present standing of the theory of sexual selection, in: Evolution, ed. G. R. de Beer: 11–42. Clarendon Press, Oxford.

—— 1939. Clines: an auxiliary method in taxonomy. Bijdr. Dierk., 27:491–520.

—— (editor). 1940. The New Systematics. Clarendon Press, Oxford.

—— 1941. Evolutionary genetics. Proc. Eighth Int. Genet. Congr., Edinburg (1939):157–164.

International Rules of Zoological Nomenclature. Published in every issue, C. R. Congr. Int. Zool.

Jaworski, E. 1939. Geographische Rassen und Standortsmodifikationen bei Seefedern. Thalassia, 3, No. 7:1–24.

Jensen, A. J. C. 1939. Fluctuations in the racial characters of the plaice and the dab. J. Cons. Perm. Int. Expl. Mer., 14:370–384.

Johansson, K. E. 1937. Über Lamellisabella zachsi und ihre systematische Stellung. Zool. Anz., 117:23–26.

Johnson, C. G. 1939. Taxonomic characters, variability and relative growth in Cimex lectularius and C. columbarius. Trans. Roy. Ent. Soc. London, 89:543–568.

Jordan, K. 1938. Where subspecies meet. Novit. Zool., 41:103–111.

Junge, G. C. A. 1934. A difference in time between the egg-laying of Larus fuscus L. and Larus argentatus Pont. in the Shetlands. Ardea, 23:169–171.

Kaltenbach, H. 1936. Die Conchylienfauna des Heiligenstädter Mergellagers. Arch. Naturg., N.F., 5:256–286.

Kattinger, E. 1929. Sexual- und Subspeziesunterschiede im Skelettbau der Vögel. J. Ornith., 77:41–149.

Keeler, C. E., and H. D. King. 1941. Multiple effects of coat color genes in the

Norway rat, with special reference to the "marks of domestication." Anat. Rec., 81 Suppl.: 48–49.

Kerkis, J. 1931. Vergleichende Studien über die Variabilität der Merkmale des Geschlechtsapparats und der äusseren Merkmale bei *Eurygaster integriceps* Put. Zool. Anz., 93:129–143.

Kinsey, A. C. 1930. The gallwasp genus Cynips. Indiana Univ. Studies, 16:1–577.

—— 1936. The Origin of Higher Categories in Cynips. Indiana Univ. Publ., Sci. Ser., No. 4:1–334.

—— 1937a. Supra-specific variation in nature and in classification. From the viewpoint of zoology. Amer. Nat., 71:206–222.

—— 1937b. An evolutionary analysis of insular and continental species. Proc. Nat. Acad. Sci., 23:5–11.

—— 1941. Local populations in the gallwasp *Biorrhiza eburnea*. Genetics, 26:158.

Klauber, L. M. 1936–1940. A statistical study of the rattlesnakes. Occ. Pap. San Diego Soc. Nat. Hist., 1, 3, 4, 5, 6.

—— 1941a. Four papers on the applications of statistical methods to herpetological problems. Bull. Zool. Soc. San Diego, 17:1–73.

—— 1941b. The long-nosed snakes of the genus *Rhinocheilus*. Trans. San Diego Nat. Hist. Soc., 9:289–332.

Kleinschmidt, O. 1900. Arten oder Formenkreise? J. Ornith., 48:134–139.

—— 1930. The formenkreis theory and the progress of the organic world [trans. from German]. H. F. and G. Witherby, London.

Klemm, W. 1939. Zur rassenmässigen Gliederung des Genus *Pagodulina* Clessin. Arch. Naturg., N.F., 8:198–262.

Knipper, H. 1939. Systematische, anatomische, ökologische und tiergeographische Studien an südosteuropäischen Heliciden. Arch. Naturg., N.F., 8:327–517.

Koch, C. 1940. Phylogenetische, biogeographische und systematische Studien über ungeflügelte Tenebrioniden. Mitt. Münch. Entom. Ges., 30:254–337, 3 maps.

—— 1941. Die Verbreitung und Rassenbildung der marokkanischen Pimelien (Col. Tenebr.). Eos, 16 (1940): 7–123.

Koelz, W. 1931. The Coregonid fishes of northeastern America. Pap. Mich. Acad. Sci. Arts Lett., 13 (1930): 303–432.

Kramer, G., and F. von Medem. 1940. Untersuchungen an Kleinpopulationen von *Lacerta sicula* Raf. auf der Sorrentiner Halbinsel und der Insel Capri. Publ. Staz. Zool. Napoli, 18:86–117.

Kramer, G., and R. Mertens. 1938a. Rassenbildung bei west-istrianischen Inseleidechsen in Abhängigkeit von Isolierungsalter und Arealgrösse. Arch. Naturg., N.F., 7:189–234.

—— 1938b. Zur Verbreitung und Systematik der festländischen Mauer-Eidechsen Istriens. Senckenbergiana, 20:48–65.

Kratz, W. 1940. Die Zeckengattung *Hyalomma*. Zeitschr. Parasitenk., 11:510–526.

Krumbiegel, I. 1932. Untersuchungen über physiologische Rassenbildung. Zool. Jahrb., Abt. Syst., 63:183–280.

—— 1936a. Morphologische Untersuchungen über Rassenbildung, ein Beitrag zum Problem der Artbildung und der geographischen Variation. Zool. Jahrb., Abt. Syst., 68:105–178.

—— 1936b. Sinnesphysiologische Untersuchungen an geographischen Rassen. ibid., 179–204.

—— 1936c. Untersuchungen über gleichsinnige geographische Variation. ibid., 68:481–516.

—— 1938. Physiologisches Verhalten als Ausdruck der Phylogenese. Zool. Anz., 123:223–240.

Lack, David. 1940a. Evolution of the Galapagos Finches. Nature, 146:324 ff.

—— 1940b. Habitat selection and speciation in birds. Brit. Birds, 34:80–84.

—— 1940c. Variation in the introduced English sparrow. Condor, 42:239–241.

—— 1942. The Galapagos Finches (Geospizinae): a study in variation. Proc. Calif. Acad. Sci. (in press).

Lieftink, M. A. 1940. Revisional notes on some species of Copera Kirby, etc. Treubia, 17:281–306.

Lincoln, F. 1933. Mallard Number 555414 returns again. Bird-Banding, 4:156.

Linsdale, J. 1928. Variations in the Fox Sparrow (Passerella iliaca), etc. Univ. Calif. Publ. Zool., 30:251–392.

Lissner, H. 1938. Über die Makrele des Adriatischen Meeres. Thalassia, 3 (8): 1–81.

Lorenz, K. 1937. Biologische Fragestellung in der Tierpsychologie. Zeitschr. Tierpsych., 1:24–32.

Lotsy, J. P. 1918. Qu'est-ce qu' une espèce? Arch. Neérl. Sci. Exact. Nat., Sér. 3b, 3:57–110.

Lowe, P. R. 1912. Observations on the genus Coereba, etc. Ibis, (9) 6:489.

—— 1936. The finches of the Galapagos in relation to Darwin's conception of species. Ibis, (13) 6:310–321.

Ludwig, W. 1940. Selektion und Stammesentwicklung. Naturwissensch., 28: 689–705.

Lynes, H. 1930. Review of the genus Cisticola. Ibis, Suppl., 673 pp.

Manton, I. 1934. The problems of Biscutella laevigata L. Zeitschr. ind. Abst. Vererb., 67:41.

Marcus, E. 1936. Tardigrada. Das Tierreich, 66. Lief.: 1–340, Akad. Wiss., Berlin.

Martin, R. F. 1940. A review of the cruciferous genus Selenia. Amer. Midl. Nat., 23:455–462.

Mather, K. 1941. Variation and selection of polygenic characters. J. Genet., 41:159.

Mather, K., and Th. Dobzhansky. 1939. Morphological differences between the "races" of Drosophila pseudoobscura. Amer. Nat., 73:5–25.

Mayr, E. 1926. Die Ausbreitung des Girlitz. J. Ornith., 74:571–671.

—— 1931a. Notes on Halcyon chloris and some of its subspecies. Amer. Mus. Novit., No. 469:1–10.

—— 1931b. A systematic list of the birds of Rennell Island, etc. Amer. Mus. Novit., No. 486:1–29.

—— 1931c. The birds of Malaita Island. Amer. Mus. Novit., No. 504:1–26.

—— 1932a. Notes on Meliphagidae from Polynesia and the Solomon Islands. Amer. Mus. Novit., No. 516:4–12.

—— 1932b. Notes on the bronze cuckoo Chalcites lucidus and its subspecies. Amer. Mus. Novit., No. 520:1–9.

—— 1932c. Notes on thickheads (Pachycephala) from the Solomon Islands. Amer. Mus. Novit., No. 522:1–22.

—— 1932d. Notes on thickheads (Pachycephala) from Polynesia. Amer. Mus. Novit., No. 531:1–32.

—— 1933. Die Vogelwelt Polynesiens. Mitt. Zool. Mus. Berlin, 19:306–323.

—— 1934. Notes on the genus Petroica. Amer. Mus. Novit., No. 714:1–19.

—— 1935. How many birds are known? Proc. Linn. Soc. New York, 45–46:19–23.

—— 1937. Notes on New Guinea birds. II. Amer. Mus. Novit., No. 939:8–9.

—— 1938a. Notes on New Guinea birds. III. Amer. Mus. Novit., No. 947:1–11.

—— 1938b. Notes on New Guinea birds. IV. Amer. Mus. Novit., No. 1006:11.

—— 1940a. Speciation phenomena in birds. Amer. Nat., 74:249–278.

—— 1940b. In: Stanford, J. K., and E. Mayr, The Vernay-Cutting Expedition to Northern Burma. Ibis, (14) 4:689–691.

—— 1940c. Pericrocotus brevirostris and its double. Ibis, (14) 4:712–722.

—— 1940d. Notes on Australian birds. I. The genus *Lalage*. Emu, 40:111–117.

—— 1941a. List of New Guinea birds. Amer. Mus., New York: 1–260.

—— 1941b. The origin and the history of the bird fauna of Polynesia. Proc. Sixth Pac. Sci. Congr. (1939), 4:197–216.

Mayr, E., *et al.* 1931 ff. Birds collected during the Whitney South Sea Expedition, Nos. 12–48. Amer. Mus. Novit., Nos. 469, 486, . . . to 1166.

Mayr, E., and D. Amadon. 1941. Geographical variation in *Demigretta sacra* (Gmelin). Amer. Mus. Novit., No. 1144:1–11.

Mayr, E., and D. Ripley. 1941. Notes on the genus *Lalage*. Amer. Mus. Novit., No. 1116:1–18.

Mayr, E., and R. M. de Schauensee. 1939. The birds of the island of Biak. Proc. Acad. Nat. Sci. Philadelphia, 91:1–37.

Mayr, E., and D. L. Serventy. 1938. A review of the genus *Acanthiza* Vigors and Horsfield. Emu, 38:245–292.

Meinertzhagen, R. 1924. An account of a journey across the southern Syrian desert, etc. Ibis, 6 (11): 88, pl. 6.

—— 1935. The races of *Larus argentatus* and *Larus fuscus*, etc. Ibis, (13) 5: 765.

Meise, W. 1928a. Die Verbreitung der Aaskrähe (Formenkreis *Corvus corone* L.). J. Ornith., 76:1–203.

—— 1928b. Rassenkreuzungen an den Arealgrenzen. Verh. Dtsch. Zool. Ges., 1928:96–105.

—— 1932. Fehlender und extrem entwickelter Sexualdimorphismus im Formenkreis *Heterometrus longimanus*. Arch. Naturg., N.F., 1:660–671.

—— 1936a. Zur Systematik und Verbreitungsgeschichte der Haus- und Weidensperlinge, *Passer domesticus* (L.) und *hispaniolensis* (T.). J. Ornith., 84:631–672.

—— 1936b. Über Artentstehung durch Kreuzung in der Vogelwelt. Biol. Zentralbl., 56:590–604.

—— 1938. Fortschritte der ornithologischen Systematik seit 1920. Proc. Eighth Int. Orn. Congr. Oxford (1934): 49–189.

Mertens, R. 1928a. Über den Rassen- und Artenwandel auf Grund des Migrationsprinzipes, dargestellt an einigen Amphibien und Reptilien. Senckenbergiana, 10:81–91.

—— 1928b. Zur Naturgeschichte der europäischen Unken. Zeitschr. Morph. Ökol., 11:613–628.

—— 1931. *Ablepharus boutoni* (Desj.) und seine geographische Variation. Zool. Jahrb., Abt. Syst., 61:63–210.

—— 1934. Die Insel-Reptilien, ihre Ausbreitung, Variation und Artbildung. Zoologica, 32 (Heft 84): 1–209.

Mertens, R., and L. Müller. 1928. Liste der Amphibien und Reptilien Europas. Abh. Senckenberg. Naturf. Ges., 41:1–62.

Miller, A. H. 1931. Systematic revision and natural history of the American Shrikes (*Lanius*). Univ. Calif. Publ. Zool., 38:11–242.

—— 1940. Climatic conditions of the pleistocene reflected by the ecological requirements of fossil birds. Proc. Sixth Pacific Sci. Congr., 1939, Geol.: 807–810.

—— 1941. Speciation in the avian genus *Junco*. Univ. Calif. Publ. Zool., 44:173–434, 33 figs.

—— 1942. Habitat selection among higher vertebrates and its relation to intraspecific variation. Amer. Nat., 76:25–35.

Moore, J. A. 1939. Temperature tolerance and rates of development in the eggs of amphibia. Ecology, 20:459–478.

Moreau, R. E. 1930. On the age of some races of birds. Ibis, (12) 6:229.

Muller, H. J. 1939. Reversibility in evolution considered from the standpoint of genetics. Biol. Rev., 14:261–280.

—— 1940. Bearings of the 'Drosophila' work on systematics. In: Huxley, J., The New Systematics: 185–268.

Müller, L., and H. Kautz. 1940. *Pieris bryoniae* O. and *Pieris napi* L. Abh. Österr. Ent. Ver., 1, 191 pp. 16 pls.

Murie, A. 1933. The ecological relationship of two subspecies of *Peromyscus* in the Glacier Park Region, Montana. Univ. Mich. Occ. Pap. Mus. Zool., 270:1–17.

Murphy, R. C. 1938. The need of insular exploration as illustrated by birds. Science, (N.S.) 88:533–539.

Myers, R. B. 1939. Morphological variation in *Ambystoma tigrinum* at various altitudes. Univ. Colorado Studies, 26, No. 2:98.

Nabours, R. K. 1929. The genetics of the Tettigidae. Bibl. Genet., 5:27–104.

Netolitzky, F. 1931. Einige Regeln in der geographischen Verbreitung geflügelter Käferrassen. Biol. Zentralbl., 51:277–290.

Nice, M. M. 1937. Studies in the Life History of the Song Sparrow I. Trans. Linn. Soc. New York, 4:1–247.

—— 1941. The role of territory in bird life. Amer. Midl. Nat., 26:441–487.

Niethammer, G. 1940. Die Schutzanpassung der Lerchen, in: Hoesch, W., and G. Niethammer, Die Vogelwelt Deutsch-Suedwestafrikas. J. Ornith., 88 (Sonderh.): 75–83.

Noble, G. K. 1934. Experimenting with the courtship of lizards. Nat. Hist., 34:1–15.

Ökland, F. 1937. Die geographischen Rassen der extramarinen Wirbeltiere Europas. Zoogeographica, 3:389–484.

Oliver, W. R. B. 1930. New Zealand Birds. Fine Arts Ltd., Wellington, N. Z.

Orr, R. T. 1940. The rabbits of California. Occ. Pap. Calif. Acad. Sci., No. 19: 1–227.

Osborn, H. F. 1927. The origin of species V. Speciation and mutation. Amer. Nat., 61:5–42.

Osgood, W. H. 1909. Revision of the mice of the American genus *Peromyscus*. N. Amer. Fauna (Bur. Biol. Surv.), 28:1–285.

Oudemans, A. C. 1936. Neues über die Amystidae (Acari). Arch. Naturg., (N.F.) 5:364–446.

Ownbey, M. 1940. A monograph of the genus *Calochortus*. Ann. Missouri Bot. Gard., 27:371–560.

Paludan, K. 1940. Contributions to the ornithology of Iran. Danish Sci. Invest. Iran, pt. 2:35, pl. 1.

Patterson, J. T. 1942. Drosophila and speciation. Science, 95:153–159.

Petersen, W. 1903. Entstehung der Arten durch physiologische Isolierung. Biol. Centralbl., 23:468–477.

—— 1932. Die Arten der Gattung Swammerdamia. Arch. Naturg., N.F., 1:197–224.

Philiptschenko, J. 1927. Variabilität und Variation. Gebrüder Borntraeger, Berlin.

Phillips, J. C. 1912. The Hawaiian Linnet, *Carpodacus mutans* Grinnell. Auk, 29:336–338.

Pickford, G. E. 1937. A monograph of the Acanthodriline earthworms of South Africa. Heffer and Sons, Cambridge.

Pictet, A. 1935. Les populations hybridées de Maniola gorge Esp., etc. Mitt. Schweiz. Ent. Ges., 16:421–441.

—— 1937. Sur des croisements de races géographiques de Lépidoptères de pays très éloignés. Mitt. Schweiz. Ent. Ges., 16:706–715.

Plate, L. 1913. Selektionsprinzip und Probleme der Artbildung: 524–549. W. Engelmann, Leipzig und Berlin.

Poulton, E. B. 1903. What is a species? Proc. Ent. Soc. London: LXXVII–CXVI.

Promptoff, A. 1930. Die geographische Variabilität des Buchfinkenschlags (*Fringilla coelebs* L.), etc. Biol. Zentralbl., 50:478–503.

Ramme, W. 1933. Revision der Phaneroptinen-Gattung *Poecilimon* Fish (Orth., Tettigon.). Mitt. Zool. Mus. Berlin, 19:497–576.

Ramsbottom, J. 1938. Linnaeus and the species concept. Proc. Linn. Soc. of London, 150th Sess.: 192–219.

Rand, A. 1936. Altitudinal variation in New Guinea birds. Amer. Mus. Novit., No. 890:1–14.

—— 1938. On the breeding habits of some birds-of-paradise in the wild. Amer. Mus. Novit., No. 993:1–8.

Reed, S. C., C. M. Williams and L. E. Chadwick. 1942. Frequency of wing-beat as a character for separating species, races and geographic varieties of Drosophila. Genetics, 27:349–361.

Reinig, W. F. 1937. Die Holarktis. G. Fischer, Jena.

—— 1939. Die Evolutionsmechanismen, erläutert an den Hummeln. Zool. Anz., Suppl., 12:170–206.

Remane, A. 1933. Verteilung und Organisation der benthonischen Mikrofauna der Kieler Bucht. Wissensch. Meeresunters. Abt. Kiel, N.F., 21:163.

—— 1939. Geltungsbereich der Mutationstheorie. Zool. Anz., Suppl., 12:206–220.

Rensch, B. 1929. Das Prinzip geographischer Rassenkreise und das Problem der Artbildung. Borntraeger Verl., Berlin.

—— 1931. Der Einfluss des Tropenklimas auf den Vogel. Proc. VII. Int. Ornith. Congr. Amsterdam 1930:197–205.

—— 1932. Über die Abhängigkeit der Grösse, des relativen Gewichts und der Oberflächenstruktur der Landschneckenschalen von den Umweltsfaktoren. Zeitschr. Morph. Ökol., 25:757–807.

—— 1933. Zool. Systematik und Artbildungsproblem. Verh. Dtsch. Zool. Ges., 1933:19–83.

—— 1934. Kurze Anweisung für zoologisch-systematische Studien. Akademische Verlagsgesellschaft, Leipzig.

—— 1936. Studien über klimatische Parallelität der Merkmalsausprägung bei Vögeln und Säugern. Arch. Naturg., N.F., 5:317–363.

—— 1937. Untersuchungen über Rassenbildung und Erblichkeit von Rassenmerkmalen bei sizilischen Landschnecken. Zeitschr. ind. Abst. Vererb., 72:564–588.

—— 1938a. Bestehen die Regeln klimatischer Parallelität bei der Merkmalsausprägung von homöothermen Tieren zu Recht? Arch. Naturg., N.F., 7:364–389.

—— 1938b. Some problems of geographical variation and species formation. Proc. Linn. Soc. London, 150th Sess.: 275–285.

—— 1938c. Einwirkung des Klimas bei der Ausprägung von Vogelrassen, mit besonderer Berücksichtigung der Flügelform und der Eizahl. Proc. Eighth Int. Orn. Congr. Oxford (1934): 285–311.

—— 1939a. Typen der Artbildung. Biol. Rev., 14:180–222.

—— 1939b. Klimatische Auslese von Grössenvarianten. Arch. Naturg., N.F., 8:89–129.

—— 1940. Die ganzheitliche Auswirkung der Grössenauslese am Vogelskelett. J. Ornith., 88:373–388.

Richards, O. W. 1927. Sexual selection and allied problems in the insects. Biol. Rev., 2:298–364.

—— 1938. The formation of species, in 'Evolution,' ed. G. R. De Beer: 95–110. Clarendon Press, Oxford.

Richter, R. 1938. Beobachtungen an einer gemischten Kolonie von Silbermöwe (*Larus argentatus* Pont.) und Heringsmöwe (*Larus fuscus graellsi* Brehm). J. Ornith., 86:366–373.

Riech, E. 1937. Systematische, anatomische, ökologische und tiergeographische

Untersuchungen über die Süsswassermollusken Papuasiens und Melanesiens. Arch. Naturg., N.F., 6:37–153.

Ripley, D. 1942. A review of the species *Anas castanea*. Auk, 59:90–99.

Roberts, H. R. 1941. A comparative study of the subfamilies of the Acrididae (Orth.), etc. Proc. Acad. Nat. Sci. Philadelphia, 93: 231–233.

Robson, G. C., and O. W. Richards. 1936. The variations of animals in nature. Longmans Green, London.

Rodeheffer, I. A. 1941. The movements of marked fish in Douglas Lake, Michigan. Pap. Mich. Acad. Sci., 26:265–280.

Rost, H. 1939. Die Entwicklung der Hypophyse der Haustauben und ihre rassentypische Ausbildung bei der Römertaube und der Möwchentaube. Zeitschr. wiss. Zool., Abt. A, 152:221–276.

Rümmler, H. 1938. Die Systematik und Verbreitung der Muriden Neuguineas. Mitt. Zool. Mus. Berlin, 23:1–297.

Runnström, Sven. 1930. Weitere Studien über die Temperaturanpassung der Fortpflanzung und Entwicklung mariner Tiere. Bergens Mus. Arbok, 1929, No. 10:1–46.

Salomonsen, F. 1931. Diluviale Isolation und Artbildung. Proc. VII. Int. Ornith. Congr. Amsterdam (1930): 413–438.

—— 1933. Revision of the group *Tchitrea affinis* Blyth. Ibis, 3(13): 730–745.

—— 1938. Mutationen bei *Lybius torquatus* (Dumont). Proc. Eighth Int. Ornith. Congr. Oxford (1934): 190–198.

Salt, George. 1941. The effects of hosts upon their insect parasites. Biol. Rev., 14:239–264.

Schenk, E. T., and J. H. McMasters. 1936. Procedure in taxonomy. Stanford Univ. Press.

Schiermann, G. 1939. "Stammesgenossenschaften" bei Vögeln. Ornith. Monatsber., 47:1–3.

Schilder, F. A., and M. Schilder. 1938. Prodrome of a monograph on living Cypraeidae. Proc. Malac. Soc., 23:119–231.

Schindewolf, O. H. 1936. Paläontologie, Entwicklungslehre und Genetik. Borntraeger, Berlin.

Schnakenbeck, W. 1931. Zum Rassenproblem bei den Fischen. Zeitschr. Morph. Ökol., 21:409–566.

Schnitter, H. 1922. Die Najaden der Schweiz. Rev. Hydrol., Suppl., 2:1–200, 15 pls.

Seitz, A. 1906 ff. The macrolepidoptera of the world. Vols. 2, 10, 14. Alfred Kernen, Stuttgart.

Semenov-Tian-Shansky, A. 1910. Die taxonomischen Grenzen der Art und ihrer Unterabteilungen. Friedländer and Sohn, Berlin.

Sewertzoff, A. N. 1931. Morphologische Gesetzmässigkeiten der Evolution. G. Fischer, Jena.

Shih, C. H. 1937. Die Abhängigkeit der Grösse und Schalendicke mariner Mollusken von der Temperatur und dem Salzgehalt des Wassers. Sitz. Ber. Ges. naturf. Fr. Berlin: 238–287.

Sick, H. 1939. Über die Dialektbildung beim "Regenruf" des Buchfinken. J. Ornith., 87:568–592.

Simms, A. D. 1931. Biological races and their significance in evolution. Ann. Appl. Biol., 18:404–452.

Simpson, G. G. 1931. Origin of mammalian faunas as illustrated by that of Florida. Amer. Nat., 65:258–276.

Simpson, G. G., and A. Roe. 1939. Quantitative Zoology. McGraw-Hill, New York.

Sonneborn, T. M. 1941. Sexuality in unicellular organisms: 666–709. In: Protozoa in biological research, ed. by G. N. Calkins and F. M. Summers. Columbia Univ. Press, New York.

Southern, H. N. 1939. The status and problem of the Bridled Guillemot. Proc. Zool. Soc. London, (A) 109:31.

Spencer, W. P. 1940. Levels of divergence in Drosophila speciation. Amer. Nat., 74:299–311.

—— 1941. Ecological factors and Drosophila speciation. Ohio J. Schi., 41:190–200.

Speyer, W. 1938. Über das Vorkommen von Lokalrassen des Kleinen Frostspanners (*Cheimatobia brumata* L.). Arb. physiol. angew. Ent. Berlin-Dahlem, 5:50–76.

Spieth, H. 1941. Taxonomic studies on the Ephemeroptera. II. The genus *Hexagenia*. Amer. Midl. Nat., 26:233–280.

Stalker, H. 1942. *Drosophila virilis-americana* Crosses. Genetics, 27:238–257.

Steinbacher, F. 1927. Die Verbreitungsgebiete einiger europäischer Vogelarten als Ergebnis der geschichtlichen Entwicklung. J. Ornith., 75:535–567.

Steinmann, P. 1941. Neue Probleme der Salmoniden Systematik. Rev. Suisse Zool., 48:525–529.

Stephenson, T. A. 1933. The relation between form and environment in corals. Great Barrier Reef Expedition, 1928–29, Sci. Rep., III, 7:200–207.

Stresemann, E. 1919. Über die europäischen Baumläufer. Verh. Ornith. Ges. Bayern, 14:39–74.

—— 1923. Mutationsstudien IV. *Rhipidura fuliginosa*. J. Ornith., 71:515–516.

—— 1924. Einiges über die afrikanischen *Terpsiphone*-Arten. J. Ornith., 72:89–96, 256–260.

—— 1926. Uebersicht über die "Mutationsstudien" I–XXIV und ihre wichtigsten Ergebnisse. J. Ornith., 74:377–385.

—— 1927–1934. Aves, in: Kükenthal, Handb. Zool., VII B: 729–853.

—— 1931. Die Zosteropiden der indo-australischen Region. Mitt. Zool. Mus. Berlin, 17:201–238.

—— 1936. Zur Frage der Artbildung in der Gattung *Geospiza*. Org. Club Nedl. Vogelk., 9:13–21.

—— 1939. Die Vögel von Celebes. J. Ornith., 87:360.

—— 1940a. Zur Kenntnis der Wespenbussarde (*Pernis*). Arch. Naturg., N.F., 9:137–193.

—— 1940b. [Bemerkungen über *Garrulus glandarius*]. Ornith. Monatsber., 48:102–104.

—— 1941. [Bemerkungen über *Zonotrichia capensis*]. Ornith. Monatsber., 49:60–61.

Streuli, A. 1932. Zur Frage der Artmerkmale und der Bastardierung von Baum- und Steinmarder (*Martes*). Zeitschr. Säugetierk., 7:58–72.

Strohmeyer, G. 1928. Systematisches und Zoogeographisches über die Cypholobini (Carab. Anthiinae). Mitt. Zool. Mus. Berlin, 14:287–462.

Strouhal, H. 1939. Variationsstatistische Untersuchungen an *Adonia variegata*. Zeitschr. Morph. Ökol., 35:288–316.

Stuart, L. C. 1941. A revision of the genus *Dryadophis*. Misc. Publ. Mus. Zool. Univ. Mich., No. 49:1–106, 4 pls.

Stull, O. G. 1940. Variations and relationships in the snakes of the genus *Pituophis*. U.S. Nat. Mus., Bull. 175:1–225.

Sturtevant, A. H. 1940. Genetic data on *Drosophila affinis*, etc. Genetics, 25:337–353.

Sturtevant, A. H., and E. Novitski. 1941. The homologies of the chromosome elements in the genus *Drosophila*. Genetics, 26:517–541.

Suchetet, A. 1896. Des hybrides à l'état sauvage, 1 (oiseaux). Lille.

Sumner, F. B. 1932. Genetic, distributional and evolutionary studies of the subspecies of deer-mice (*Peromyscus*). Bibl. Genet., 9:1–106.

Sutton, G. M. 1931. The blue goose and lesser snow goose on Southampton Island, Hudson Bay. Auk, 48:335–364.

—— 1932. The birds of Southampton Island. Mem. Carnegie Mus., 12, pt. 2, sect. 2:30–41.

Swarth, H. S. 1934. The bird fauna of the Galapagos Islands in relation to species formation. Biol. Rev., 9:213–234.

Sweadner, W. R. 1937. Hybridisation and the phylogeny of the genus *Platysamia*. Ann. Carnegie Mus., 25:163–242.

Teissier, G. 1934. Dysharmonies et discontinuités dans la croissance. Actualités sci. industr., 95:1–39.

Thienemann, A. 1938. Rassenbildung bei *Planaria alpina*. Jub.-Festschr. Grig. Antipa: 1–21 (from Zool. Ber., 49 (1940): 84–85).

Thill, H. 1937. Beiträge zur Kenntnis der *Aurelia aurita* L. Zeitschr. wiss. Zool., Abt. A, 150:51–96.

Thomson, D'A. W. 1917. On growth and form. Cambridge Univ. Press, Cambridge.

Thomson, G. M. 1922. The naturalization of animals and plants in New Zealand. Univ. Press, Cambridge.

Thorpe, W. H. 1930. Biological races in insects and allied groups. Biol. Rev., 5:177.

—— 1940. Ecology and the future of systematics. in: Huxley, J., The New Systematics: 340–364.

Ticehurst, Cl. B. 1938a. A Systematic Review of the Genus Phylloscopus. Brit. Mus. London.

—— 1938b. On the birds of northern Burma. Ibis, 2 (14): 93–94.

—— 1939. On the birds of northern Burma. Ibis, 3 (14): 220–224.

Timofeeff-Ressovsky, N. W. 1935. Über geographische Temperaturrassen bei *Drosophila funebris* F. Arch. Naturg,. N.F., 4:245–357.

—— 1940a. Mutations and geographical variation. in: Huxley, J., The New Systematics: 73–136.

—— 1940b. Zur Analyse des Polymorphismus bei *Adalia bipunctata*. Biol. Zentralbl., 69:130–137.

Turbott, E. G. 1940. A bird census on Taranga (The Hen). Emu, 40:158–161.

Uhlmann, E. 1923. Entwicklungsgedanke und Artbegriff. G. Fischer, Jena.

Usinger, R. L. 1941. Problems of insect speciation in the Hawaiian Islands. Amer. Nat., 75:251–263.

Vandel, A. 1934. La parthénogenèse géographique. Bull. Biol. France Belgique, 68:419–463.

Venables, L. S. V. 1940. Nesting behaviour of the Galapagos Mockingbird. The Ibis, 4 (14): 629–639.

Wagler, E. 1937. Die Systematik der Voralpencoregonen. Int. Rev. ges. Hydrob. Hydrogr., 35:345–446.

Wagner, M. 1889. Die Entstehung der Arten durch räumliche Sonderung. Benno Schwalbe, Basel.

Welch, D'Alte A. 1938. Distribution and variation of *Achatinella mustelina* Mighels in the Waianae Mountains, Oahu. Bernice P. Bishop Mus., Bull. 152: 1–64, 13 pls.

Wertheim, P. 1936. Über die Gliederung innerhalb des Rassenkreises *Diplodinium* (*Ostracodinium*) *gracile*. Arch. Naturg., N.F., 5:296–312.

Wetmore, A. 1927. The Birds of Porto Rico and the Virgin Islands. Sci. Survey Porto Rico, etc., N.Y. Acad. Sci., 9:509.

—— 1940. A systematic classification for the birds of the world. Smiths. Misc. Coll., 99, No. 7:1–11.

Whitman, C. O. 1919. The behavior of pigeons (Edited by H. A. Carr). Carnegie Inst. Washington, Publ. 257, III: 1–161.

Wilhelmi, R. W. 1940. Serological reactions and species specificity of some helminths. Biol. Bull., 79:64–90.

Williams, C. B. 1940. On "Type" Specimens. Ann. Ent. Soc. Amer., 33:621–624.

Willis, J. C. 1940. The course of evolution by differentiation, etc. Univ. Press, Cambridge.

Wimpenny, R. S. 1941. Organic polarity. Some ecological and physiological aspects. Quart. Rev. Biol., 16:389–425.

Witschi, E. 1930. The geographical distribution of the sex races of the European grass frog (Rana temporaria, L.). J. Exp. Zool., 56:149–165.

Woltereck, E. 1937. Systematisch-variationsanalytische Untersuchungen über die Rassen- und Artbildung bei Süsswassergarneelen aus der Gattung Caridina. Int. Rev. ges. Hydrol. Hydrogr., 34:208–262.

Woltereck, R. 1921. Variation und Artbildung. Int. Rev. ges. Hydrol. Hydrogr., 9:1–152.

—— 1931. Wie entsteht eine endemische Rasse oder Art? Biol. Zentralbl., 51: 231–253.

Worthington, E. B. 1937. On the evolution of fish in the great lakes of Africa. Int. Rev. ges. Hydrol. Hydrogr., 35:304–317.

—— 1940. Geographical differentiation in fresh waters with special reference to fish. In: Huxley, J., The New Systematics: 287–302.

Wright, S. 1929. Fisher's theory of dominance. Amer. Nat., 63:274–279.

—— 1931. Evolution in Mendelian populations. Genetics, 16:97–159.

—— 1932. The roles of mutation, inbreeding, crossbreeding, and selection in evolution. Proc. 6th Int. Congress of Genetics, 1:356–366.

—— 1937. The distribution of gene frequencies in populations. Proc. Nat. Acad. Sci., 23:307–320.

—— 1940a. The statistical consequences of Mendelian heredity in relation to speciation. In: Huxley, J., The New Systematics: 161–183.

—— 1940b. Breeding structure of populations in relation to speciation. Amer. Nat., 74:232–248.

—— 1941a. The physiology of the gene. Physiol. Rev., 21:487–527.

—— 1941b. The "Age and Area" concept extended. Ecology, 22:345–347.

—— 1941c. The material basis of evolution. Sci. Monthly, 53:165–170.

Wunder, W. 1939. Die "Hungerform" und die "Mastform" des Karpfens (Cyprinus carpio). Zeitschr. Morph. Ökol., 35:594–614.

Yocum, H. B., and R. R. Huestis. 1928. Histological differences in the thyroid glands from two subspecies of Peromyscus. Anat. Rec., 39:57.

Zarapkin, S. R. 1934. Zur Phänoanalyse von geographischen Rassen und Arten. Arch. Naturg., N.F., 3:161–186.

Zimmer, J. T. 1931 ff. Notes on Peruvian Birds, 1 ff. Amer. Mus. Novit., No. 500, and subsequent issues.

Zimmermann, K. 1931. Studien über individuelle und geographische Variabilität paläarktischer Polistes und verwandter Vespiden. Zeitschr. Morph. Ökol., 22: 173–230.

—— 1935. Zur Rassenanalyse der mitteleuropäischen Feldmäuse. Arch. Naturg., N.F., 4:258.

—— 1936. Zur Kenntnis der europäischen Waldmäuse (Sylvaemus sylvaticus L. and S. flavicollis Melch.). Arch. Naturg., N.F., 5:116–133.

Zimmermann, S. 1932. Über die Verbreitung und die Formen des Genus Orcula Held in den Ostalpen. Arch. Naturg., N.F., 1:1–56.

Zumpt, F. 1940. Die Verbreitung der Glossina palpalis—Subspecies im Belgischen Kongogebiet. Rev. Zool. Bot. Afrique, 33:136–149.

INDEX

Aberrant types and predation, 272
Acanthiza, 90; *pusilla* and *ewingi*, 172, 174, 175
Accidental evolution, 86
Accipiter novaehollandiae, 78, 81
Achatinella, 142, 176, 214; *mustelina*, 34, 35, 93, 219, 220
Acrocephalus, 54, 169
Adalia bipunctata, 76
Adaptation, definition, 85; to background, 86
Adaptive variation, 85-88; complex (indirect) selective factors, 87; directly selective characters, 86
Adensamer, W., 28
Adonia variegata, 35
Aegithalos, 264
Agama stellio, 46
Age variation, 25
Aggressive period, 238
Alauda arvensis and *gulgula*, 167
Alaudidae, soil adaptation of, 86
Albinism, 73, 74
Alces alces, 31
Alkins, W. E., 34, 202, 243
Allee, W. C., Hesse, R., Schmidt, K. P., 234
Allen, J. A., 41, 89, 90, 92, 265
Allochronic species, delimitation, 153
Allocotops, 169
Allometry, 40, 293
Allopatric, definition, 149
Allopatric hybridization, 259
Allopatric species gaps, 148-54; doubtful, 152; gaps between sympatric and allopatric, 154-62; origin of, in zones of intergradation, 188
Allopatric species delimitation, 151-53
Allotetraploidy, 191
Alpatov, W. W., 139
Altitude preference, an isolating mechanism, 250
Altitudinal races, 196 ff.
Amadon, D., Mayr, E., and, 78, 237

Ambystoma maculatum, 47; —*tigrinum*, 47, 93, 135
Ameiva, species and subspecies, 133
American Museum of Natural History, bird collection, 8; Whitney South Sea Expedition, 12
Amherst pheasant, 259
Ammomanes deserti annae, 86
Amphibia, polytypic species, 135
Anas, 219, 243; *castanea*, 52
Anatidae, and hybridization, 259
Anderson, E., 68, 122
Anguiostomum, 191
Anguis fragilis, 46
Animals, differences in speciation of plants and, 273; early systems, 277; ecotypes among, 195; geographic variation, 127; hybrid swarms, 149; number of species of living, 275; sedentary, 240; speed of speciation, 222
Annelids, 191; size and distribution of marine and land fauna, 234
Anodonta, 28, 61
Anopheles, *maculipennis* and sibling species, 205-6
Anser, 219, 242
Anthornis melanocephala, 235
Antirrhinum, 122
Ants, 30, 139, 203
Aphids, 192, 212
Apis mellifica, 139
Aplonis gigas, 37
Aplysiidae, 14
Apodemus sylvaticus and *flavicollis*, 202, 231
Apogamy, 122
Apus apus and *pallidus*, 167
Arachnids, polytypic species, 141
Archaeopteryx, 296, 298
Archbold Expeditions, 131
Archipelago speciation, 174
Arctic coloration, 87
Ardea herodias wardi and *occidentalis*, 150

Ardeidae, 73
Arianta arbustorum, 62, 194
Arkell, W. J., and Moy-Thomas, J. A.
 279, 289
Artenkreis, 169
Ascaris lumbricoides, 210
Asexual reproduction, 191
Astrapia, 153, 170, 260, 283; *nigra*, 169,
 229, 230
Astrarchia, 167
Aurelia aurita, 144
Autopolyploidy, 191

Babblers, 182, 201, 228, 279
Background adaptation, 86
Bailey, R. M., Hubbs, C. L. and, 268
Bailey, J. L., Jr., 53
Balance of nature, 238
Banta, A. M., and Wood, T. R., 46
Barriers, biological, 247; breakdown,
 176, 258; ecological, 226, 231; ecolog-
 ical vs. geographic, 229; faculty to
 overcome, 238, 239; fresh-water ani-
 mal, 234; lifting of, 263; restriction
 of random dispersal by geographic,
 226–38; subspecific, 229; vertical,
 232; waterfalls, 234
Bates, M., 205, 206, 207, 246
Bateson, W., 49, 71, 264
Bather, F. A., quoted, 16
Bats, 246, change in pigmentation, 87
Baur, E., 67, 122
Beebe, W., 60
Beer, G. R. de, 50, 292
Bees, 139 orientation by visual cues, 241;
 parasitic genera, 278; *see also*
 Bumblebees
Beetles, 6, 18, 41, 76, 229; flightless, 139,
 228; polytypic species, 139
Behavior differences restrict random
 mating, 254
Bembidiinae, 90
Benson, S. B., 87
Berg, L. S., 136
Bergmann's rule, 89, 90, 94, 261
Bernard, H. M., quoted, 109
Beurlen, K., 292
Biological discontinuities, *see* Discon-
 tinuities
Biological isolating mechanisms, *see*
 Isolating mechanisms
Biological races, 193, 200. 203 ff. *passim*,
 208–11; definition, 208

Biological species concept, 146
Biology of speciation, *see* Speciation,
 biology of
Biometric methods, 14, 132, 133
Biorrhiza eburnea, 76
Biostatistics, treatment of, 14, 132, 133
Birckhead, H., Ripley, D., and, 239
Birds, adaptive variation, 85 ff.; altitudinal variation, 197; border-line
 cases, 164 ff.; classification into species
 and subspecies, 130; collections, 8, 12;
 courtship patterns, 55; differences in
 degree of subspeciation, 218; dispersal
 faculty, 227; double colonization of
 islands, 173; ecological rules applying
 to, 90; effect of water barriers, 227;
 engagement period, 255; evolution,
 218, 297; extinct species, 224; flightless, 278, 296; fluctuating population
 size, 237; geographic races, 128; habitat preference, 56, 246; hen-feathered
 races, 48; homing faculty, 240, 241;
 hybrids, 260 ff., 264; individual variants, 149, 150; large genera of, 290;
 mating behavior, 55, 256; migratory
 movements, 55; molting period, 50;
 monotypic species, 124; number of
 genera and of species recognized, 286;
 number of species and subspecies, 155;
 patterns of coloration, 42; phenotypical changes in, 60; physiology of
 plumage and plumage change in, 48–
 52; plumage change in captivity, 60;
 polytypic species, 123, 125, 128, 132;
 proportions, 39–41; races per polytypic and monotypic species, 246;
 range of subspecies, 219; seasonal
 isolation, 251; seasonal races, 199;
 size of population, 235; song races, 54,
 256; speed of speciation, 221, 222,
 223; structural polymorphism, 80;
 transient polymorphism, 76; unnecessary genera, 287; wing length, 14, 36
Birds of paradise, 30, 41, 121, 130, 153,
 167, 170, 229, 230, 265, 283; geographic variation, 83; intergeneric
 hybridization among, 260, 261
Bischoff, H., 210
Biscutella, 122
Bitterns, polymorphism, 74
Bivalves, 257
Black bear, clinal variation of polymorphism, 95
Black cock, 261

Black Hills deermouse, 235
Blair, A. P., 84, 95, 253, 262, 267
Blanchard, B. D., 132, 253
Blending inheritance, 68
Blossom, P. M., Dice L. R., and. 87, 223
   quoted 244
Blue goose, 150, 242
Böker, H., 292, 295
Bombina bombina and *variegata*, 178, 253
Bombus, 139, 222, 236; color phases, 80;
   polytypic species, 125
Bond, J., 77
Border invasions. 176-80
Border-line cases, 164-73; overlap of
   ranges. 176
Bovey, P., 80
Boycott, A. E., 28, 62, 142
Brachiopods, 128, 144, 217
Brachypternus erythronotus and *beng-*
   halensis intermedius, 173
Brachyura, speed of speciation, 223
Bragg, A. N., and Smith, C. C., 203
Branta, 171, 219, 243; species, 242
Breeding habits, colonial or semi-
   colonial, 242
Breeding seasons, 251
Brehm, C. L., 203
Breuning, St., 139
Brewster's warbler, 262
Bridgeless gap, 148, 149, 152
Bronze grackle, 264
Brown creeper, sibling species, 203
Bryozoa, 191, 257
Buch, Leopold von, 157, 162; quoted, 156
Buchka, E., 229
Bufo, 203, 253, 262, 267; *americanus*, 95:
   bufo, 47; *fowleri*, 84, 95
Bugs, 176, 210, 239; *see also* Insects
Bull snakes, 179
Bumblebees, *see Bombus*
Buteo species, 105, 150
Butterflies, 8, 42, 87, 163, 174, 183, 202,
   209, 235, 255; color variants, 80; cor-
   relation between climate and pigment,
   90; geographic variation, 52; migra-
   tory behavior, 56; polytypic species,
   136; species and races, 125; transient
   polymorphism, 76
Buxton, P. A., 272
Byers, C. F., 250
   quoted, 177

Cacatua galerita triton, 37, 89, 197
Calochortus, 122

Canis. 259
Capercaillie, 261
Carabus, 42, 93, 96, 125, 139; *cancellatus*,
   18; *monilis* and *violaceus*, 229; *nemor-*
   alis, 46, 53
Carduelis carduelis, 60. 262, 264
Carp, 63
Carpenter, F. M., *et al.*, 223
Carpodacus mexicanus frontalis and
   mutans, 60
Carr, A. F., 249
Castle, W. E., 294
Categories, collective units, 102; infraspecific, 103-8; monophyletic, 276;
   polyphyletic, 279, 280; subjective,
   281; terminology, 103
   higher, 107, 276-80; reaction against
   excessive splitting of, 286 ff.; and
   evolution, 275-98; nature of. 280-91;
   origin. 298
   systematic, 17, 275; and the new
   species concept, 102-22; gradient, 172
Cave animals, aberrant evolution, 234;
   crickets, 7, 140, 166; spiders, 141;
   swiftlets, 15, 116, 201
Cepaea, 203, 255; *hortensis* and *nemor-*
   alis, 20, 32, 34, 75, 78, 105, 202, 248,
   263; *vindobonesis*, 263
Cerambycids, 176
Cercomacra cinerascens and subspecies,
   228
Ceriocera, 204
Certhia, 177; *familiaris* and *brachydac-*
   tyla, 204
Cestodes, parasitic, 191
Ceuthophilus, 7, 136, 140, 166
Chaffinch, song races, 54
Chalcites lucidus, 56
Chamberlin, R. V., and Ivie, W., 141
Changes, post-mortem, 29
Chapin, J. P., 54, 199, 231
Chapman, F. M., 54, 55, 127, 132, 197,
   201, 232, 265, 266; quoted, 117
Character gradients, 94-98; steepening
   of, 99
Characters, conservative, 296
Characters, taxonomic, *see* Taxonomic
   characters
Charmosyna papou, geographic varia-
   tion of melanism, 74, 79
Chasen, F. N., 132
Cheimatobia brumata, 52
Chen and species, 150, 242, 243
Chiffchaff, 54

Chinese jay, 29
Chloris chloris, 262
Chromosomes, 65; differences found in, 45
Chrysis ignita, 210
Chrysoena luteovirens, 167
Chrysolophus amherstiae and *pictus*, 259
Chrysophaps, 167, 284
Cicada, seventeen-year, 198
Cichlidae, 213, 272
Cicinnurus, 260
Cicurina, polytypic species, 141
Ciliates, 207, 210
Cimex, 210
Ciona intestinalis, 46
Cissa chinensis, 29
Cisticola, 12, 51, 290
Cladocera, 212
Clark, F. H., 31, 40
Classifications, 10; horizontal, 279; of
    observations relating to speciation
    factors, 216, 217; phylogenetic, 276 ff.;
    practical, 277; principles of, 275;
    simplified by introduction of poly-
    typic species concept, 126; taxonomic
    characters and, 21; type method, 109
Clausen, J., Hiesey, W. M., and Keck,
    D. D., quoted, 193
Clausilia rugosa and *cravenensis*, 34, 202,
    243
Clausiliidae, 22, 171
Climate, influence on geographic varia-
    tion, 87, 88
Climatic races, 194
Clines, 37, 94–98; non-adaptive, 96
Clones, 192
Close-inbreeding, obligatory, 192
Cloth louse, 210
Clupea harengus, 145, 198
Clytorhynchus, 169
Coccid, 191
Coccinellidae, 74, 90, 139
Cochran, D. M., quoted, 133
Cockatoo, 37, 89, 197
Coelacanthid fish, 5
Coelenterates, 257
    sessile, 143, 191
Coenonympha, 137; species and races,
    125; *pamphilus*, 105
Coereba, geographic variation of melan-
    ism, 74
    flaveola atrata, 77
Coker, R. E., 62
Colaptes, 171
    auratus and *cafer*, 265

Cold-blooded animals, phenotypical
    changes, 61–63
Cole, A. C., 203
Colias philodice, 76
Collecting of material, 12
Collembola, 212
Collocalia, 15, 116, 121, 130, 200, 201
Colman, J., 35
Colonization, double, 173–76
Colonizing periods, 239
Coloration, adaptive, 86, 87, 88
Color patterns, 42, 78
Columba laurivora and *bollii*, 173
Competition, 271
Complex, 108
Conditioning and speciation, 256
Conotrachelus, 5
Conspecifity of allopatric and allo-
    chronic forms, 121
Contact zone, 264
Continuous variation, 71, 72, 84–85
Cooper, A., 218
Cope, E. D., 294
Copsychus, 79
Corals, 27, 143
Coregonus, 63, 135
Corn plant, 10
Corvus, 171, 264, 265–266; *corax*, 57,
    89, 249
Cosmopolitan species, 211–13; parasites,
    210; speciation of, 212
Cotton species, 69
Courtship dances, 255
Courtship patterns, triple function, 254
Cowan, I. McT., 95, 131
Coyotes, 259
Craig, F. W., 198
Crampton, H. E., 8, 41, 80, 142, 220, 222
—— Grace S. Forbes and, 53
Crane, J., 255
Craspedophora, 260
Criteria of species, 113–22
Crossability, 119, 120
Crotalus and species, 179
Crows, 171, 264, 265
Crustaceans, 143, 213; size and distribu-
    tion of marine and land fauna, 234
Cryptopora, geographic races, 144
Ctenophthalmus agyrtes and *nobilis*, 231
Cuckoo bees, 278–279
Cuckoos, 56; parasitic, 55
Cuénot, L., 65, 103, 131, 144, 151, 199,
    218, 225, 253
    quoted, 149

Culcita, geographic races, 144
Cushing, J. E., 55, 256
Cuttlefish, 144, 199, 253
Cyanorhamphus auriceps forbesi, 235
Cyclic changes, 237, 238
Cyclomorphosis, 62
Cynipidae, 136, 166, 192, 268; polytypic species, 139
Cynips, 5, 8, 12, 30, 236; species, 139, 219, 221; *dugesi* complex, 139
Cypholoba, 139
Cypraea, 144; *carneola*, 145; *leviathan*, 145
Cyprinidae, 213, 271
Cyprinus carpio, 63

Dale, F. H., 90
Dall, W. H., quoted, 27
Daphnia, 46, 62, 192; *cucullata*, 62
Darwin, Charles, 3, 23, 36, 67, 109, 110, 113, 147, 156, 157, 162, 190, 277; quoted 115
Davenport, D., 105, 125, 137
Davis, W. B., 90
De Buck, A., Schoute, E., and Swellengrebel, N. H., 205
Deer mouse, 106, 235, 244; clines, 96; overlapping circle of races, 184
Degerbøl, M., 220
Degner, E., 142
Delacour, J., 79
Delichon urbica, 262
Delimitation of allochronic species, 153; allopatric species, 151–53; genera, 281; sympatric species, 149–51
Delkeskamp, K., 139
Dementiev, G. P., 196, 198, 264
Demigretta sacra, 78, 237, 243
Dendrobiastes bonthaina and *rufigula*, 173
Dendroica, 152, 171, 250; *dominica* and *potomac*, 150; *petechia*, 56
Dépèret, C., 294
Description, purpose of, 13
Diagnostic characters, 18–20, 289
Dice, L. R., 87, 94, 96, 106, 118, 131, 179, 193, 196, 228, 235, 244, 249, 255; quoted, 34, 85
—— Sumner, F. B., and, 64
—— and Blossom, P. M., 87, 233 quoted, 244
Dichoceros bicornis, 231
Dicranostephes, 169, 284
Dicrurus bracteatus, 169; *montanus* and *hottentottus*, 173

Diphyllodes, 260, 283; *magnificus*, 169
Diplopods, 142
Diptera, geographic variation, 140
Discontinuities, 23, 156, 157, 216; genetics of, 159; origin of, correlated with evolutionary changes, 147
Discontinuous variation, 71, 72–84
Dispersal, and geographic variation, 243–46; restriction of random, by geographic barriers, 226–38; by internal factors, 238–47
Diver, C., 3, 20, 62 64, 75, 80, 142, 202, 250, 255; quoted, 248
Diversity and divergence, 23, 216, 240
Dobzhansky, Theodosius, 3, 35, 42, 43, 45, 64, 65, 67, 68, 69, 71, 73, 74, 76, 80, 90, 115, 118, 131, 139, 152, 155, 158, 163, 188, 204, 209, 217, 220, 225, 256, 257, 259, 266, 292 quoted, 157, 276; species definition, 119
—— and Wright, S., 35
—— Mather, K.. and, 205
Doederlein, L., 115, 143, 144
Dollo's Law, 295
Dorylus, 30
Double invasions, 173–76
Doves, 57, 170, 239
Dowdeswell, W. H., Fisher, R. A., and Ford, E. B., 235
Draco, nonadaptive clines, 96
Dragon flies, 141, 177; habitats, 249
Drepanididae, 176, 271
Drosophila, 6, 13, 25, 45, 64, 74, 120, 140, 237; polytypic species with geographic races, 140; reduced fertility, 163; sibling group, 200; sterility of crossings, 259; wing vibrations, 255 species, 140; *americana*, 270; *funebris*, 46; *macrospina*, 140, 171; *melanogaster*, 10, 120, 140, 217; *pseudoobscura*, 35, 78, 140, 204, 208, 220
Dryadophis, 172, 177
Dual species, 151
Duck hawk, 53
Ducks, 219, 241, 243, 248; fertility, 259; pair formation, 241; sexual dimorphism: nuptial plumage, 52
Ducula pacifica, 167, 168; species, 170
Dunn, E. R., 47, 132, 135
Du Rietz, G. E., 103
Dynamics of species, 113

Earthworms, 143
Echiniscus intermedius, 213; *wendti*, 212

Echinodermes, 257
Echinometra lucunter, 144
Ecological race, 193–99
Ecological rules, 88–98; exceptions, 93; marine animals, 93
  applying to birds, 90; to mammals, 92; to snails, 92; to warm-blooded vertebrates, 90; to intraspecific variation, 94
Ecology, isolating factors, 247, 248–54; of speciation, 216; preferences, 53; relationship of related species, 250
Ecophenotypes, 27–29, 194
Ecotypes, 194
Egrets, 74
Eiselt, J., 132
Eller, K., 42, 136, 174
Elmidae, 284
Elton, C. S., 238, 246, 256
Emberiza melanocephala and *icterica*, 264
Emerson, A. E., 119, 204, 296
Empidonax, 116, 121, 255
Encaustes, 139
Endemism and ecology in birds, 232
Endrödi, S. von, 42, 139
Engagement period, 255, 260
Engel, H., 144
Engraulicypris, 271
Entoprocts, 191
Environment, adaptive responses to specific, 59 ff.; correlation between geographic variation and, 89; factors in ecologic races, 195; influencing speciation, 216, 217
Ephemerids, 198
Epidermal structure, subject to geographic variation, 41
Epimachus, 260
Eremophila, 86
Erinaceus, 267
Erosaria miliaris and *lamarckii*, 145
Erythropygia, 169
Ethological, definition, 254*n*
Ethological function, 254
Ethological isolating factors, 254–56
Eumeces schneideri, 132
Eupetes caerulescens and *nigricrissus*, 182
Eupithecia innotata Hufn., and *unedonata* Mab, 254
Eurygaster integriceps, 44
Eurystomus orientalis, 253
Eustephanus fernandensis and *galeritus*, 175
Evolution, accidental, 86; approach of geneticist and taxonomist to problems

of, 11; competition a retarding factor, 271; convergent, 294; divergent without origin of new species, 288; higher categories and, 275–98; importance of systematics in study of, 3; in small populations, 236; in the sea, 234; intraspecific, 291; processes, 291 ff.; rate of, 297; reticulate, 280; role played by selection, 270; significance of individual variation in study of, 32; slowness of, 218; specialization, 293; species in, 147–85; speed of, 223; stagnant, 217; study of factors of, 10; supraspecific, 275–91
Ewing, H. E., 143, 210
Expansion, range, 238 ff.
Explosive speciation in lakes, 213–15
Extinction species, 223–25

Faeroe house mouse, 220
Falco peregrinus, 53
Family, 102
Faunas, fresh-water, 214
Feeding habits, changes of, 209
Fence lizards, 241
Ferris, G. F., 11, 14
Fertility, reduction of, 163, 226, 257
Fertilization, individual, 257; in plants, 122; mass, 257
Fiddler crabs, 255
Fiedler, K., 5
Finnegan, S., 223
Fisher, R. A., 75, 135, 293
——, Dowdeswell, W. H., and Ford, E. B., 235
Fishes, 75, 79, 171, 196; barriers, 234; breeding season, 253; evolution, 221; habitat differences, 56; in isolated desert springs, 234; insular hybrids, 268; methods of reproduction, 257; phenotypical races, 63; racial studies of marine organisms made on, 144; seasonal races, 198; sedentary, 240
  fresh-water, 213; correlation between environment and body form 93; local races, 62; polytypic species, 135
Fitch, H. S., 133, 241, 262
Fleas, 143, 202
Fleming, C. A., 235, 251
Flies, 6, 140, 204; sibling species, 203
Floaters, 212
Flycatcher, 49, 81, 116, 255, 279
Forbes, Grace S., and Crampton, H. E., 53

Forbes. W. T. M., 184
Ford, E. B., 73, 75, 76, 80
——, Dowdeswell, W. H., Fisher, R. A., and, 235
Form, 108
Formenkreis, 111, 169
Foulehaio carunculata, 37
"Founder" principle, 237
Fox sparrow, 41
Frank, F., 90, fig. 91
Franz, V., 292
Fraser, A. C., Gordon M., and, 76, 106
Friedmann, H., 61
Fringilla coelebs, 54
Fringilla teydea and *coelebs canariensis*, 173
Frogs, 135, 178; grass, 47; temperature requirements, 46
Fruit doves, 170, 239
Fuchs, A., and Käufel, F., 41, 44, 142
Fulton, B. B., 204
Fungia fungites, geographic races, 143

Galactodes, 169
Galapagos finches, 109, 235
Galerita, 86
Gall insects, 210
Gallinula chloropus, 169
Gall mites, 210
Gall wasps, 5, 12, 30, 76, 166, 169, 192, 210, 219, 236; insular hybrids, 268; polytypic species, 125
Galton, F., 71
Gammarid crustaceans, 213
Gaps, *see* Allopatric species gaps; Sympatric species gaps
Garrulax pectoralis and *moniliger*, 201
Garrulus glandarius, 108
Garter snakes, 133, 134, 262
Gause, G. F., 143
Geese, 219, 243; social and reproductive habits, 242
Generations, alternating genetic, 30
Generic characters, 286
Genes, connection between body and, 68; loss in small populations, 235, 236, 237; multiple (pleiotropic) effect of, 292
Genetic basis of species formation, 69
Genetic changes, high frequency of small, 292
Genetic isolating factors, 258
Geneticists, approach to problems of evolution, 11; differences between taxonomists and, 10, 64; mutual understanding between systematists, and, 3
Genetics, most fundamental theses of, 64; of geographic variation, 59–70; of individual variability, 30; of speciation, 67
Genetics and the Origin of Species (Dobzhansky), 70
Genital armatures, 43, 44, 256
Gennaeus, 265
Genotypical variation, *see under* Variation, individual
Genus, 102; are borders real? 281; as a collective category, 289; attempts to combine two simultaneous functions in, 290; definition, 283; lacks objective reality, 281; monotypic, 213, 286; 287; morphological concept, 286; a natural unit? 290
Geographic race, *see* Subspecies
Geographic representation, 111
Geographic speciation, 166; alternatives, 186–89; definition, 155; depends on geographic variation, 127; process, 154–62; proof for, 162–185; *see also* speciation
Geographic variation, 23, 32, 33–70, 71–101; absence of, 146; adaptive, 85–88; all differences between species are subject to, 162; and population structure, 98–101; Call-notes of birds, 54; characters subject to, 36–59; coloration, 42; continuous, 71, 72, 84–85; courtship patterns, 55; cytological structures, 45; degree of, of related species in same region, 172; difficulties encountered in study of, 106; discontinuous, 71, 72–84; dispersal restricting factors and, 243–46; epidermal structure subject to, 41; exception to prevalence of, 128; general pigmentation, 42; genetics of, 59–70; genital armatures, 43; habitat preference, 56; habits and life history, 53; heterogynism, 50; in sclerotized structures, 42; internal structures, 44; irregular, 37; morphological characters, 36–45; of chromosome number, 45; of feeding habits or food preferences, 55; of number of molts, 52; of plumage changes, 50; physiological characters, 45–48, 52–53; physiology of plumage and plumage change in birds, 48–52; physiology of sex and reproduction:

Geographic variation (*Continued*)
hermaphroditism, 47; polymorphism, 77–84; proportions, 39–41; quantitative, qualitative, and meristic, 71; role of, 59; rules applying to warm-blooded vertebrates, 90; sex ratio, 48; sexual dimorphism, 48 ff., 52; skeleton, 41; species formation by, 180; temperature tolerance and preference, 45; throughout animal system, 127; vertical distribution, 57

Geospiza, hybrid populations, 268; *magnirostris* and *fortis*, 235

Geospizidae, 109, 175, 271

Gerhardt, U., 20

Gerould, J. H., 76

Gertsch, W., 5, 141

Ghigi, A., 265

Gislén, T., quoted, 212

Gliding intergradation, 84

Gloger, C. W. L., 89; ecological rule, 90

Glossina palpalis, 140

Gloyd, H. K., 133, 179

Goin, C. J., and Netting, M. G., 135

Golden pheasant, 259

Golden warbler, 56

Golden wasp, 210

Golden-winged warbler, 262

Goldfinch, 60, 262, 264

Goldschmidt, R., 43, 48, 52, 64, 65, 69, 112, 114, 118, 124, 127, 131, 137, 138, 148, 149, 162, 163, 184, 220, 222, 256, 297; on correlation of species formation with clines, 96; quoted, 73, 137, 155

Goodeidae, 136, 289

Goodey, T., 211

Gordon, M., 62, 64, 75, 76, 79
—— and Fraser, A. C., 76, 106

Gossypium, 69

Grackle, 266

Gradient of systematic categories, 172; character gradients, *see* clines

Grasshoppers, 87, 279, 290

Grassland birds, 197

Gray-cheeked thrush, 148

Great blue heron, 150

Great titmouse, 182

Great white heron, 150

Greenman, J. M., quoted, 283

Greenway, J., 224

Gregory, W. K., 292, 295

Griggs, R. F., 292

Grinnell, J., 56, 131, 246

Grobman, A. B., 133

Group, 108

Group variation, 23

Grütte, E., 278, 279

Gulick, J. T., 142

Gypsy moth, 48

Haas, F., 28

Habitat, differences, 57, 248–51; forms, 27–29, 62; preferences, 267; selection, 246; specialization, 193

Habits and life history, 53

Haecker, V., 74

Halcyon chloris, 167, 181, 182; *leucocephala*, 189

Hall, E. R., 131
—— and Hoffmeister, D. F., 37

Handlirsch, A., quoted, 289

Haplochilichthys pelagicus, 271

Harland, S. C., 68, 69

Harmonia axyridis, color variants, 80

Hart, J. L., Tester, A. L., and McHugh, J. L., 241

Hartert, E., 49, 86, 112 *tab.*, 124, 126, 132

Hasebroek, K., 220

Hawks, 41, 78, 290; change in pigmentation, 88

Head louse, 210

Hedgehog, 255, 267

Heikertinger, F., 17

Heincke, F., 144

Heinroth, O., 242, 256, 296

Helicidae, geographic variation, 92

Helicigona, 125, 290

Helix aspersa, 248; *pomatia*, 62

Hellmayr, C. E., 50

Helmcke, J.-G., 144

Hemiptera, 141, 171, 172, 174, 223

Hen-feathered bird races, 48

Hennig, W., 96, 289

Herald, E. S., 146

Hereditary variation, *see under* Variation, individual

Heredity, *see* Blending inheritance; Mendelian inheritance

Hering, M., 151, 204

Hermaphroditism, 47, 128, 191

Hermit thrush, 148

Herons, 237; polymorphism among, 73

Herpetology, 132

Herre, A. W. C. T., 213

Herre, W., 135, 178

Herring, 145, 198, 253

Herter, K., 46, 255, 267

Hertwig, P., 259
Hesse, R., Allee, W. C., and Schmidt, K. P., 234
Heterodera schachti, 211
Heterogynism, definition, 50
Heterozygotes, 204
Hickey, J., 54
Hiesey, W. M., Clausen, J., and Keck, D. D., quoted, 193
Hile, R., 62, 63, 135
—— and Juday, Ch., 56
Hindwood, K. A., 224
Hinton, H. E., 284
Hippolais, species pairs, 178
Hirudinea, 191
Hirundo rustica, 262
Hoffmeister, D. F., E. R. Hall and, 37
Hogben, L., 186, 191, 192, 254
Holotype, 15
Homing, 240, 241–43
Homogeneity, genetic: of small populations, 235, 236
Homozygosity, 204
Honeybee, 139
Honey eaters, size variation, tab. 39; structural polymorphism, 80
Hooper, E. T., 233, 245
Hornbill, 41, 230
Horned lark, 86
Host races, 209; conditioning to new, 210
House finch, 60
House sparrow, 60, 182, 241, 268
House wren, 237
Hovanitz, W., 52, 87, 90
Howard, H., and Miller, A. H., 224
Hubbell, Th. H., 7, 136, 140
Hubbs, C. L., 6n, 62, 64, 69, 93, 135, 221, 234, 268, 289
—— and Bailey, R. M., 268
—— and Turner, C. L., 136, 289
Huestis, R. R., Yocum, H. B., and, 45
Human anatomy, differences between races, 44
Human lice, 210
Hummingbirds, 41, 56 121, 175, 260; geographic variation, 83
Husted, L., and Ruebush, T. K., 45, 143
Hutchinson, J. B., 69
Huxley, J. S., 3, 6, 95, 113, 131, 173, 216, 254, 266, 272, 293; quoted, 188, 189, 196, 226
Hyalomma, 141
Hybridization, 258; allopatric, 259; due to human interference, 262; inter-

generic, 260; introgressive, 74; speciation associated with, 119, 270; sympatric, 259; zones of, 188; *see also under* Intergradation
Hybrid populations or hybrid zones, 263–70; narrowness, 266; stabilized, 265, 268, 270; variability, 268
Hybrid fertility in birds, 259
Hybrids, 178, 180; common in nature, 122; occasional, between sympatric species, 260–63
Hybrid swarms, 122; in animals, 149
Hylocichla and species, 148
Hymenoptera, differences of appearance in sexes, 30; parasitic, 6, 139; polytypic species, 139

Icerya purchasi, 191
Identification, 9, 12
Inbreeding, geese, 242; obligatory close-inbreeding, 192
Incipient species, 155
Individuals, speciation through, 190
Individual variation, *see* Variation, individual
Insects, 176; background selection, 87; changes in feeding habits, 209, 210; correlation between climate and pigment, 90; ecological barriers, 231; genital armatures, 43; geographic variation of polymorphism in, 80; giant genera, 290; hybrids, 265; orientation by visual cues, 241; origin of dangerous pests of cultivated plants, 209; polytypic species, 136–41; reduced fertility, 163; speed of speciation, 223; structural polymorphism, 80; subspecies, 125; variability of social, 29
Instantaneous speciation, *see* Speciation, sympatric instantaneous
Insular hybrid populations, 268
Interbreeding, intraspecific, 223, 258; random, 225; *see also* Hybridization; Panmixia
Intergeneric crosses, *see* Hybridization, intergeneric
Intergradation, between species, 114; between subspecies, 106; intergradation principle, 133; origin of species gaps in zones of, 188; zone of, 98, 99, 100, 188, 263, 265, 266
Internal factors, restriction of random dispersal, 238–47

Internal structures, geographic variation, 44
"International Rules of Zoological Nomenclature," 13, 16
Invasions, border, 176–80; double, 173–76; multiple, 157
Invertebrates, aberrant characters, 236; polytypic species, 142; variability, 219
Ipswich sparrow, 164, 222
Irreversibility, 295
Islands, as evolutionary traps, 224, 225; ecological competition, 250; reason for active speciation in, 227; role in extinction process, 224; speciation, 173, 227; species, 236
Isolated forms, 164
Isolating mechanisms, 23, 225; and the method of reproduction, 257; breakdown of, and its consequences, 258–70; classification, 247; conditioned habits as, 55; ecological factors, 247, 248–54; ethological factors, 254–56; habitat differences, 248–51; of plants, 273; mechanical factors, 256; restriction of random mating, 226, 247–57; two classes of, 226
Isolation, by habitat, 232; effects of, 179; geographic, 226, 229; incompleteness of, 245; in the sea, 234; isolative factors and species formation, 225; reproductive, 119 ff., 152, 164, 248, 255; seasonal, 251–54; see also Populations, isolated
Ivie, W., Chamberlin, R. V., and, 141

Jaworski, E., 143
Jennings, H. S., 207
Jensen, A. J. C., quoted, 145
Johansson, K. E., 5, 67
Johnson, C. G., 210
Jordanons, 122
Jordan, K., 111, 112, 124, 136, 143, 202, 231
Journal of Mammalogy, 131
Juday, Ch., Hile, R., and 56
Junonia lavinia, 183
Junco, 8, 85, 170, 171, 172, 229, 265; hiemalis cismontanus 270
Junge, G. C. A., 251
Juvenile stages, 25

Kaltenbach, H., 93
Kattinger, E., 41
Käufel, F., Fuchs, A., and, 41, 44, 142

Kautz, H., Müller, L., and, 8, 52, 56, 202
Kea, 209
Keck, D. D., Hiesey, W. M., Clausen, J., and, quoted, 193
Keeler, C. E., and King, H. D., quoted, 88
Kendeigh, Ch., 237
Kerkis, J., 44
Key characters, 18–20, 289
Kimball, R. F., 207
King, H. D., Keeler, C. E., and, quoted, 88
Kingfisher, 152, 153, 167, 181, 199, 236; racket-tailed, 41
King parrot, 30
Kinsey, A. C., 3, 5, 8, 12, 30, 76, 118, 123, 124, 136, 139, 162, 166, 169, 192, 210, 218, 236, 265, 268, quoted, 117
Klauber, L. M., 41, 133, 135, 267
Kleinschmidt, O., 86, 87, 111, 112, 113, 114, 126, 169
Klemm, W., 30, 92, 142, 178
Knipper, H., 92, 93, 125, 142, 290
Kobelt, W., 142
Koch, C., 139
Koelz, W., 62
Kramer, G., and Mertens, R., 203, 222, 234, 245
Kratz, W., 141
Krumbiegel, I., 46, 53, 93, 96, 139, 296

Lacerta lepida and species, 171
—— muralis and melisselensis, 203
—— sicula, 46, 203, 222, 234, 245
—— vivipara, 46
Lack, David, 60, 132, 176, 235, 246, 249, 250, 270, 271
  quoted, 268
Ladybird beetle, 35, 74; color variants, 80
Lady bug, 76
Lagopus lagopus, 165
—— scoticus, 165, 222
Lakes, fresh-water: species flocks in, 214
Lalage, 182; species, 40, 42, 50, 51, 172, 173
Land snails, 142
Lanius, 171; collurio kobylini, loudoni, and phoenicuroides, 264
Larius (Eclectus) roratus, 30
Larks, 87, 246; cryptically colored, 86
Larus, 171; argentatus, 180, 182, 251; fuscus 251
Larvae, development, 25, 52

Lasiocampa quercus, 163
Lates, 215, 272
Latimeria, 5
Lawrence's warbler, 262
Leiocidaris pistillaris, geographic races, 143
Lepidopterorum Catalogus, 137
Lepus, 220
Lesser Snow Goose, 150, 242
Leucichthys artedi, 62
Lieftink, M. A., 141
Life cycle of species, 25, 224
Limanda limanda, 145
Limax, 20
Limnaea peregra, 64
Lincoln, F., 241
Lingula, 217
Linnaeus, 109, 111, 112, 150
  genus concept, 286; species concept, 102, 103, 108, 110, 111, 115, 117, 125; *Systema Naturae*, 115; terminology for systematic categories, 102, 108
Linsdale, J., 41, 132
Lissner, H., 146
Literature, application of polytypic species in modern zoölogical writing, 130; taxonomic zoölogical, 131
Littorina obtusa, 35
Lizards, 171, 203, 222, 234, 241, 245
  temperature preference, 46
Localization of individuals, 240
Locard, A., 28, 61
Lonchura and species, 230
Lophorina, 260
Lorenz, K., 256, 296
Loss convergences, 278, 279
Lotsy, J. P., 118, 155, 259
Louse, 143
Lowe, P. R., 270
Ludwig, W., 86
Lumpers and splitters, 178, 280
Luscinia, species pairs, 263
Lybius torquatus, 77
Lycaena, 255
Lygaeid bugs, 176
Lymantria, 64; *dispar*, 48, 52, 137, 138, 163; *mathura* and *monacha*, 137, 138; polytypic species, 137; species and subspecies, 138
Lymnaea, 53, 61, 62, 142
Lynes, H., 12, 52, 132
Lyrurus tetrix, 261

Macgregoria, 260

Machairodontidae, 294
McHugh, J. L., Hart, J. L., Tester, A. L., and, 241
Mackerel, 146
McMasters, J. H., Schenk, E. T., and, 11, 16
Macrobiotus hufelandii, 212
Macroevolution, 291–98
Macroevolutionary principles, 293–98
Macrolepidoptera, 137
Macrotaxonomic characters, 297
Macrotaxonomy, 275–91
Magicicada septendecim, 198
Malaria mosquitoes, 205
Mammals, adaptive variation, 85 ff.; background adaptation, 87; dispersal faculty, 245; ecological rules applying to, 92; literature, 131; polytypic species, 131; variability in endemic races of rock-inhabiting, 244
Manakins, 261
Manton, I., 122
Manucodia, 200, 260, 283
Marcus, E., 212, 213
Marine animals, ecological rules, 93; individual fertilization, 257; microscopic, 5; polytypic species, 143; show little variation in space, 128; slowness of evolution, 218; speciation, 223; temperature races found in, 46
Marsupials, 61, 294
Martes foina, and *martes*, 202
Martin, R. F., 122
Material, available for taxonomic work, 7; collecting of, 12
Mather, K., 293
—— and Dobzhansky, Th., 205
Mathews, G. M., 281, 286
Mating, effect of behavior differences, 254; interspecific, 254, 255; reduction of success, 256; restriction of random, 226, 247–57
Mating types, 207
Mayflies, 141, 198
Mayr, E., 37, 38, 41, 42, 49, 50, 51, 56, 57, 82, 97, 115, 124, 129, 132, 152, 159, 167, 169, 170, 173, 180, 181, 197, 200, 201, 221, 223, 227, 228, 232, 239, 240, 249, 251, 260, 261, 268, 270, 281, 288; quoted, 118, 120, 165
—— and Amadon, D., 78, 237
—— and Ripley, D., 40, 42
—— and de Schauensee, R. M., 38
—— and Serventy, D. L., 90, 174

Mayrornis versicolor, and *lessoni orientalis*, 175
Measurements, value of, 14
Mechanical isolating factors, 256
Megalurus timoriensis and subspecies, 233
Megapodius, 57, 152, 167, 268
Meinertzhagen, R., 86, 167
Meise, W., 50, 77, 92, 132, 141, 152, 170, 262, 264, 265, 266, 268, 270
Melania, 144; species, 31
Melanins, geographic variation, 90
Melanism, 73
Melanocichla lugubris, 169
Melidectes belfordi, 197; races and subspecies, 80
—— *leucostephes*, 39
Melipotes, and species 38
Mell, R., 41
Melopsittacus undulatus, 60
Melospiza melodia, 56, 237, 246, 249
Mendelian inheritance, 65, 67
Meristic variation, 71
Mertens, R., 124, 132, 171, 178, 236, 253
—— and Müller, L., 135
——, Kramer, G., and 203, 222, 234, 245
Mesostoma ehrenbergii and *wardii*, 45
Metazoa, 191
Mice, 31, 131, 179, 184, 220; cline, 96; geographic variation of size in meadow, 90; habitats, 250
Microevolution, 291
Microscelis leucocephalus, 83
Microscopic animals, carried by wind currents, 212
Microsubspecies, 107, 194, 195
Microtus, 90
Migratory behavior, 55
Miller, A H., 8, 32, 85, 124, 132, 156, 171, 246, 165, 270
—— Howard, H., and, 224
Mirafra africanoides, *fasciolata deserti*, and *sabota hoeschi*, 247
Miro traversi, 235
Misogamy, *see* Reproductive isolation
Missing link between reptiles and birds, 296
Mites, red, 5
Mockingbirds, begging postures, 55
Modifiers, 68
Moffit, J., 132, 242
Mollusks, habitat forms, 27; marine, 61, 144; polytypic species, 142
Molting period of birds, 50

Monarcha castaneoventris, 81, 152; species 82, 218
Monophyletic, definition, 280
Monophyletic category, 276
Moore, J. A., 46, 47, 135
Moose, 31
Moreau, R. E., 222
Morgan, T. H., 67
Morphological characters, 19, 36–45; size variation, 36; which tend to be correlated with climatic factors, 95
Morphological genera, 167
Morphological genus concept, 286
Mosquitoes, malaria, 205
Motacilla cinerea, 239
——*flava*, 53
Moths, 52, 179, 209, 220, 248, 254; hybrids, 265; polytypic species, 136; reduced fertility, 163
Mountains, speciation in, 229, 234
Mouse flea, 231
Moy-Thomas, J. A., Arkell, W. J., and, 279, 289
Muller, H. J., 45, 64, 124, 132, 159, 292, 293, 295, 296
Müller, L., and Kautz, H., 8, 52, 56, 202
——Mertens, R., and, 135
Murie, A., 184
Murphy, R. C., 49, 92
Murre, clines, 95, 96
Muscicapa, species pairs, 178
Muscicapidae, 279
Musculus faeroeensis, 220
Museum specimens, color deterioration, 29
Mussels, fresh-water, 28
phenotypic variation, 61
Mutability factors, influencing speciation, 216, 217
Mutation concept, 65
Mutation rates, 217
Mutations. 292; definition, 66; homologous series of, 73; nature of, 67; random, 295; recessive, 234; recurrent, 225; reversible, 293, 296; small, 67; systemic, 155, 297; *see also* Geographic variation
Myers, R. B., 93
Myiolestes megarhynchus, 42, 43
Myriapods, 142
Myrmotherula longipennis and subspecies, 228
——*menetriesii* and subspecies, 228

Nabours, R. K., 73
Names, basis of, 16; use of vernacular and Latin, 105
Nasutitermes, 204
Natrix sipedon, 249
Natural system, 275; advantages, difficulties, 276
Nematode, 191, 211
Nemeophila plantaginis, 163
Neseis, 171, 176; species, 173
Nesospiza acunhae and *wilkinsi*, 175
Nestor notabilis, 209
Nests, 53
Netolitsky, F., 90
Netting, M. G., Goin, C. J., and, 135
New Systematics, The, 4
Newts, 178
Nice, M. M., 56, 237, 241
Niche characteristics, *see* Ecological factors
Niethammer, G., 86; quoted, 246
Nile perch, 215
Noble, G. K., 241
Nomenclature, binary and binomial, 108; difficulties caused by name-changing, 17; rules, 16; ternary, 110
Nongenetic variation, *see under* Variation, individual
Non-segregation of species characters, 68
Novitski, E., Sturtevant, A. H., and, 74, 294
Nuthatch, species and subspecies, 126
Nyroca, 219
Nysius, 174, 176, 239

Oberholser, H. C., 281, 286
Objectivity of a systematic unit, 148, 280
Obligatory close-inbreeding, 192
Ocean, *see* Sea
Oceanic islands, defined, 173
Oedirhinus, 167, 284
Oenothera, 66
Ökland, F., 113, 124, 136
Oldham, Ch., 62
Old World flycatchers, 279
Oligochaeta, 191
Olive-backed thrush, 148
Oliver, W. R. B., 77
Orcula, 171, 178
Organic reconstruction, *see* Reconstruction, organic
Organisms, classification of, 275
Origin of Species (Darwin), 3, 109, 147

Ornithology, subspecies concept, 129; polytypic species, 132
Orr, R. T., 131
Orthogenesis, 293
Orthogenetic series, 291
Orthonyx, 169
Orthoptera, geographic variation, 140
Oryctes, 42; *nasicornis*, 139
Osborn, H. F., on speciation and mutation, 66
Osgood, W. H., 184
Ostrea virginica, 27
Oudemans, A. C., 5
Overlap, of terminal links of same species, 180–85; partial distributional, 176–85
Overlapping ranges, 250, 251
Ovis, 265
Ownbey, M., 122
Oyster, 27

Pachycephala, 82, 200, 250; hybrid populations, 152, 268, 269, 270; *pectoralis*, 42, 48, 50, 57, 125, 218
Pachyptila and species, 251
Pagodulina, 30, 92, 178
Pair formation, 255, 260; and population structure, 242
Paleontology, 289, 292; species concept, 153
Paludan, K., 264
Panmixia, 225, 226, 234, 236, 241
Papilio machaon and *hospiton*, 174
Papuorthonyx, 169
Paradigalla, 260; *brevicauda* and *carunculata*, 40
Paradisaea, 97, 130, 169, 260, 283; *see also* Birds of paradise
Paradisaeidae, 116, 260
Paradise flycatcher, 79
Paramecium, 152, 207
Parasites, 6, 139, 210, 231
Parasitism, 279
Paratypes, 15
Paripotency, 74
Parnassius literature, 137
Parotia, 153, 170, 260
Parrot, 37, 209, 235; king, 30
Parthenogenesis, 28, 191
Partula, 8, 142, 220, 222
Parula warbler (*P. americana*), 150
Parus atricapillus, correlation between climate and feather pigments, 90; *caeruleus* and *cyanus*, hybrids, 262; *major*, 182

Passer, hybrid populations, 268, 270; *domesticus*, 60, 182, 241; *hispaniolensis*, 182

Passerculus princeps, 164, 222; *sandwichensis savanna*, 56, 164

Passerella iliaca, 41

Patterson, J. T., 6, 45, 69, 140, 164, 171, 200, 270

Pediculus, 210

Pennatula phosphorea, 143

Peregrine falcon, 53

Pericrocotus brevirostris and *ethologus*, 201

Peromyscus, 31, 34, 40, 64, 87, 131, 196, 249, 250; *leucopus* and *gossypinus*, 179; *maniculatus* and subspecies, 45, 85, 94, 96, 106, 235, 244; overlapping circle of races, 184; *polionotus*, 245

Peters, J. L., 167, 281

Petersen, W., 209, 255

Petroica multicolor, 48

Phaeomelanin, geographic variation, 90

Phasianidae (pheasants), 116, 248, 259, 265; fertility, 259

Phenotypical changes, in birds, 60; in cold-blooded animals, 61–63; *see also* Variation, individual

Phenotypical races, 194

Philiptschenko, J., 23

Phillips, J. C., 60

Phlegopsis nigromaculata, geographic races, 228

Phonygammus, 260

Phylloscopus, 8, 20, 55, 250, 255; overlap of terminal links of subspecies, 182, 183; species and races, 54, 95, 125, 182

Phylogenetic system, 276 ff.

Phylogenetic tree, 281, 291

Physiological characteristics, geographic variation, 45–53; Physiological factors, influencing speciation, 216

Pickford, G. E., 143

Pictet, A., 163, 264

Pieris and species, 8, 53, 56; sibling species, 202

Pigeons, 167, 248, 290; fertility, 259; pituitary of domestic, 45

Pigmentation, geographic variation, 42, 87

Pimelia, 139, 228

Pinarolestes, 169

Pipridae, 261

Pitohui dichrous, 94

Pitta kochi and *erythrogaster*, 173

Pituophis and species, 179

Planaria alpina, 47

Planarians, 143

Plant lice, 192

Plants, adaptability to local conditions, 59; clines, 98; differences in speciation of animals and, 273; double invasion of islands, 173; geographic speciation, 122

Plate, L., 234

Platyhelminthes, 191

Platypoecilus, 106, 136; species, 75, 79, 171

Platysamia, 248, 265; *cecropia* and related species, 179

Pleiotropic genes, 88

Plesicoris rugicollis, 209

Plethodontidae, 166

Pleuronectes platessa, 145

Plumage, geographic variation of, changes, 50; physiology of, and plumage change, 48–52

Pocket gophers, size variation, 90

Podargus, 37

Pogonofora, 5

Pogonomyrmex, 203

Poikilothermal animals, *see* Insects; Snails

Polistes, 90, 139

Polychaetes, 257

Polychromatism, 72n

Polyembryony, 192

Polygenes, 292

Polymorphism, 31, 72–77, 220; and speciation, 80; balanced, 76; classification of, 75; found in *Bombus*, 139; geographically variable, 77–84; neutral, 75; structural, 80; transient, 76, 81

Polyommatus icarus, 235

Polyploidy, 122, 191, 225

Polytypic species, *see* Species, polytypic

Populations, basic taxonomic unit, 7; changes from population to, 98; concept of isolated, as incipient species, 33; definition, 24; determining characters of, 25; differences between local, 33–36; fluctuating, 237; hybrid, 152, 263–70; isolated, 38, 100, 116, 152, 158, 225, 235 (*see also* Isolating mechanism; Isolation); local, 24, 225; shifting, 239; size and variability, 234–37; structure and variation, 98–101

Porphyriornis, 169
Porthetria, 137
Poulton, E. B., 148*n*
Predation, 272
Priority, law of, 16
Progomphus, and species, 177, 250
Promptoff, A., 54
Proportions, geographic variation of organs and body structures, 39–41
Proterhinus weevils, 176
Protozoa, 128, 143, 191; transportation, 212
Protura, 212
Pseudechiniscus suillus, 212
Pseudemys floridana, 249
Psittrichas fulgidus, 37
Ptilinopus, species, and subspecies, 57, 167, 170, 172, 175, 239
Ptiloprora guisei, 197
Pulmonate Mollusca, 191
Pupillidae, 22
Purple grackle, 265

Qualitative variation, 71
Quantitative variation, 71
Quiscalus, 266; species, 264, 265

Rabbits, 131, 221
Races, altitudinal, 196 ff.; ecological, 193–99; formation of local, 243; geographic, *see* geograhpic variation; seasonal, 198; temperature, 46
Ramme, W., 140, 290
Ramsbottom, J., 102
Rana, physiological races, 47, 135; *esculenta*, 47, 135, 178, 253; *pipiens*, 46, 47; *ridibunda*, 178, 253; *temporaria*, 47
Rand, A., 92, 94, 197, 232, 260
Range expansion, 238 ff.
Ranges, interlacing of, 267; overlapping, 250–251
Rangifer, 41
Rassenkreis, 111, 112, 113, 114, 138, 162, 173
Ratites, 278, 294
Rats, pleiotropic genes, 88
Rattlesnakes, 179
Raven, 57; geographic variation, 89
Recognition marks, 254
Recombinations, 67
Reconstruction, organic: harmonius, 295
Red fox, clinical variation of polymorphism, 95

Red grouse, 165, 222
Red-shafted flicker, 265
Reed, S. C., 205
Reef heron, 237; color phases, 78
Reinig, W. F., 56, 80, 139, 222, 236, 264
Reisen in der Regentschaft Algier (Wagner), 228
Remane, A., 5, 65
Rensch, B., 3, 11, 32, 34, 41, 44, 53, 59, 61, 62, 78, 90, 92, 93, 94, 103, 108, 112, 124, 130, 141, 142, 143, 162, 163, 165, 169, 170, 171, 173, 182, 193, 194, 214, 219, 245, 288, 292, 293, 295; ecological rules, 89; quoted, 22, 105, 106, 126 f.; survey of occurrence of geographic variation, 128; wing rule, 95
Reproduction, isolating mechanism and the method of, 257; physiological factors subject to geographic variation, 47
Reproductive isolation, 119 ff., 152, 164, 255
Reptiles, 41, 46, 218, 294, 296; aberrant characters, 236; literature, 132; polytypic species, 132; temperature preference, 46; *see also* Crocodiles; Lizzards; Snakes; Turtles
Reversibility, 295
Rhinocheilus, 267
Rhipidura, 82, 218; *flabellifera*, 76; *rufifrons*, 47, 218
Rhynchocephalians, 218
Richards, O. W., 254; quoted, 278; Robson, G. C., and, 23, 73, 103, 131, 218, 226
Richter, R., 251
Ridgeway, R., 286
Riech, E., 31, 142, 144
Riparia obsoleta and *rupestris*, 167
Ripley, D., 52
—— and Birckhead, 239
—— Mayr, E. and, 40, 42
Rivers, as barriers, 228
Roberts, A., 281, 286
Roberts, H. R., quoted, 279
Robson, G. C., and Richards, D. W., 23, 73, 103, 131, 218, 226
Rodeheffer, I. A., quoted, 241
Rodents, 87; *see also* Mice; Rabbits; Rats
Roe, A., Simpson, G. G., and, 14, 71, 135
Romanes, G. J., quoted, 120
Romeria, 296
Rost, H., 45
Rotifers, 128; transportation, 212

Round worm, 210
Ruebush, T. K., Husted, L., and, 45, 143
Rümmler, H., 131
Runnström, Sven, 46
Rusts, 220

Salamanders, 166; spotted, 47
Salomonsen, F., 77, 79, 177, 178
Salt, George, 211
Salvelinus, 135
Sarasin, F. and P., 142
Savanna sparrow, 56, 164
Scale insects, resistance to poisons, 220
Sceloporus occidentalis, 241
Schauensee, R. M. de, Mayr, E., and 38
Schenk, E. T., and McMasters, J. H.,
  11, 16
Schiermann, G., 53
Schilder, F. A., and Schilder, M., 124,
  144, 145
Schindewolf, O. H., 279, 292, 296, 297
Schizotypische Artzerplitterung, 214
Schlegel, H., 110
Schmidt, K. P., Hesse, R., Allee, W.C., 234
Schlegelia, 169
Schnakenbeck, W., 145, 198, 253
Schnitzer, H., quoted, 28
Schoute, E., De Buck, A., and Swellen-
  grebel, N. H., 205
Sclerotized structures, geographic varia-
  tion in, 42
Scorpions, 50; polytypic species, 141
Sea, isolation and evolution in the, 234
Sea birds, 237
Sea-feather, 143
Seasonal generations, 26
Seasonal isolation, 251–54
Seasonal races, 198
Seasonal variation, 26
Sea star, 144
Sea urchin, geographic races, 143
Secondary intergradation, 157
Seitz, A., 42, 137
Selasphorus alleni and race sedentarius
  Grinnell, 56
Selection, 70, 292, 293, 295
Selective factors, and species formation,
  270–73
Selective process, see Adaptation; Adap-
  tive variation
Selenia, 122
Seleucides, 260; ignotus, 29
Semenov-Tian-Shansky, A., 103
Semi-species, 165

Separation theory, 157
Sepia officinalis, 144, 199, 253
Serinus canaria serinus, 238
Serresius, 167, 168, 284
Serventy, D. L., Mayr, E., and, 90, 174
Seventeen-year cicada, 198
"Sewall Wright effect," 192, 195
Sewertzoff, A. N., 292
Sex races, 47, 48
Sex stuff, 258
Sexual armatures, 43, 44, 256
Sexual attraction, reduced, 163
Sexual dimorphism, 30, 260, 261; in
  birds, 48 ff.
Sexual isolation, 163
Sexual selection, intraspecific, 254
Seymouria, 296
Sheep, 131, 265
Shells, marine: polytypic species, 145
Shih, C. H., 62
Shrimps, fresh-water, 214
Sibling species, 116, 139, 140, 150, 151,
  200–208, 210, 288; definition, 151, 200
Sick, H., 54
Silow, R. A., 69
Silver pheasants, 265
Simms, A. D., quoted, 209
Simpson, G. G., 224
—— and Roe, A., 14, 71, 135
Sitta, 126, 264
Size, a taxonomic character, 36; increase,
  in phylogeny, 293
Slugs, 20
Smith, C. C., Bragg, A. N. and, 203
Snails, 8, 22, 30, 34, 44, 62, 105, 176,
  178, 194, 219, 220, 222, 229, 243, 290;
  ecological rules applying to, 92; geographic variation, 41; land, 142; polytypic species, 125; sibling species, 202;
  spiraling of shells, 80; superspecies,
  polytypic species, 171; fresh-water, 28,
  62; geographic variation of microgeographic races, 53; phenotypic variation, 61
—garden, 32, 34, 75, 78, 105; color
  patterns, 78
Snakes, 172, 177, 179, 262, 267; habitats,
  249
Snedecor, G. W., 135
Soil, correlation between coloration and,
  86
Solaster papposus, 144
Song birds, inheritance of song patterns,
  256; races, 54

Song sparrow, 56, 237, 246, 249

Sonneborn, T. M., 207

Southern, H. N., 95, 96

Sparrows, 56, 164; hybrid populations, 268; *see also* Song sparrows

Specialization, 294

Speciation, alternatives to geographic, 186–89; biology of, 216–74; by force of distance, 180; by isolation, 225; classification of processes, 187; clines and, 96; definition: dual meaning, 23, 155; depends on geographic variation, 127; differences in, in plants and animals, 273; effects of geographic isolation on, 100; explosive, in lakes, 213–15; extinction the counterpart of, 223; factors influencing, 216; genetic basis, 64–70; geographic process, 154–62, 166;importance of host races, 209; influence of competition and predation on, 271 ff.; influence of population size, 236; in mountains, 229, 234; instantaneous, 225; instantaneous or gradual, 187; internal factors, 217–25; island, 173; isolative factors and, 225, 257; nongeographic, 186–215; of cosmopolitan species, 212; primarily external factors, 225–47; reduction of mating success, 256; restriction of random mating (biological isolating mechanisms), 226, 247–57; role of competition, 271; selective factors and species formation, 270–73; semigeographic, 188; speed of, 220–23; stages of, 159–62; through hybridization, 270; through individuals, 190; types of, 186; without much evolutionary divergence, 288

sympatric, 187, 189–215, 272; evidence for, very scanty, 215; gradual, 192; instantaneous, 190–92

Species, 102

characters, 116, 162

classification, 10; *see also* Taxonomic characters); composed of genetically different populations, 64; continental, 162; cosmopolitan, 211–13; criteria and definitions, 113–22, 247; description, 18; description of a new, 13; different kinds of, 114; dynamics of, 113; effect of change in criteria, 111; extinction, 223–25; formation, *see* Speciation; gaps, 148–62, 188; hybrids between sympatric, 260–63; identification of,

9; incipient, 155; instantaneous creation of, 296; intermediates between, 110; isolated, 111, 162, 166, 237, 239; origin of, 3, 147, 187 (*see also* Speciation); *ortstreue* (philopatric), 195; panmictic, 225, 226, 234, 236, 241; polymorphic, 237; reaction system, 69; species flocks in fresh-water lakes, 214; species group, as a subgeneric unit, 290; "species" of the paleontologist, 154; subdivisions, 7, 193; use of trinomials for geographic subdivisions of, 110; ways of delimiting, 148; without geographic variation, 128

in evolution, 147–85; borderline cases, 164; gaps between allopatric species, 148–54; process of geographic speciation, 154–62; proof, 162–85

monotypic, definition, 113; prevalence of, in groups of animals, 124, 146

polytypic, 111, 114, 116, 166, 286; amphibia, 135; application, 128–30; application of concept in taxonomic groups, 130–46; arachnids, 141; beetles, 139; birds, 132; butterflies and moths, 136; concept based on principle of geographic variation, 127; definition, 113; flies, 140; fresh-water fish, 135; hymenoptera, 139; in nature and in systematics, 123–46; insects, 136–41; mammals, 131; marine animals, 143–46; mollusks, 142; other invertebrates, 142; prevalence of, 123–25; reptiles, 132; vertebrates, 131–36

Species concept: based on sterility, 119; biological, 119; changing, 108–13, 129; genetic, 118; morphological, 115–18, 121; new, 102–22; practical, 115

Specific recognition marks, 254, 261

Spencer, W. P., 69, 140, 163, 200

Speyer, W., 52

Sphaerophoria scripta and *menthastri*, 203

Spiders, 5, 212; geographic variation, 141

Spieth, H., 141, 265

Spizitornis fernandezianus and *parvulus*, 38

Splitters, and lumpers, 280

Splitting, excessive, 286 ff.

Sponges, 257, 191

Spore formation, 191

Stability, the basic principle of the rules, 17

Stadler, L. J., 67

Stagnation, evolutionary, 217

Stalker, H., 164
Starling, 29, 37, 171
Statistical methods, 135
Stegmann, B., 132
Steinmann, P., 135, 178
Stephenson, T. A., 143
Sterility, 163, 257; species concept based on, 119
Stiasny, G., 144
Stresemann, E., 40, 75, 76, 77, 79, 92, 108, 132, 158, 167, 177, 250, 251, 264, 270, 281, 288; quoted, 119
Streuli, A., 202
Strohmeyer, G., 139
Strouhal, H., 35
Stuart, L. C., 132, 172, 177
Stull, O. G., 179
Sturnus vulgaris, 29
Sturtevant, A. H., 69, 74
—— and Novitski, E., 74, 294
Subgenus, 290
Subspeciation, by distance, 244; degree of, 245; influence of population size, 236; polymorphism and, 80; speed of, 220
Subspecies, 102, 193, 194; age of, 221 all genetically different, 118; altitudinal, 197; border-line cases, 164, 170; definition, 106; diagnosis, 13; microsubspecies, 107, 194, 195; originally described as species, 130; practical aspects, 106; range of, 219
Suchetet, A., 262
Sumner, F. B., 87, 118, 245
—— and Dice, L. R., 64
Superspecies, border cases, 169, 171; definition, 169
Supraspecies, term, 169*n*
Sutton, G. M., 242, 243
Swallow-tail butterflies, 136, 174
Swamping, 244, 245
Swarth, H. S., 223
Sweadner, W. R., 179, 248, 265
Swellengrebel, N. H., De Buck, A., Schoute, E., and, 205
Sympatric, definition, 148
Sympatric hybridization, *see* Hybridization, sympatric
Sympatric species gaps, 148–54; gaps between sympatric and allopatric, 154–62
Sympatric species, delimitation, 149–51; reproductive isolation, 121
Sympatric speciation, 187, 189–215, 260–63, 272

Syngnathus californiensis, 146
Synoicus ypsilophorus and subspecies, 233
Synonyms, 16
Syrphidae, 140
Syrphus, 203
Systema Naturae (Linnaeus), 115, 150
Systematics, definition, 6*n*; knowledge of, 5; methods, principles, 3–17; old and new, 6–8, 291; status of, 4–8
Systematist, approach of new, to material, 7; difference between geneticist and, 10; field of activity, 9; functions, 8–11; mutual understanding between geneticists, 3; procedure, 11

Taeniaparadisea, 167
Tanysiptera, 284
    galatea, 152, 153, 172, 176, 236; relative tail and wing length, 41
    hydrocharis, 172, 176
Tardigrades, 212, 213
Taxonomic categories, *see* Categories
Taxonomic characters, 18–32, 116, 162; adaptational, 21; constancy of, 22; definition, 20; diagnostic, 18–20; environmental modification of, 61; geographic variation, *see* Geographic variation; phylogenetically conservative, 21; variation, 22–31
Taxonomic unit, 7
Taxonomists, approach to problems of evolution, 11; develop technique of ecologist, 9; diversity of opinion among 4, 280; idealists and realists, 281
Taxonomy, definition, 6*n*; material, 7, 109; methods, 11, 109; of parasites, 279; publications, 11; simplification of, 125; *see also* Systematics
Teissier, G., 293
Temperature, effect upon warm-blooded land animals, 88, 89; tolerance and preference, 45
Tenebrionids, 139
Terminal subspecies, 167
Terminology, need to be improved and modernized, 132; neutral terms, 108; use of vernacular and Latin names, 105
Termites, 204
Terpsiphone, 79
Territorial songs, 255
Territory, 241
Tester, A. L., Hart, J. L., McHugh, J. L., and, 241
Tetrao urogallus, 261

Textbooks, 11
Thamnophis, 262; *ordinoides* group, inter-
breeding and overlapping, 134
Thaumastes fernandensis and *galeritus*,
38
Thienemann, A., 47, 143
Thill, H., 144
Thomomys, 90
Thomson, D'Arcy W., 293
Thomson, G. M., 61
Thornbill, 174
Thorpe, W. H., 204, 208, 209, 283;
quoted, 207
Thrushes, 55, 57, 79, 148, 224, 225, 239,
249
Thyliphaps, 284
Ticehurst, Cl. B., 8, 20, 54, 95, 125, 132,
182, 183, 265; quoted, 201
Tick, 141
Timaliidae, 279
Time, individual variability in, 25–27
Timofeeff-Ressovsky, N. W., 3, 46, 64,
73, 76, 226, 239, 292
Toads, 84, 178, 203, 253; cline, 95; hy-
brids, 267
Todirhamphus, 167, 284
Topotypical material, 15
Transient polymorphism, *see* Polymor-
phism, transient
Transplantation experiments, 64
Tree creeper, 177
Tree crickets, 204
Trichogramma evanescens, 211
Trinomials, 110, 133
Triturus and species, 178
Trochilidae, 116, 260
Troglodytes aedon, 237
Tsetse fly, 140
Tunicates, 191, 257
Turbellarians, 45, 47, 191
Turbott, E. G., 235
Turdoides jardinei, and subspecies, 228
Turdus, 55, 224; *javanicus-poliocephalus*,
239; *poliocephalus*, 57, 58, 82, 249
Turner, C. L., Hubbs, C. L., and, 136
Tylenchus dipsaci, 211
Type locality, 15
Types, definition: function of a type, 15;
instantaneous origin of new, 296
Type specimen, 14, 15

Uca, 255
Uhlmann, E., 103
Upupa epops, 199

Uranornis, 169
Uria aalge, 96
Usinger, R. L., 141, 171, 174, 214, 223,
239; quoted, 172, 176, 272
Uvarow, B. P., 140

Vandel, A., 48, 191
Variability, degree of, 28, 31, 217–19
Variation adaptive, 85–88; altitudinal,
232; classification, 23; intraspecific,
114, 298; of taxonomic characters, 22–
31; *see also* Geographic variation
individual, 13, 14, 23, 25–32, 104, 105,
149, 150; in age, 25; classification: non-
genetic (phenotypical), 25–29; heredi-
tary (genotypical), 29–31; importance
of, 31–32; in time, 25; seasonal, 26;
sexes, generations, 30
*Variation of Birds Under the Influence of
Climate, The* (Gloger), 89
Variety, elimination of variety names,
104; term, 103
Vavilow, N. O., 73
Venables, L. S. V., 55
Vermes, 257
Vermivora, 152; species, 262
Vernacular names, use of, 105
Vertebrates, polytypic species, 131–36;
rules applying to warm-blooded, 90
Vertigo arctica, 22
Vincent, J., 77
Vireo olivaceus, 52
Vogelzug, 240
Vries, H. de, 65, 155
V. T. (Preferred Temperature), 46

Waagen, W., mutation concept, 65
Wagler, E., 135
Wagner, M., 156, 157, 228, 229
Wagtail, 239
Wallace, A. R., 36, 109, 162
Warblers, 8, 12, 51, 54, 152, 182, 255,
262, 290
Wasp, 139; mutillid, 30
Water barrier, 227, 228, 233
Water beetles, 284
Water temperatures, factor in breeding
season of aquatic animals, 253
Weevils, 5, 176
Welch, D'Alte A., 35, 93, 142, 214, 219,
220
Wertheim, P., 210
Wetmore, A., 56, 288
Whale bird, 251

Whistler, *see Pachycephala*
White-eye, 116, 239, 290
White-throated sparrows, 61
White-winged triller, 50
Whitman, C. O., 256
Whitney, Harry Payne, funds donated by family of, 12
Whitney South Sea Expedition, 12
Wilhelmi, R. W., quoted, 117
Williams, C. B., quoted, 15
Willis, J. C., 159, 173, 235, 288
Willow sparrow, 182, 268
Wimpenny, R. S., 93
Wing vibrations, 255
Witschi, E., 47, 135
Woltereck, E., 213
Woltereck, R., 62, 214
Wood, T. R., Banta, A. M., and, 46
Worms, chromosomal differences, 45; host ranges, 210; turbellarian, 45, 47, 191
Worthington, E. B., 135, 196, 215, 234, 271, 272
Wright, Sewall, 99, 192, 195, 216, 217, 225, 234, 235, 236, 238, 244, 271, 288, 296; quoted, 158
—— Th. Dobzhansky and, 35
Wunder, W., 63

Xerocrassa cretica, 44

Yellow-shafted flicker, 265
Yellow-throated warbler, 150
Yellow wagtail, 53
Yocum, H. B., and Huestis, R. R., 45

Zarapkin, S. R., 18, 139
Zea mays, 10
Zeitschrift für Säugetierkunde, 131
Zimmer, John T., 50, 228
Zimmermann, K., 90, 96, 139, 202
Zimmermann, S., 171, 178
Zonotrichia albicollis, 61; *capensis*, 54, 55, 127
Zosterops, 116, 182, 200, 290; *albogularis*, and *tenuirostris*, 158, 173; *lateralis*, 158, 173, 239; *rendovae* and species, 170, 227
Zumpt, F., 140
Zygaena ephialtes, color phases, 80

CATALOG OF DOVER BOOKS

The more difficult books are indicated by an asterisk (*)

Books Explaining Science and Mathematics

WHAT IS SCIENCE?, N. Campbell. The role of experiment and measurement, the function of mathematics, the nature of scientific laws, the difference between laws and theories, the limitations of science, and many similarly provocative topics are treated clearly and without technicalities by an eminent scientist. "Still an excellent introduction to scientific philosophy," H. Margenau in PHYSICS TODAY. "A first-rate primer . . . deserves a wide audience," SCIENTIFIC AMERICAN. 192pp. 5⅜ x 8.   S43 Paperbound **$1.25**

THE NATURE OF PHYSICAL THEORY, P. W. Bridgman. A Nobel Laureate's clear, non-technical lectures on difficulties and paradoxes connected with frontier research on the physical sciences. Concerned with such central concepts as thought, logic, mathematics, relativity, probability, wave mechanics, etc. he analyzes the contributions of such men as Newton, Einstein, Bohr, Heisenberg, and many others. "Lucid and entertaining . . . recommended to anyone who wants to get some insight into current philosophies of science," THE NEW PHILOSOPHY. Index. xi + 138pp. 5⅜ x 8.   S33 Paperbound **$1.25**

EXPERIMENT AND THEORY IN PHYSICS, Max Born. A Nobel Laureate examines the nature of experiment and theory in theoretical physics and analyzes the advances made by the great physicists of our day: Heisenberg, Einstein, Bohr, Planck, Dirac, and others. The actual process of creation is detailed step-by-step by one who participated. A fine examination of the scientific method at work. 44pp. 5⅜ x 8.   S308 Paperbound **75¢**

THE PSYCHOLOGY OF INVENTION IN THE MATHEMATICAL FIELD, J. Hadamard. The reports of such men as Descartes, Pascal, Einstein, Poincaré, and others are considered in this investigation of the method of idea-creation in mathematics and other sciences and the thinking process in general. How do ideas originate? What is the role of the unconscious? What is Poincaré's forgetting hypothesis? are some of the fascinating questions treated. A penetrating analysis of Einstein's thought processes concludes the book. xiii + 145pp. 5⅜ x 8.   T107 Paperbound **$1.25**

THE NATURE OF LIGHT AND COLOUR IN THE OPEN AIR, M. Minnaert. Why are shadows sometimes blue, sometimes green, or other colors depending on the light and surroundings? What causes mirages? Why do multiple suns and moons appear in the sky? Professor Minnaert explains these unusual phenomena and hundreds of others in simple, easy-to-understand terms based on optical laws and the properties of light and color. No mathematics is required but artists, scientists, students, and everyone fascinated by these "tricks" of nature will find thousands of useful and amazing pieces of information. Hundreds of observational experiments are suggested which require no special equipment. 200 illustrations; 42 photos. xvi + 362pp. 5⅜ x 8.   T196 Paperbound **$1.95**

THE UNIVERSE OF LIGHT, W. Bragg. Sir William Bragg, Nobel Laureate and great modern physicist, is also well known for his powers of clear exposition. Here he analyzes all aspects of light for the layman: lenses, reflection, refraction, the optics of vision, x-rays, the photoelectric effect, etc. He tells you what causes the color of spectra, rainbows, and soap bubbles, how magic mirrors work, and much more. Dozens of simple experiments are described. Preface. Index. 199 line drawings and photographs, including 2 full-page color plates. x + 283pp. 5⅜ x 8.   T538 Paperbound **$1.85**

SOAP-BUBBLES: THEIR COLOURS AND THE FORCES THAT MOULD THEM, C. V. Boys. For continuing popularity and validity as scientific primer, few books can match this volume of easily-followed experiments, explanations. Lucid exposition of complexities of liquid films, surface tension and related phenomena, bubbles' reaction to heat, motion, music, magnetic fields. Experiments with capillary attraction, soap bubbles on frames, composite bubbles, liquid cylinders and jets, bubbles other than soap, etc. Wonderful introduction to scientific method, natural laws that have many ramifications in areas of modern physics. Only complete edition in print. New Introduction by S. Z. Lewin, New York University. 83 illustrations; 1 full-page color plate. xii + 190pp. 5⅜ x 8½.   T542 Paperbound **95¢**

Classics of Science

THE DIDEROT PICTORIAL ENCYCLOPEDIA OF TRADES AND INDUSTRY, MANUFACTURING AND THE TECHNICAL ARTS IN PLATES SELECTED FROM "L'ENCYCLOPEDIE OU DICTIONNAIRE RAISONNE DES SCIENCES, DES ARTS, ET DES METIERS" OF DENIS DIDEROT, edited with text by C. Gillispie. The first modern selection of plates from the high point of 18th century French engraving, Diderot's famous Encyclopedia. Over 2000 illustrations on 485 full page plates, most of them original size, illustrating the trades and industries of one of the most fascinating periods of modern history, 18th century France. These magnificent engravings provide an invaluable glimpse into the past for the student of early technology, a lively and accurate social document to students of cultures, an outstanding find to the lover of fine engravings. The plates teem with life, with men, women, and children performing all of the thousands of operations necessary to the trades before and during the early stages of the industrial revolution. Plates are in sequence, and show general operations, closeups of difficult operations, and details of complex machinery. Such important and interesting trades and industries are illustrated as sowing, harvesting, beekeeping, cheesemaking, operating windmills, milling flour, charcoal burning, tobacco processing, indigo, fishing, arts of war, salt extraction, mining, smelting iron, casting iron, steel, extracting mercury, zinc, sulphur, copper, etc., slating, tinning, silverplating, gilding, making gunpowder, cannons, bells, shoeing horses, tanning, papermaking, printing, dying, and more than 40 other categories. 920pp. 9 x 12. Heavy library cloth.　　　　　　　　　　　T421 Two volume set **$18.50**

THE PRINCIPLES OF SCIENCE, A TREATISE ON LOGIC AND THE SCIENTIFIC METHOD, W. Stanley Jevons. Treating such topics as Inductive and Deductive Logic, the Theory of Number, Probability, and the Limits of Scientific Method, this milestone in the development of symbolic logic remains a stimulating contribution to the investigation of inferential validity in the natural and social sciences. It significantly advances Boole's logic, and describes a machine which is a foundation of modern electronic calculators. In his introduction, Ernest Nagel of Columbia University says, "(Jevons) . . . continues to be of interest as an attempt to articulate the logic of scientific inquiry." Index. liii + 786pp. 5⅜ x 8.
S446 Paperbound **$2.98**

*DIALOGUES CONCERNING TWO NEW SCIENCES, Galileo Galilei. A classic of experimental science which has had a profound and enduring influence on the entire history of mechanics and engineering. Galileo based this, his finest work, on 30 years of experimentation. It offers a fascinating and vivid exposition of dynamics, elasticity, sound, ballistics, strength of materials, and the scientific method. Translated by H. Crew and A. de Salvio. 126 diagrams. Index. xxi + 288pp. 5⅜ x 8.　　　　　　　　　　　S99 Paperbound **$1.75**

DE MAGNETE, William Gilbert. This classic work on magnetism founded a new science. Gilbert was the first to use the word "electricity," to recognize mass as distinct from weight, to discover the effect of heat on magnetic bodies; invented an electroscope, differentiated between static electricity and magnetism, conceived of the earth as a magnet. Written by the first great experimental scientist, this lively work is valuable not only as an historical landmark, but as the delightfully easy-to-follow record of a perpetually searching, ingenious mind. Translated by P. F. Mottelay. 25 page biographical memoir. 90 fix. lix + 368pp. 5⅜ x 8.　　　　　　　　　　　　　　　　　　　S470 Paperbound **$2.00**

*OPTICKS, Sir Isaac Newton. An enormous storehouse of insights and discoveries on light, reflection, color, refraction, theories of wave and corpuscular propagation of light, optical apparatus, and mathematical devices which have recently been reevaluated in terms of modern physics and placed in the top-most ranks of Newton's work! Foreword by Albert Einstein. Preface by I. B. Cohen of Harvard U. 7 pages of portraits, facsimile pages, letters, etc. cxvi + 412pp. 5⅜ x 8.　　　　　　　　　　　　　　S205 Paperbound **$2.25**

A SURVEY OF PHYSICAL THEORY, M. Planck. Lucid essays on modern physics for the general reader by the Nobel Laureate and creator of the quantum revolution. Planck explains how the new concepts came into being; explores the clash between theories of mechanics, electrodynamics, and thermodynamics; and traces the evolution of the concept of light through Newton, Huygens, Maxwell, and his own quantum theory, providing unparalleled insights into his development of this momentous modern concept. Bibliography. Index. vii + 121pp. 5⅜ x 8.
S650 Paperbound **$1.15**

A SOURCE BOOK IN MATHEMATICS, D. E. Smith. English translations of the original papers that announced the great discoveries in mathematics from the Renaissance to the end of the 19th century: succinct selections from 125 different treatises and articles, most of them unavailable elsewhere in English—Newton, Leibniz, Pascal, Riemann, Bernoulli, etc. 24 articles trace developments in the field of number, 18 cover algebra, 36 are on geometry, and 13 on calculus. Biographical-historical introductions to each article. Two volume set. Index in each. Total of 115 illustrations. Total of xxviii + 742pp. 5⅜ x 8.　　　　S552 Vol I Paperbound **$1.85**
S553 Vol II Paperbound **$1.85**
The set, boxed **$3.50**

CATALOGUE OF DOVER BOOKS

*THE THIRTEEN BOOKS OF EUCLID'S ELEMENTS, edited by T. L. Heath. This is the complete EUCLID — the definitive edition of one of the greatest classics of the western world. Complete English translation of the Heiberg text with spurious Book XIV. Detailed 150-page introduction discusses aspects of Greek and medieval mathematics: Euclid, texts, commentators, etc. Paralleling the text is an elaborate critical exposition analyzing each definition, proposition, postulate, etc., and covering textual matters, mathematical analyses, refutations, extensions, etc. Unabridged reproduction of the Cambridge 2nd edition. 3 volumes. Total of 995 figures, 1426pp. 5⅜ x 8. S88, 89, 90 — 3 vol. set, Paperbound **$6.75**

*THE GEOMETRY OF RENE DESCARTES. The great work which founded analytic geometry. The renowned Smith-Latham translation faced with the original French text containing all of Descartes' own diagrams! Contains: Problems the Construction of Which Requires Only Straight Lines and Circles; On the Nature of Curved Lines; On the Construction of Solid or Supersolid Problems. Notes. Diagrams. 258pp. S68 Paperbound **$1.60**

*A PHILOSOPHICAL ESSAY ON PROBABILITIES, P. Laplace. Without recourse to any mathematics above grammar school, Laplace develops a philosophically, mathematically and historically classical exposition of the nature of probability: its functions and limitations, operations in practical affairs, calculations in games of chance, insurance, government, astronomy, and countless other fields. New introduction by E. T. Bell. viii + 196pp. S166 Paperbound **$1.35**

DE RE METALLICA, Georgius Agricola. Written over 400 years ago, for 200 years the most authoritative first-hand account of the production of metals, translated in 1912 by former President Herbert Hoover and his wife, and today still one of the most beautiful and fascinating volumes ever produced in the history of science! 12 books, exhaustively annotated, give a wonderfully lucid and vivid picture of the history of mining, selection of sites, types of deposits, excavating pits, sinking shafts, ventilating, pumps, crushing machinery, assaying, smelting, refining metals, making salt, alum, nitre, glass, and many other topics. This definitive edition contains all 289 of the 16th century woodcuts which made the original an artistic masterpiece. It makes a superb gift for geologists, engineers, libraries, artists, historians, and everyone interested in science and early illustrative art. Biographical, historical introductions. Bibliography, survey of ancient authors. Indices. 289 illustrations. 672pp. 6¾ x 10¾. Deluxe library edition. S6 Clothbound **$10.00**

GEOGRAPHICAL ESSAYS, W. M. Davis. Modern geography and geomorphology rest on the fundamental work of this scientist. His new concepts of earth-processes revolutionized science and his broad interpretation of the scope of geography created a deeper understanding of the interrelation of the landscape and the forces that mold it. This first inexpensive unabridged edition covers theory of geography, methods of advanced geographic teaching, descriptions of geographic areas, analyses of land-shaping processes, and much besides. Not only a factual and historical classic, it is still widely read for its reflections of modern scientific thought. Introduction. 130 figures. Index. vi + 777pp. 5⅜ x 8.
S383 Paperbound **$2.95**

CHARLES BABBAGE AND HIS CALCULATING ENGINES, edited by P. Morrison and E. Morrison. Friend of Darwin, Humboldt, and Laplace, Babbage was a leading pioneer in large-scale mathematical machines and a prophetic herald of modern operational research—true father of Harvard's relay computer Mark I. His Difference Engine and Analytical Engine were the first successful machines in the field. This volume contains a valuable introduction on his life and work; major excerpts from his fascinating autobiography, revealing his eccentric and unusual personality; and extensive selections from "Babbage's Calculating Engines," a compilation of hard-to-find journal articles, both by Babbage and by such eminent contributors as the Countess of Lovelace, L. F. Menabrea, and Dionysius Lardner. 11 illustrations. Appendix of miscellaneous papers. Index. Bibliography. xxxviii + 400pp. 5⅜ x 8. T12 Paperbound **$2.00**

*THE WORKS OF ARCHIMEDES WITH THE METHOD OF ARCHIMEDES, edited by T. L. Heath. All the known works of the greatest mathematician of antiquity including the recently discovered METHOD OF ARCHIMEDES. This last is the only work we have which shows exactly how early mathematicians discovered their proofs before setting them down in their final perfection. A 186 page study by the eminent scholar Heath discusses Archimedes and the history of Greek mathematics. Bibliography. 563pp. 5⅜ x 8. S9 Paperbound **$2.25**

Nature, Biology, Medicine

NATURE RECREATION: Group Guidance for the Out-of-doors, William Gould Vinal. Intended for both the uninitiated nature instructor and the education student on the college level, this complete "how-to" program surveys the entire area of nature education for the young. Philosophy of nature recreation; requirements, responsibilities, important information for group leaders; nature games; suggested group projects; conducting meetings and getting discussions started; etc. Scores of immediately applicable teaching aids, plus completely updated sources of information, pamphlets, field guides, recordings, etc. Bibliography. 74 photographs. + 310pp. 5⅜ x 8½.   T1015 Paperbound **$1.75**

HOW TO KNOW THE WILD FLOWERS, Mrs. William Starr Dana. Classic nature book that has introduced thousands to wonders of American wild flowers. Color-season principle of organization is easy to use, even by those with no botanical training, and the genial, refreshing discussions of history, folklore, uses of over 1,000 native and escape flowers, foliage plants are informative as well as fun to read. Over 170 full-page plates, collected from several editions, may be colored in to make permanent records of finds. Revised to conform with 1950 edition of Gray's Manual of Botany. xlii + 438pp. 5⅜ x 8½.   T332 Paperbound **$1.85**

HOW TO KNOW THE FERNS, F. T. Parsons. Ferns, among our most lovely native plants, are all too little known. This classic of nature lore will enable the layman to identify almost any American fern he may come across. After an introduction on the structure and life of ferns, the 57 most important ferns are fully pictured and described (arranged upon a simple identification key). Index of Latin and English names. 61 illustrations and 42 full-page plates. xiv + 215pp. 5⅜ x 8.   T740 Paperbound **$1.25**

MANUAL OF THE TREES OF NORTH AMERICA, Charles Sprague Sargent. Still unsurpassed as most comprehensive, reliable study of North American tree characteristics, precise locations and distribution. By dean of American dendrologists. Every tree native to U.S., Canada, Alaska, 185 genera, 717 species, described in detail—leaves, flowers, fruit, winterbuds, bark, wood, growth habits etc. plus discussion of varieties and local variants, immaturity variations. Over 100 keys, including unusual 11-page analytical key to genera, aid in identification. 783 clear illustrations of flowers, fruit, leaves. An unmatched permanent reference work for all nature lovers. Second enlarged (1926) edition. Synopsis of families. Analytical key to genera. Glossary of technical terms. Index. 783 illustrations, 1 map. Two volumes. Total of 982pp. 5⅜ x 8.   T277 Vol. I Paperbound **$2.00**
                     T278 Vol. II Paperbound **$2.00**
                     The set **$4.00**

TREES OF THE EASTERN AND CENTRAL UNITED STATES AND CANADA, W. M. Harlow. A revised edition of a standard middle-level guide to native trees and important escapes. More than 140 trees are described in detail, and illustrated with more than 600 drawings and photographs. Supplementary keys will enable the careful reader to identify almost any tree he might encounter. xiii + 288pp. 5⅜ x 8.   T395 Paperbound **$1.35**

GUIDE TO SOUTHERN TREES, Ellwood S. Harrar and J. George Harrar. All the essential information about trees indigenous to the South, in an extremely handy format. Introductory essay on methods of tree classification and study, nomenclature, chief divisions of Southern trees, etc. Approximately 100 keys and synopses allow for swift, accurate identification of trees. Numerous excellent illustrations, non-technical text make this a useful book for teachers of biology or natural science, nature lovers, amateur naturalists. Revised 1962 edition. Index. Bibliography. Glossary of technical terms. 920 illustrations; 201 full-page plates. ix + 709pp. 4⅝ x 6⅜.   T945 Paperbound **$2.25**

FRUIT KEY AND TWIG KEY TO TREES AND SHRUBS, W. M. Harlow. Bound together in one volume for the first time, these handy and accurate keys to fruit and twig identification are the only guides of their sort with photographs (up to 3 times natural size). "Fruit Key": Key to over 120 different deciduous and evergreen fruits. 139 photographs and 11 line drawings. Synoptic summary of fruit types. Bibliography. 2 Indexes (common and scientific names). "Twig Key": Key to over 160 different twigs and buds. 173 photographs. Glossary of technical terms. Bibliography. 2 Indexes (common and scientific names). Two volumes bound as one. Total of xvii + 126pp. 5⅝ x 8⅜.   T511 Paperbound **$1.25**

INSECT LIFE AND INSECT NATURAL HISTORY, S. W. Frost. A work emphasizing habits, social life, and ecological relations of insects, rather than more academic aspects of classification and morphology. Prof. Frost's enthusiasm and knowledge are everywhere evident as he discusses insect associations and specialized habits like leaf-rolling, leaf-mining, and case-making, the gall insects, the boring insects, aquatic insects, etc. He examines all sorts of matters not usually covered in general works, such as: insects as human food, insect music and musicians, insect response to electric and radio waves, use of insects in art and literature. The admirably executed purpose of this book, which covers the middle ground between elementary treatment and scholarly monographs, is to excite the reader to observe for himself. Over 700 illustrations. Extensive bibliography. x + 524pp. 5⅜ x 8.   T517 Paperbound **$2.45**

CATALOGUE OF DOVER BOOKS

COMMON SPIDERS OF THE UNITED STATES, J. H. Emerton. Here is a nature hobby you can pursue right in your own cellar! Only non-technical, but thorough, reliable guide to spiders for the layman. Over 200 spiders from all parts of the country, arranged by scientific classification, are identified by shape and color, number of eyes, habitat and range, habits, etc. Full text, 501 line drawings and photographs, and valuable introduction explain webs, poisons, threads, capturing and preserving spiders, etc. Index. New synoptic key by S. W. Frost. xxiv + 225pp. 5⅜ x 8. **T223 Paperbound $1.35**

THE LIFE STORY OF THE FISH: HIS MANNERS AND MORALS, Brian Curtis. A comprehensive, non-technical survey of just about everything worth knowing about fish. Written for the aquarist, the angler, and the layman with an inquisitive mind, the text covers such topics as evolution, external covering and protective coloration, physics and physiology of vision, maintenance of equilibrium, function of the lateral line canal for auditory and temperature senses, nervous system, function of the air bladder, reproductive system and methods—courtship, mating, spawning, care of young—and many more. Also sections on game fish, the problems of conservation and a fascinating chapter on fish curiosities. "Clear, simple language . . . excellent judgment in choice of subjects . . . delightful sense of humor," New York Times. Revised (1949) edition. Index. Bibliography of 72 items. 6 full-page photographic plates. xii + 284pp. 5⅜ x 8. **T929 Paperbound $1.50**

BATS, Glover Morrill Allen. The most comprehensive study of bats as a life-form by the world's foremost authority. A thorough summary of just about everything known about this fascinating and mysterious flying mammal, including its unique location sense, hibernation and cycles, its habitats and distribution, its wing structure and flying habits, and its relationship to man in the long history of folklore and superstition. Written on a middle-level, the book can be profitably studied by a trained zoologist and thoroughly enjoyed by the layman. "An absorbing text with excellent illustrations. Bats should have more friends and fewer thoughtless detractors as a result of the publication of this volume," William Beebe, Books. Extensive bibliography. 57 photographs and illustrations. x + 368pp. 5⅜ x 8½. **T984 Paperbound $2.00**

BIRDS AND THEIR ATTRIBUTES, Glover Morrill Allen. A fine general introduction to birds as living organisms, especially valuable because of emphasis on structure, physiology, habits, behavior. Discusses relationship of bird to man, early attempts at scientific ornithology, feathers and coloration, skeletal structure including bills, legs and feet, wings. Also food habits, evolution and present distribution, feeding and nest-building, still unsolved questions of migrations and location sense, many more similar topics. Final chapter on classification, nomenclature. A good popular-level summary for the biologist; a first-rate introduction for the layman. Reprint of 1925 edition. References and index. 51 illustrations. viii + 338pp. 5⅜ x 8½. **T957 Paperbound $1.85**

LIFE HISTORIES OF NORTH AMERICAN BIRDS, Arthur Cleveland Bent. Bent's monumental series of books on North American birds, prepared and published under auspices of Smithsonian Institute, is the definitive coverage of the subject, the most-used single source of information. Now the entire set is to be made available by Dover in inexpensive editions. This encyclopedic collection of detailed, specific observations utilizes reports of hundreds of contemporary observers, writings of such naturalists as Audubon, Burroughs, William Brewster, as well as author's own extensive investigations. Contains literally everything known about life history of each bird considered: nesting, eggs, plumage, distribution and migration, voice, enemies, courtship, etc. These not over-technical works are musts for ornithologists, conservationists, amateur naturalists, anyone seriously interested in American birds.

BIRDS OF PREY. More than 100 subspecies of hawks, falcons, eagles, buzzards, condors and owls, from the common barn owl to the extinct caracara of Guadaloupe Island. 400 photographs. Two volume set. Index for each volume. Bibliographies of 403, 520 items. 197 full-page plates. Total of 907pp. 5⅜ x 8½. Vol. I **T931 Paperbound $2.50**
Vol. II **T932 Paperbound $2.50**

WILD FOWL. Ducks, geese, swans, and tree ducks—73 different subspecies. Two volume set. Index for each volume. Bibliographies of 124, 144 items. 106 full-page plates. Total of 685pp. 5⅜ x 8½. Vol. I **T285 Paperbound $2.50**
Vol. II **T286 Paperbound $2.50**

SHORE BIRDS. 81 varieties (sandpipers, woodcocks, plovers, snipes, phalaropes, curlews, oyster catchers, etc.). More than 200 photographs of eggs, nesting sites, adult and young of important species. Two volume set. Index for each volume. Bibliographies of 261, 188 items. 121 full-page plates. Total of 860pp. 5⅜ x 8½. Vol. I **T933 Paperbound $2.35**
Vol. II **T934 Paperbound $2.35**

THE LIFE OF PASTEUR, R. Vallery-Radot. 13th edition of this definitive biography, cited in Encyclopaedia Britannica. Authoritative, scholarly, well-documented with contemporary quotes, observations; gives complete picture of Pasteur's personal life; especially thorough presentation of scientific activities with silkworms, fermentation, hydrophobia, inoculation, etc. Introduction by Sir William Osler. Index. 505pp. 5⅜ x 8. **T632 Paperbound $2.00**

CATALOGUE OF DOVER BOOKS

AMERICAN WILDLIFE AND PLANTS: A GUIDE TO WILDLIFE FOOD HABITS, Alexander C. Martin, Herbert S. Zim, and Arnold L. Nelson. A tremendous amount of material from 25 years of concentrated researches by U.S. Fish and Wildlife Service is collected, correlated, condensed into this 500-page volume. Learn of food, feeding habits of more than 1,000 species of U.S. mammals, birds, fish, their distribution and migratory habits, the most important plant-animal relationships. Last third of book devoted to all genera of plants that furnish food to American wildlife. ". . . should prove a classic in its field and a must for every naturalist," Harold E. Anthony, NATURAL HISTORY. Republication of first (1951) edition. Index. Hundreds of illustrations, tables, range maps, etc. ix + 500pp. 5⅜ x 8.　　　　　T793 Paperbound **$2.25**

RACING PIGEONS, C. Osman. A complete, practical, up-to-date, and authoritative book on racing pigeons by a British expert. Covers the anatomy of the pigeon, the homing instinct, the pigeon's life cycle, food and feeding, lofts and aviaries, breeding winners, preparing for races, winning systems, common diseases, and much more. Indispensable for beginner and expert alike. 24 photographs by the author. 10 line drawings. Index. 192pp. 5⅛ x 7⅛.
T513 Clothbound **$3.00**

ANTONY VAN LEEUWENHOEK AND HIS "LITTLE ANIMALS," selected, translated, and edited from his printed works, unpublished manuscripts, contemporary records by Clifford Dobell. 100-page biographical study of the first microbiologist, bacteriologist, micrologist. 4 chapters of the papers that founded protozoology, bacteriology, with many of Leeuwenhoek's illustrative drawings, observations and letters to Royal Society, discussion of Leeuwenhoek's name, language, dwelling, draughtsmen, method, microscope bring to life an excited, naive, completely self-taught genius. 25 years of research went into its compilation by a Fellow of the Royal Society. More than an important book for students and workers in the sciences, it may also be read with pleasure by anyone interested in meeting one of the most interesting and remarkable men in history of science. 32 illustrations. Bibliography of over 400 items. Index. vii + 435pp. 5⅜ x 8.　　　　　S594 Paperbound **$2.25**

MICROGRAPHIA, Robert Hooke. Hooke, 17th-century British universal genius, was a major pioneer in celestial mechanics, optics, gravity, and many other fields, but his greatest contribution was this book, now reprinted in its entirety from the original 1655 edition, which gave microscopy its first great impetus. With all the freshness of discovery, he describes his microscope, and his observations of cork, the edge of a razor, insects' eyes, fabrics, and dozens of other objects. 38 plates, full-size or larger, contain all the original illustrations. A fundamental classic in the fields of combustion and heat theory, light and color theory, botany and zoology, hygrometry, and many others. Contains such farsighted predictions as the famous anticipation of artificial silk. Final section is concerned with Hooke's observations of the moon and stars. 348pp. 5⅜ x 8½.　　　　　T8 Paperbound **$2.00**

THE AUTOBIOGRAPHY OF CHARLES DARWIN AND SELECTED LETTERS, edited by Francis Darwin. The personal record of the professional and private life of the author of "Origin of Species," whose ideas have shaped our thinking as have few others. His early life; the historic voyage aboard the "Beagle"; the furor surrounding evolution and his replies; revealing anecdotes; reminiscences by his son; letters to Henslow, Lyell, Hooker, Huxley, Wallace, Kingsley, and others; his thought on religion and vivisection. Appendix. Index. 365pp. 5⅜ x 8.
T479 Paperbound **$1.65**

THE MALAY ARCHIPELAGO, Alfred Russel Wallace. A great classic of natural history and travel. The observations of one of the founders of modern biology whose work also provides foundation for scientific study of botany and zoology in many parts of the world. Based on 8 years' personal exploration. Descriptions of the island groupings and peoples, accounts of abundant, strange animals, startling birds and insects—many previously unknown—on either side of the Wallace line, dividing animal life into Indian on the West and Australian on the East and named for the author. Unrivalled travel experience, packed full of intellectual excitement, infectious enthusiasm, this will arouse the empathy of any lay reader interested in strange places and new theories. 62 drawings and maps. Three appendices on crania, 59 languages, and vocabularies. Index. xvii + 515pp. 5⅜ x 8½.
T187 Paperbound **$2.00**

STUDIES ON THE STRUCTURE AND DEVELOPMENT OF VERTEBRATES, Edwin S. Goodrich. This definitive study by the greatest modern comparative anatomist covers the skeleton, fins and limbs, head region morphology, skull, skeletal visceral arches and labial cartilages, middle ear and ear ossicles, visceral clefts and gills, subdivisions of body cavity, vascular, respiratory, excretory, and peripheral nervous systems of vertebrates from fish to the higher mammals. 754 pictures. 69 page biographical study by C. C. Hardy. Bibliography of 1186 references. "For many a day this will certainly be the standard textbook," Journal of Anatomy. Index. Two volumes total 906pp. 5⅜ x 8.　　　　2 volume set S449-50 Paperbound **$5.00**

FINGER PRINTS, PALMS AND SOLES: AN INTRODUCTION TO DERMATOGLYPHICS, Harold Cummins and Charles Midlo. One of the most fascinating of sciences receives careful, thorough treatment. Primitive knowledge of dermatoglyphics; early investigators; fundamental patterns and pattern types; technical methods of classification, identification. Detailed, unique descriptions of uses: identification of twins; paternity cases; racial variation; genetic process; relation of prints to body measurement, criminality and character, blood groups, handedness. New chapter adds information on identification in action, with accounts of criminal cases in which prints played major role. 2nd enlarged edition. 149 figures. 49 tables. 361-item bibliography. Index. xii + 319pp. 5⅝ x 8⅜.　　　　　T778 Paperbound **$1.95**

CATALOGUE OF DOVER BOOKS

HEREDITY AND YOUR LIFE, A. M. Winchester. Authoritative, concise explanation of human genetics, in non-technical terms. What factors determine characteristics of future generations, how they may be altered, history of genetics, application of knowledge to control health, intelligence, number of entire populations. Physiology of reproduction, chromosomes, genes, blood types, Rh factor, dominant, recessive traits, birth by proxy, sexual abnormalities, radiation, much more. Index. 75 illus. 345pp. 5⅜ x 8.   T598 Paperbound **$1.50**

THE ORIGIN OF LIFE, A. I. Oparin. This is the first modern statement of the theory that life evolved from complex nitro-carbon compounds. A historical introduction covers theories of the origin of life from the Greeks to modern times and then the techniques of biochemistry as applied to the problem by Dr. Oparin. The exposition presupposes a knowledge of chemistry but can be read with profit by everyone interested in this absorbing question. "Easily the most scholarly authority on the question," NEW YORK TIMES. Bibliography. Index. xxv + 270pp. 5⅜ x 8.   T213 Paperbound **$1.75**

SOURCE BOOK OF MEDICAL HISTORY, edited by Logan Clendening. Chronological compilation of the most significant medical writings of 4000 years, carefully edited to save reading time, isolate important contributions. 124 selections by 120 authors, each with introduction, short biography. Covers every area of medical thought and practice: Hippocrates, Galen, Vesalius, Malpighi, Pasteur, Florence Nightingale, Walter Reed, Lavoisier, Leeuwenhoek, Parkinson, Beaumont, many more. Includes selections from non-medical literature to show lay view of medicine through the ages. Will give anyone interested in medicine, regardless of reason, an immediate, dramatic view of its growth and development. 124 papers. Classified bibliographies. Index. xiv + 685pp. 5⅜ x 8.   T621 Paperbound **$2.75**

CLASSICS OF CARDIOLOGY, F. A. Willius, T. E. Keys. Monumental collection of 52 papers by great researchers, physicians on the anatomy, physiology and pathology of the heart and the circulation, and the diagnosis and therapy of their diseases. These are the original writings of Harvey, Sénac, Auenbrugger, Withering, Stokes, Einthoven, Osler, and 44 others from 1628 to 1912. 27 of the papers are complete, the rest in major excerpts; all are in English. The biographical notes and introductory essays make this a full history of cardiology—with exclusively first-hand material. 103 portraits, diagrams, and facsimiles of title pages. Chronological table. Total of xx + 858pp. 5⅝ x 8⅜. Two volume set.   T912 Vol I Paper bound **$2.00**
T913 Vol II Paperbound **$2.00**
The set **$4.00**

A WAY OF LIFE, by Sir William Osler. An inspirational classic that has helped countless business and professional men since the beloved physician and philosopher first delivered it at Yale in 1913. In warm human terms Osler tells how he managed to make the most of every day by an edifying mental and physical regimen. Illustrated.   **FREE**

INTRODUCTION TO THE STUDY OF EXPERIMENTAL MEDICINE, Claude Bernard. The only major work of Claude Bernard now available in English, this classic records Bernard's efforts to transform physiology into an exact science. He examines the roles of chance and error and incorrect hypothesis in leading to scientific truth and describes many classic experiments on the action of curare, carbon monoxide, and other poisons, the functions of the pancreas, the glycogenic function of the liver, and many others. Introduction. Foreword by I. B. Cohen. xxv + 266pp. 5⅜ x 8.   T400 Paperbound **$1.50**

A WAY OF LIFE AND OTHER SELECTED WRITINGS, Sir William Osler. Physician and humanist, Osler writes brilliantly on philosophy, religion, and literature in "The Student Life," "Books and Men," "Creators, Transmuters, and Transmitters," "The Old Humanities and the New Science," and the title essay. His medical history is equally acute in discussions of Thomas Browne, Gui Patin, Robert Burton, Michael Servetus, William Beaumont, Laënnec. 5 more of his best essays. 5 photographs. Introduction by G. L. Keynes, M.D., F.R.C.S. Index. xx + 278pp. 5⅜ x 8.   T488 Paperbound **$1.50**

FROM MAGIC TO SCIENCE, Charles Singer. Great historian of science examines aspects of medical science from the Roman Empire through the Renaissance. Especially valuable are the sections on early herbals, probably the best coverage of this subject available, and on "The Visions of Hildegarde of Bingen" which are explained by physiological means. Also covered are Arabian and Galenic influences, astrology, the Sphere of Pythagoras, Leonardo da Vinci, Vesalius, Paracelsus, et al. Frequent quotations and translations. New introduction by the author. New unabridged, corrected edition. 158 unusual illustrations from classical and medieval sources. Index. xxvii + 365pp. 5⅜ x 8.   T390 Paperbound **$2.00**

A SHORT HISTORY OF ANATOMY AND PHYSIOLOGY FROM THE GREEKS TO HARVEY, C. Singer. An intermediate history formerly entitled THE EVOLUTION OF ANATOMY, this work conveys the thrill of discovery as the nature of the human body is gradually clarified by hundreds of scientists from the Greeks to the Renaissance. Diogenes, Hippocrates, and other early workers, up to Leonardo da Vinci, Vesalius, Harvey, and others, with 139 illustrations from medieval manuscripts, classical sculpture, etc. Index. 221pp. 5⅜ x 8.   T389 Paperbound **$1.75**

Psychology

YOGA: A SCIENTIFIC EVALUATION, Kovoor T. Behanan. A complete reprinting of the book that for the first time gave Western readers a sane, scientific explanation and analysis of yoga. The author draws on controlled laboratory experiments and personal records of a year as a disciple of a yoga, to investigate yoga psychology, concepts of knowledge, physiology, "supernatural" phenomena, and the ability to tap the deepest human powers. In this study under the auspices of Yale University Institute of Human Relations, the strictest principles of physiological and psychological inquiry are followed throughout. Foreword by W. A. Miles, Yale University. 17 photographs. Glossary. Index. xx + 270pp. 5⅜ x 8. T505 Paperbound **$1.75**

CONDITIONED REFLEXES: AN INVESTIGATION OF THE PHYSIOLOGICAL ACTIVITIES OF THE CEREBRAL CORTEX, I. P. Pavlov. Full, authorized translation of Pavlov's own survey of his work in experimental psychology reviews entire course of experiments, summarizes conclusions, outlines psychological system based on famous "conditioned reflex" concept. Details of technical means used in experiments, observations on formation of conditioned reflexes, function of cerebral hemispheres, results of damage, nature of sleep, typology of nervous system, significance of experiments for human psychology. Trans. by Dr. G. V. Anrep, Cambridge Univ. 235-item bibliography. 18 figures. 445pp. 5⅜ x 8. S614 Paperbound **$2.25**

EXPLANATION OF HUMAN BEHAVIOUR, F. V. Smith. A major intermediate-level introduction to and criticism of 8 complete systems of the psychology of human behavior, with unusual emphasis on theory of investigation and methodology. Part I is an illuminating analysis of the problems involved in the explanation of observed phenomena, and the differing viewpoints on the nature of causality. Parts II and III are a closely detailed survey of the systems of McDougall, Gordon Allport, Lewin, the Gestalt group, Freud, Watson, Hull, and Tolman. Biographical notes. Bibliography of over 800 items. 2 Indexes. 38 figures. xii + 460pp. 5½ x 8¾. T253 Clothbound **$6.00**

SEX IN PSYCHO-ANALYSIS (formerly CONTRIBUTIONS TO PSYCHO-ANALYSIS), S. Ferenczi. Written by an associate of Freud, this volume presents countless insights on such topics as impotence, transference, analysis and children, dreams, symbols, obscene words, masturbation and male homosexuality, paranoia and psycho-analysis, the sense of reality, hypnotism and therapy, and many others. Also includes full text of THE DEVELOPMENT OF PSYCHO-ANALYSIS by Ferenczi and Otto Rank. Two books bound as one. Total of 406pp. 5⅜ x 8. T324 Paperbound **$1.85**

BEYOND PSYCHOLOGY, Otto Rank. One of Rank's most mature contributions, focussing on the irrational basis of human behavior as a basic fact of our lives. The psychoanalytic techniques of myth analysis trace to their source the ultimates of human existence: fear of death, personality, the social organization, the need for love and creativity, etc. Dr. Rank finds them stemming from a common irrational source, man's fear of final destruction. A seminal work in modern psychology, this work sheds light on areas ranging from the concept of immortal soul to the sources of state power. 291pp. 5⅜ x 8. T485 Paperbound **$2.00**

ILLUSIONS AND DELUSIONS OF THE SUPERNATURAL AND THE OCCULT, D. H. Rawcliffe. Holds up to rational examination hundreds of persistent delusions including crystal gazing, automatic writing, table turning, mediumistic trances, mental healing, stigmata, lycanthropy, live burial, the Indian Rope Trick, spiritualism, dowsing, telepathy, clairvoyance, ghosts, ESP, etc. The author explains and exposes the mental and physical deceptions involved, making this not only an exposé of supernatural phenomena, but a valuable exposition of characteristic types of abnormal psychology. Originally titled "The Psychology of the Occult." 14 illustrations. Index. 551pp. 5⅜ x 8. T503 Paperbound **$2.00**

THE PRINCIPLES OF PSYCHOLOGY, William James. The full long-course, unabridged, of one of the great classics of Western literature and science. Wonderfully lucid descriptions of human mental activity, the stream of thought, consciousness, time perception, memory, imagination, emotions, reason, abnormal phenomena, and similar topics. Original contributions are integrated with the work of such men as Berkeley, Binet, Mills, Darwin, Hume, Kant, Royce, Schopenhauer, Spinoza, Locke, Descartes, Galton, Wundt, Lotze, Herbart, Fechner, and scores of others. All contrasting interpretations of mental phenomena are examined in detail — introspective analysis, philosophical interpretation, and experimental research. "A classic," JOURNAL OF CONSULTING PSYCHOLOGY. "The main lines are as valid as ever," PSYCHO-ANALYTICAL QUARTERLY. "Standard reading . . . a classic of interpretation," PSYCHIATRIC QUARTERLY. 94 illustrations. 1408pp. 2 volumes. 5⅜ x 8. Vol. 1, T381 Paperbound **$2.50** / Vol. 2, T382 Paperbound **$2.50**

THE DYNAMICS OF THERAPY IN A CONTROLLED RELATIONSHIP, Jessie Taft. One of the most important works in literature of child psychology, out of print for 25 years. Outstanding disciple of Rank describes all aspects of relationship or Rankian therapy through concise, simple elucidation of theory underlying her actual contacts with two seven-year olds. Therapists, social caseworkers, psychologists, counselors, and laymen who work with children will all find this important work an invaluable summation of method, theory of child psychology. xix + 296pp. 5⅜ x 8. T325 Paperbound **$1.75**

Puzzles, Mathematical Recreations

SYMBOLIC LOGIC and THE GAME OF LOGIC, Lewis Carroll. "Symbolic Logic" is not concerned with modern symbolic logic, but is instead a collection of over 380 problems posed with charm and imagination, using the syllogism, and a fascinating diagrammatic method of drawing conclusions. In "The Game of Logic" Carroll's whimsical imagination devises a logical game played with 2 diagrams and counters (included) to manipulate hundreds of tricky syllogisms. The final section, "Hit or Miss" is a lagniappe of 101 additional puzzles in the delightful Carroll manner. Until this reprint edition, both of these books were rarities costing up to $15 each. Symbolic Logic: Index. xxxi + 199pp. The Game of Logic: 96pp. 2 vols. bound as one. 5⅜ x 8. **T492 Paperbound $1.50**

PILLOW PROBLEMS and A TANGLED TALE, Lewis Carroll. One of the rarest of all Carroll's works, "Pillow Problems" contains 72 original math puzzles, all typically ingenious. Particularly fascinating are Carroll's answers which remain exactly as he thought them out, reflecting his actual mental process. The problems in "A Tangled Tale" are in story form, originally appearing as a monthly magazine serial. Carroll not only gives the solutions, but uses answers sent in by readers to discuss wrong approaches and misleading paths, and grades them for insight. Both of these books were rarities until this edition, "Pillow Problems" costing up to $25, and "A Tangled Tale" $15. Pillow Problems: Preface and Introduction by Lewis Carroll. xx + 109pp. A Tangled Tale: 6 illustrations. 152pp. Two vols. bound as one. 5⅜ x 8. **T493 Paperbound $1.50**

AMUSEMENTS IN MATHEMATICS, Henry Ernest Dudeney. The foremost British originator of mathematical puzzles is always intriguing, witty, and paradoxical in this classic, one of the largest collections of mathematical amusements. More than 430 puzzles, problems, and paradoxes. Mazes and games, problems on number manipulation, unicursal and other route problems, puzzles on measuring, weighing, packing, age, kinship, chessboards, joiners', crossing river, plane figure dissection, and many others. Solutions. More than 450 illustrations. vii + 258pp. 5⅜ x 8. **T473 Paperbound $1.25**

THE CANTERBURY PUZZLES, Henry Dudeney. Chaucer's pilgrims set one another problems in story form. Also Adventures of the Puzzle Club, the Strange Escape of the King's Jester, the Monks of Riddlewell, the Squire's Christmas Puzzle Party, and others. All puzzles are original, based on dissecting plane figures, arithmetic, algebra, elementary calculus and other branches of mathematics, and purely logical ingenuity. "The limit of ingenuity and intricacy," The Observer. Over 110 puzzles. Full Solutions. 150 illustrations. vii + 225pp. 5⅜ x 8. **T474 Paperbound $1.25**

MATHEMATICAL EXCURSIONS, H. A. Merrill. Even if you hardly remember your high school math, you'll enjoy the 90 stimulating problems contained in this book and you will come to understand a great many mathematical principles with surprisingly little effort. Many useful shortcuts and diversions not generally known are included: division by inspection, Russian peasant multiplication, memory systems for pi, building odd and even magic squares, square roots by geometry, dyadic systems, and many more. Solutions to difficult problems. 50 illustrations. 145pp. 5⅜ x 8. **T350 Paperbound $1.00**

MAGIC SQUARES AND CUBES, W. S. Andrews. Only book-length treatment in English, a thorough non-technical description and analysis. Here are nasik, overlapping, pandiagonal, serrated squares; magic circles, cubes, spheres, rhombuses. Try your hand at 4-dimensional magical figures! Much unusual folklore and tradition included. High school algebra is sufficient. 754 diagrams and illustrations. viii + 419pp. 5⅜ x 8. **T658 Paperbound $1.85**

CALIBAN'S PROBLEM BOOK: MATHEMATICAL, INFERENTIAL AND CRYPTOGRAPHIC PUZZLES, H. Phillips (Caliban), S. T. Shovelton, G. S. Marshall. 105 ingenious problems by the greatest living creator of puzzles based on logic and inference. Rigorous, modern, piquant; reflecting their author's unusual personality, these intermediate and advanced puzzles all involve the ability to reason clearly through complex situations; some call for mathematical knowledge, ranging from algebra to number theory. Solutions. xi + 180pp. 5⅜ x 8.
T736 Paperbound $1.25

MATHEMATICAL PUZZLES FOR BEGINNERS AND ENTHUSIASTS, G. Mott-Smith. 188 mathematical puzzles based on algebra, dissection of plane figures, permutations, and probability, that will test and improve your powers of inference and interpretation. The Odic Force, The Spider's Cousin, Ellipse Drawing, theory and strategy of card and board games like tit-tat-toe, go moku, salvo, and many others. 100 pages of detailed mathematical explanations. Appendix of primes, square roots, etc. 135 illustrations. 2nd revised edition. 248pp. 5⅜ x 8.
T198 Paperbound $1.00

MATHEMAGIC, MAGIC PUZZLES, AND GAMES WITH NUMBERS, R. V. Heath. More than 60 new puzzles and stunts based on the properties of numbers. Easy techniques for multiplying large numbers mentally, revealing hidden numbers magically, finding the date of any day in any year, and dozens more. Over 30 pages devoted to magic squares, triangles, cubes, circles, etc. Edited by J. S. Meyer. 76 illustrations. 128pp. 5⅜ x 8. **T110 Paperbound $1.00**

CATALOGUE OF DOVER BOOKS

MATHEMATICAL RECREATIONS, M. Kraitchik. One of the most thorough compilations of unusual mathematical problems for beginners and advanced mathematicians. Historical problems from Greek, Medieval, Arabic, Hindu sources. 50 pages devoted to pastimes derived from figurate numbers, Mersenne numbers, Fermat numbers, primes and probability. 40 pages of magic, Euler, Latin, panmagic squares. 25 new positional and permutational games of permanent value: fairy chess, latruncles, reversi, jinx, ruma, lasca, tricolor, tetrachrome, etc. Complete rigorous solutions. Revised second edition. 181 illustrations. 333pp. 5⅜ x 8.
T163 Paperbound **$1.75**

MATHEMATICAL PUZZLES OF SAM LOYD, selected and edited by M. Gardner. Choice puzzles by the greatest American puzzle creator and innovator. Selected from his famous collection, "Cyclopedia of Puzzles," they retain the unique style and historical flavor of the originals. There are posers based on arithmetic, algebra, probability, game theory, route tracing, topology, counter, sliding block, operations research, geometrical dissection. Includes the famous "14-15" puzzle which was a national craze, and his "Horse of a Different Color" which sold millions of copies. 117 of his most ingenious puzzles in all, 120 line drawings and diagrams. Solutions. Selected references. xx + 167pp. 5⅜ x 8.
T498 Paperbound **$1.00**

MATHEMATICAL PUZZLES OF SAM LOYD, Vol. II, selected and edited by Martin Gardner. The outstanding 2nd selection from the great American innovator's "Cyclopedia of Puzzles": speed and distance problems, clock problems, plane and solid geometry, calculus problems, etc. Analytical table of contents that groups the puzzles according to the type of mathematics necessary to solve them. 166 puzzles, 150 original line drawings and diagrams. Selected references. xiv + 177pp. 5⅜ x 8.
T709 Paperbound **$1.00**

ARITHMETICAL EXCURSIONS: AN ENRICHMENT OF ELEMENTARY MATHEMATICS, H. Bowers and J. Bowers. A lively and lighthearted collection of facts and entertainments for anyone who enjoys manipulating numbers or solving arithmetical puzzles: methods of arithmetic never taught in school, little-known facts about the most simple numbers, and clear explanations of more sophisticated topics; mysteries and folklore of numbers, the "Hin-dog-abic" number system, etc. First publication. Index. 529 numbered problems and diversions, all with answers. Bibliography. 60 figures. xiv + 320pp. 5⅜ x 8.
T770 Paperbound **$1.65**

CRYPTANALYSIS, H. F. Gaines. Formerly entitled ELEMENTARY CRYPTANALYSIS, this introductory-intermediate level text is the best book in print on cryptograms and their solution. It covers all major techniques of the past, and contains much that is not generally known except to experts. Full details about concealment, substitution, and transposition ciphers; periodic mixed alphabets, multafid, Kasiski and Vigenere methods, Ohaver patterns, Playfair, and scores of other topics. 6 language letter and word frequency appendix. 167 problems, now furnished with solutions. Index. 173 figures. vi + 230pp. 5⅜ x 8.
T97 Paperbound **$2.00**

CRYPTOGRAPHY, L. D. Smith. An excellent introductory work on ciphers and their solution, the history of secret writing, and actual methods and problems in such techniques as transposition and substitution. Appendices describe the enciphering of Japanese, the Baconian biliteral cipher, and contain frequency tables and a bibliography for further study. Over 150 problems with solutions. 160pp. 5⅜ x 8.
T247 Paperbound **$1.00**

PUZZLE QUIZ AND STUNT FUN, J. Meyer. The solution to party doldrums. 238 challenging puzzles, stunts and tricks. Mathematical puzzles like The Clever Carpenter, Atom Bomb; mysteries and deductions like The Bridge of Sighs, The Nine Pearls, Dog Logic; observation puzzles like Cigarette Smokers, Telephone Dial; over 200 others including magic squares, tongue twisters, puns, anagrams, and many others. All problems solved fully. 250pp. 5⅜ x 8.
T337 Paperbound **$1.00**

101 PUZZLES IN THOUGHT AND LOGIC, C. R. Wylie, Jr. Brand new problems you need no special knowledge to solve! Take the kinks out of your mental "muscles" and enjoy solving murder problems, the detection of lying fishermen, the logical identification of color by a blindman, and dozens more. Introduction with simplified explanation of general scientific method and puzzle solving. 128pp. 5⅜ x 8.
T367 Paperbound **$1.00**

MY BEST PROBLEMS IN MATHEMATICS, Hubert Phillips ("Caliban"). Only elementary mathematics needed to solve these 100 witty, catchy problems by a master problem creator. Problems on the odds in cards and dice, problems in geometry, algebra, permutations, even problems that require no math at all—just a logical mind, clear thinking. Solutions completely worked out. If you enjoy mysteries, alerting your perceptive powers and exercising your detective's eye, you'll find these cryptic puzzles a challenging delight. Original 1961 publication. 100 puzzles, solutions. x + 107pp. 5⅝ x 8.
T91 Paperbound **$1.00**

MY BEST PUZZLES IN LOGIC AND REASONING, Hubert Phillips ("Caliban"). A new collection of 100 inferential and logical puzzles chosen from the best that have appeared in England, available for first time in U.S. By the most endlessly resourceful puzzle creator now living. All data presented are both necessary and sufficient to allow a single unambiguous answer. No special knowledge is required for problems ranging from relatively simple to completely original one-of-a-kinds. Guaranteed to please beginners and experts of all ages. Original publication. 100 puzzles, full solutions. x + 107pp. 5⅜ x 8.
T119 Paperbound **$1.00**

CATALOGUE OF DOVER BOOKS

THE BOOK OF MODERN PUZZLES, G. L. Kaufman. A completely new series of puzzles as fascinating as crossword and deduction puzzles but based upon different principles and techniques. Simple 2-minute teasers, word labyrinths, design and pattern puzzles, logic and observation puzzles — over 150 braincrackers. Answers to all problems. 116 illustrations. 192pp. 5⅜ x 8.
T143 Paperbound **$1.00**

NEW WORD PUZZLES, G. L. Kaufman. 100 ENTIRELY NEW puzzles based on words and their combinations that will delight crossword puzzle, Scrabble and Jotto fans. Chess words, based on the moves of the chess king; design-onyms, symmetrical designs made of synonyms; rhymed double-crostics; syllable sentences; addle letter anagrams; alphagrams; linkograms; and many others all brand new. Full solutions. Space to work problems. 196 figures. vi + 122pp. 5⅜ x 8.
T344 Paperbound **$1.00**

MAZES AND LABYRINTHS: A BOOK OF PUZZLES, W. Shepherd. Mazes, formerly associated with mystery and ritual, are still among the most intriguing of intellectual puzzles. This is a novel and different collection of 50 amusements that embody the principle of the maze: mazes in the classical tradition; 3-dimensional, ribbon, and Möbius-strip mazes; hidden messages; spatial arrangements; etc.—almost all built on amusing story situations. 84 illustrations. Essay on maze psychology. Solutions. xv + 122pp. 5⅜ x 8.
T731 Paperbound **$1.00**

MAGIC TRICKS & CARD TRICKS, W. Jonson. Two books bound as one. 52 tricks with cards, 37 tricks with coins, bills, eggs, smoke, ribbons, slates, etc. Details on presentation, misdirection, and routining will help you master such famous tricks as the Changing Card, Card in the Pocket, Four Aces, Coin Through the Hand, Bill in the Egg, Afghan Bands, and over 75 others. If you follow the lucid exposition and key diagrams carefully, you will finish these two books with an astonishing mastery of magic. 106 figures. 224pp. 5⅜ x 8. T909 Paperbound **$1.00**

PANORAMA OF MAGIC, Milbourne Christopher. A profusely illustrated history of stage magic, a unique selection of prints and engravings from the author's private collection of magic memorabilia, the largest of its kind. Apparatus, stage settings and costumes; ingenious ads distributed by the performers and satiric broadsides passed around in the streets ridiculing pompous showmen; programs; decorative souvenirs. The lively text, by one of America's foremost professional magicians, is full of anecdotes about almost legendary wizards: Dede, the Egyptian; Philadelphia, the wonder-worker; Robert-Houdin, "the father of modern magic;" Harry Houdini; scores more. Altogether a pleasure package for anyone interested in magic, stage setting and design, ethnology, psychology, or simply in unusual people. A Dover original. 295 illustrations; 8 in full color. Index. viii + 216pp. 8⅜ x 11¼.
T774 Paperbound **$2.25**

HOUDINI ON MAGIC, Harry Houdini. One of the greatest magicians of modern times explains his most prized secrets. How locks are picked, with illustrated picks and skeleton keys; how a girl is sawed into twins; how to walk through a brick wall — Houdini's explanations of 44 stage tricks with many diagrams. Also included is a fascinating discussion of great magicians of the past and the story of his fight against fraudulent mediums and spiritualists. Edited by W.B. Gibson and M.N. Young. Bibliography. 155 figures, photos. xv + 280pp. 5⅜ x 8.
T384 Paperbound **$1.25**

MATHEMATICS, MAGIC AND MYSTERY, Martin Gardner. Why do card tricks work? How do magicians perform astonishing mathematical feats? How is stage mind-reading possible? This is the first book length study explaining the application of probability, set theory, theory of numbers, topology, etc., to achieve many startling tricks. Non-technical, accurate, detailed! 115 sections discuss tricks with cards, dice, coins, knots, geometrical vanishing illusions, how a Curry square "demonstrates" that the sum of the parts may be greater than the whole, and dozens of others. No sleight of hand necessary! 135 illustrations. xii + 174pp. 5⅜ x 8.
T335 Paperbound **$1.00**

EASY-TO-DO ENTERTAINMENTS AND DIVERSIONS WITH COINS, CARDS, STRING, PAPER AND MATCHES, R. M. Abraham. Over 300 tricks, games and puzzles will provide young readers with absorbing fun. Sections on card games; paper-folding; tricks with coins, matches and pieces of string; games for the agile; toy-making from common household objects; mathematical recreations; and 50 miscellaneous pastimes. Anyone in charge of groups of youngsters, including hard-pressed parents, and in need of suggestions on how to keep children sensibly amused and quietly content will find this book indispensable. Clear, simple text, copious number of delightful line drawings and illustrative diagrams. Originally titled "Winter Nights Entertainments." Introduction by Lord Baden Powell. 329 illustrations. v + 186pp. 5⅜ x 8½.
T921 Paperbound **$1.00**

STRING FIGURES AND HOW TO MAKE THEM, Caroline Furness Jayne. 107 string figures plus variations selected from the best primitive and modern examples developed by Navajo, Apache, pygmies of Africa, Eskimo, in Europe, Australia, China, etc. The most readily understandable, easy-to-follow book in English on perennially popular recreation. Crystal-clear exposition; step-by-step diagrams. Everyone from kindergarten children to adults looking for unusual diversion will be endlessly amused. Index. Bibliography. Introduction by A. C. Haddon. 17 full-page plates. 960 illustrations. xxiii + 401pp. 5⅜ x 8½.
T152 Paperbound **$2.00**

Entertainments, Humor

ODDITIES AND CURIOSITIES OF WORDS AND LITERATURE, C. Bombaugh, edited by M. Gardner.
The largest collection of idiosyncratic prose and poetry techniques in English, a legendary
work in the curious and amusing bypaths of literary recreations and the play technique in
literature—so important in modern works. Contains alphabetic poetry, acrostics, palindromes,
scissors verse, centos, emblematic poetry, famous literary puns, hoaxes, notorious slips of
the press, hilarious mistranslations, and much more. Revised and enlarged with modern
material by Martin Gardner. 368pp. 5⅜ x 8. **T759 Paperbound $1.50**

A NONSENSE ANTHOLOGY, collected by Carolyn Wells. 245 of the best nonsense verses ever
written, including nonsense puns, absurd arguments, mock epics and sagas, nonsense ballads,
odes, "sick" verses, dog-Latin verses, French nonsense verses, songs. By Edward Lear,
Lewis Carroll, Gelett Burgess, W. S. Gilbert, Hilaire Belloc, Peter Newell, Oliver Herford, etc.,
83 writers in all plus over four score anonymous nonsense verses. A special section of
limericks, plus famous nonsense such as Carroll's "Jabberwocky" and Lear's "The Jumblies"
and much excellent verse virtually impossible to locate elsewhere. For 50 years considered
the best anthology available. Index of first lines specially prepared for this edition.
Introduction by Carolyn Wells. 3 indexes: Title, Author, First lines. xxxiii + 279pp.
T499 Paperbound $1.35

**THE BAD CHILD'S BOOK OF BEASTS, MORE BEASTS FOR WORSE CHILDREN, and A MORAL ALPHA-
BET, H. Belloc.** Hardly an anthology of humorous verse has appeared in the last 50 years
without at least a couple of these famous nonsense verses. But one must see the entire volumes—with all the delightful original illustrations by Sir Basil Blackwood—to appreciate
fully Belloc's charming and witty verses that play so subacidly on the platitudes of life and
morals that beset his day—and ours. A great humor classic. Three books in one. Total of
157pp. 5⅜ x 8. **T749 Paperbound $1.00**

THE DEVIL'S DICTIONARY, Ambrose Bierce. Sardonic and irreverent barbs puncturing the
pomposities and absurdities of American politics, business, religion, literature, and arts,
by the country's greatest satirist in the classic tradition. Epigrammatic as Shaw, piercing
as Swift, American as Mark Twain, Will Rogers, and Fred Allen, Bierce will always remain
the favorite of a small coterie of enthusiasts, and of writers and speakers whom he supplies
with "some of the most gorgeous witticisms of the English language" (H. L. Mencken).
Over 1000 entries in alphabetical order. 144pp. 5⅜ x 8. **T487 Paperbound $1.00**

THE PURPLE COW AND OTHER NONSENSE, Gelett Burgess. The best of Burgess's early nonsense,
selected from the first edition of the "Burgess Nonsense Book." Contains many of his most
unusual and truly awe-inspiring pieces: 36 nonsense quatrains, the Poems of Patagonia, Alpha-
bet of Famous Goops, and the other hilarious (and rare) adult nonsense that place him in the
forefront of American humorists. All pieces are accompanied by the original Burgess illustrations. 123 illustrations. xiii + 113pp. 5⅜ x 8. **T772 Paperbound $1.00**

**MY PIOUS FRIENDS AND DRUNKEN COMPANIONS and MORE PIOUS FRIENDS AND DRUNKEN
COMPANIONS, Frank Shay.** Folksingers, amateur and professional, and everyone who loves
singing: here, available for the first time in 30 years, is this valued collection of 132 ballads,
blues, vaudeville numbers, drinking songs, sea chanties, comedy songs. Songs of pre-Beatnik
Bohemia; songs from all over America, England, France, Australia; the great songs of the
Naughty Nineties and early twentieth-century America. Over a third with music. Woodcuts
by John Held, Jr. convey perfectly the brash insouciance of an era of rollicking unabashed
song. 12 illustrations by John Held, Jr. Two indexes (Titles and First lines and Choruses).
Introductions by the author. Two volumes bound as one. Total of xvi + 235pp. 5⅜ x 8½.
T946 Paperbound $1.00

HOW TO TELL THE BIRDS FROM THE FLOWERS, R. W. Wood. How not to confuse a carrot with
a parrot, a grape with an ape, a puffin with nuffin. Delightful drawings, clever puns, absurd
little poems point out far-fetched resemblances in nature. The author was a leading
physicist. Introduction by Margaret Wood White. 106 illus. 60pp. 5⅜ x 8.
T523 Paperbound 75¢

PECK'S BAD BOY AND HIS PA, George W. Peck. The complete edition, containing both
volumes, of one of the most widely read American humor books. The endless ingenious
pranks played by bad boy "Hennery" on his pa and the grocery man, the outraged pomposity
of Pa, the perpetual ridiculing of middle class institutions, are as entertaining today as they
were in 1883. No pale sophistications or subtleties, but rather humor vigorous, raw, earthy,
imaginative, and, as folk humor often is, sadistic. This peculiarly fascinating book is also
valuable to historians and students of American culture as a portrait of an age. 100
original illustrations by True Williams. Introduction by E. F. Bleiler. 347pp. 5⅜ x 8.
T497 Paperbound $1.35

CATALOGUE OF DOVER BOOKS

THE HUMOROUS VERSE OF LEWIS CARROLL. Almost every poem Carroll ever wrote, the largest collection ever published, including much never published elsewhere: 150 parodies, burlesques, riddles, ballads, acrostics, etc., with 130 original illustrations by Tenniel, Carroll, and others. "Addicts will be grateful . . . there is nothing for the faithful to do but sit down and fall to the banquet," N. Y. Times. Index to first lines. xiv + 446pp. 5⅜ x 8.
T654 Paperbound **$1.85**

DIVERSIONS AND DIGRESSIONS OF LEWIS CARROLL. A major new treasure for Carroll fans! Rare privately published humor, fantasy, puzzles, and games by Carroll at his whimsical best, with a new vein of frank satire. Includes many new mathematical amusements and recreations, among them the fragmentary Part III of "Curiosa Mathematica." Contains "The Rectory Umbrella," "The New Belfry," "The Vision of the Three T's," and much more. New 32-page supplement of rare photographs taken by Carroll. x + 375pp. 5⅜ x 8.
T732 Paperbound **$1.65**

THE COMPLETE NONSENSE OF EDWARD LEAR. This is the only complete edition of this master of gentle madness available at a popular price. A BOOK OF NONSENSE, NONSENSE SONGS, MORE NONSENSE SONGS AND STORIES in their entirety with all the old favorites that have delighted children and adults for years. The Dong With A Luminous Nose, The Jumblies, The Owl and the Pussycat, and hundreds of other bits of wonderful nonsense. 214 limericks, 3 sets of Nonsense Botany, 5 Nonsense Alphabets, 546 drawings by Lear himself, and much more. 320pp. 5⅜ x 8.
T167 Paperbound **$1.00**

THE MELANCHOLY LUTE, The Humorous Verse of Franklin P. Adams ("FPA"). The author's own selection of light verse, drawn from thirty years of FPA's column, "The Conning Tower," syndicated all over the English-speaking world. Witty, perceptive, literate, these ninety-six poems range from parodies of other poets, Millay, Longfellow, Edgar Guest, Kipling, Masefield, etc., and free and hilarious translations of Horace and other Latin poets, to satiric comments on fabled American institutions—the New York Subways, preposterous ads, suburbanites, sensational journalism, etc. They reveal with vigor and clarity the humor, integrity and restraint of a wise and gentle American satirist. Introduction by Robert Hutchinson. vi + 122pp. 5⅜ x 8½.
T108 Paperbound **$1.00**

SINGULAR TRAVELS, CAMPAIGNS, AND ADVENTURES OF BARON MUNCHAUSEN, R. E. Raspe, with 90 illustrations by Gustave Doré. The first edition in over 150 years to reestablish the deeds of the Prince of Liars exactly as Raspe first recorded them in 1785—the genuine Baron Munchausen, one of the most popular personalities in English literature. Included also are the best of the many sequels, written by other hands. Introduction on Raspe by J. Carswell. Bibliography of early editions. xliv + 192pp. 5⅜ x 8.
T698 Paperbound **$1.00**

THE WIT AND HUMOR OF OSCAR WILDE, ed. by Alvin Redman. Wilde at his most brilliant, in 1000 epigrams exposing weaknesses and hypocrisies of "civilized" society. Divided into 49 categories—sin, wealth, women, America, etc.—to aid writers, speakers. Includes excerpts from his trials, books, plays, criticism. Formerly "The Epigrams of Oscar Wilde." Introduction by Vyvyan Holland, Wilde's only living son. Introductory essay by editor. 260pp. 5⅜ x 8.
T602 Paperbound **$1.00**

MAX AND MORITZ, Wilhelm Busch. Busch is one of the great humorists of all time, as well as the father of the modern comic strip. This volume, translated by H. A. Klein and other hands, contains the perennial favorite "Max and Moritz" (translated by C. T. Brooks), Plisch and Plum, Das Rabennest, Eispeter, and seven other whimsical, sardonic, jovial, diabolical cartoon and verse stories. Lively English translations parallel the original German. This work has delighted millions, since it first appeared in the 19th century, and is guaranteed to please almost anyone. Edited by H. A. Klein, with an afterword. x + 205pp. 5⅝ x 8½.
T181 Paperbound **$1.00**

HYPOCRITICAL HELENA, Wilhelm Busch. A companion volume to "Max and Moritz," with the title piece (Die Fromme Helena) and 10 other highly amusing cartoon and verse stories, all newly translated by H. A. Klein and M. C. Klein: Adventure on New Year's Eve (Abenteuer in der Neujahrsnacht), Hangover on the Morning after New Year's Eve (Der Katzenjammer am Neujahrsmorgen), etc. English and German in parallel columns. Hours of pleasure, also a fine language aid. x + 205pp. 5⅝ x 8½.
T184 Paperbound **$1.00**

THE BEAR THAT WASN'T, Frank Tashlin. What does it mean? Is it simply delightful wry humor, or a charming story of a bear who wakes up in the midst of a factory, or a satire on Big Business, or an existential cartoon-story of the human condition, or a symbolization of the struggle between conformity and the individual? New York Herald Tribune said of the first edition: ". . . a fable for grownups that will be fun for children. Sit down with the book and get your own bearings." Long an underground favorite with readers of all ages and opinions. v + 51pp. Illustrated. 5⅜ x 8½.
T939 Paperbound **75¢**

RUTHLESS RHYMES FOR HEARTLESS HOMES and MORE RUTHLESS RHYMES FOR HEARTLESS HOMES, Harry Graham ("Col. D. Streamer"). Two volumes of Little Willy and 48 other poetic disasters. A bright, new reprint of oft-quoted, never forgotten, devastating humor by a precursor of today's "sick" joke school. For connoisseurs of wicked, wacky humor and all who delight in the comedy of manners. Original drawings are a perfect complement. 61 illustrations. Index. vi + 69pp. Two vols. bound as one. 5⅜ x 8½.
T930 Paperbound **75¢**

Fiction

FLATLAND, E. A. Abbott. A science-fiction classic of life in a 2-dimensional world that is also a first-rate introduction to such aspects of modern science as relativity and hyperspace. Political, moral, satirical, and humorous overtones have made FLATLAND fascinating reading for thousands. 7th edition. New introduction by Banesh Hoffmann. 16 illustrations. 128pp. 5⅜ x 8. **T1 Paperbound $1.00**

THE WONDERFUL WIZARD OF OZ, L. F. Baum. Only edition in print with all the original W. W. Denslow illustrations in full color—as much a part of "The Wizard" as Tenniel's drawings are of "Alice in Wonderland." "The Wizard" is still America's best-loved fairy tale, in which, as the author expresses it, "The wonderment and joy are retained and the heartaches and nightmares left out." Now today's young readers can enjoy every word and wonderful picture of the original book. New introduction by Martin Gardner. A Baum bibliography. 23 full-page color plates. viii + 268pp. 5⅜ x 8. **T691 Paperbound $1.45**

THE MARVELOUS LAND OF OZ, L. F. Baum. This is the equally enchanting sequel to the "Wizard," continuing the adventures of the Scarecrow and the Tin Woodman. The hero this time is a little boy named Tip, and all the delightful Oz magic is still present. This is the Oz book with the Animated Saw-Horse, the Woggle-Bug, and Jack Pumpkinhead. All the original John R. Neill illustrations, 10 in full color. 287 pp. 5⅜ x 8. **T692 Paperbound $1.45**

FIVE GREAT DOG NOVELS, edited by Blanche Cirker. The complete original texts of five classic dog novels that have delighted and thrilled millions of children and adults throughout the world with their stories of loyalty, adventure, and courage. Full texts of Jack London's "The Call of the Wild"; John Brown's "Rab and His Friends"; Alfred Ollivant's "Bob, Son of Battle"; Marshall Saunders's "Beautiful Joe"; and Ouida's "A Dog of Flanders." 21 Illustrations from the original editions. 495pp. 5⅜ x 8. **T777 Paperbound $1.75**

TO THE SUN? and OFF ON A COMET!, Jules Verne. Complete texts of two of the most imaginative flights into fancy in world literature display the high adventure that have kept Verne's novels read for nearly a century. Only unabridged edition of the best translation, by Edward Roth. Large, easily readable type. 50 illustrations selected from first editions. 462pp. 5⅜ x 8. **T634 Paperbound $1.75**

FROM THE EARTH TO THE MOON and ALL AROUND THE MOON, Jules Verne. Complete editions of 2 of Verne's most successful novels, in finest Edward Roth translations, now available after many years out of print. Verne's visions of submarines, airplanes, television, rockets, interplanetary travel; of scientific and not-so-scientific beliefs; of peculiarities of Americans; all delight and engross us today as much as when they first appeared. Large, easily readable type. 42 illus. from first French edition. 476pp. 5⅜ x 8. **T633 Paperbound $1.75**

THE CRUISE OF THE CACHALOT, Frank T. Bullen. Out of the experiences of many years on the high-seas, First Mate Bullen created this novel of adventure aboard an American whaler, shipping out of New Bedford, Mass., when American whaling was at the height of its splendor. Originally published in 1899, the story of the round-the-world cruise of the "Cachalot" in pursuit of the sperm whale has thrilled generations of readers. A maritime classic that will fascinate anyone interested in reading about the sea or looking for a solid old-fashioned yarn, while the vivid recreation of a brief but important chapter of Americana and the British author's often biting commentary on nineteenth-century Yankee mores offer insights into the colorful era of America's coming of age. 8 plates. xiii + 271pp. 5⅜ x 8½. **T774 Paperbound $1.00**

28 SCIENCE FICTION STORIES OF H. G. WELLS. Two full unabridged novels, MEN LIKE GODS and STAR BEGOTTEN, plus 26 short stories by the master science-fiction writer of all time! Stories of space, time, invention, exploration, future adventure—an indispensable part of the library of everyone interested in science and adventure. PARTIAL CONTENTS: Men Like Gods, The Country of the Blind, In the Abyss, The Crystal Egg, The Man Who Could Work Miracles, A Story of the Days to Come, The Valley of Spiders, and 21 more! 928pp. 5⅜ x 8. **T265 Clothbound $4.50**

DAVID HARUM, E. N. Westcott. This novel of one of the most lovable, humorous characters in American literature is a prime example of regional humor. It continues to delight people who like their humor dry, their characters quaint, and their plots ingenuous. First book edition to contain complete novel plus chapter found after author's death. Illustrations from first illustrated edition. 192pp. 5⅜ x 8. **T580 Paperbound $1.15**

GESTA ROMANORUM, trans. by Charles Swan, ed. by Wynnard Hooper. 181 tales of Greeks, Romans, Britons, Biblical characters, comprise one of greatest medieval story collections, source of plots for writers including Shakespeare, Chaucer, Gower, etc. Imaginative tales of wars, incest, thwarted love, magic, fantasy, allegory, humor, tell about kings, prostitutes, philosophers, fair damsels, knights, Noah, pirates, all walks, stations of life. Introduction. Notes. 500pp. 5⅜ x 8. **T535 Paperbound $1.85**

CATALOGUE OF DOVER BOOKS

3 ADVENTURE NOVELS by H. Rider Haggard. Complete texts of "She," "King Solomon's Mines," "Allan Quatermain." Qualities of discovery, desire for immortality, search for the primitive, for what is unadorned by civilization, have kept these novels of African adventure excitingly alive to readers from R. L. Stevenson to George Orwell. 636pp. 5⅜ x 8.
T584 Paperbound **$2.00**

THE CASTING AWAY OF MRS. LECKS AND MRS. ALESHINE, F. R. Stockton. A charming light novel by Frank Stockton, one of America's finest humorists (and author of "The Lady, or the Tiger?"). This book has made millions of Americans laugh at the reflection of themselves in two middle-aged American women involved in some of the strangest adventures on record. You will laugh, too, as they endure shipwreck, desert island, and blizzard with maddening tranquillity. Also contains complete text of "The Dusantes," sequel to "The Casting Away." 49 original illustrations by F. D. Steele. vii + 142pp. 5⅜ x 8.   T743 Paperbound **$1.00**

THREE PROPHETIC NOVELS OF H. G. WELLS. Complete texts of 3 timeless science fiction novels by the greatest master of the art, with remarkable prophecies of technological and social changes that are really taking place!—"When the Sleeper Wakes" (first printing in 50 years), "A Story of the Days to Come," and "The Time Machine" (only truly complete text available). Introduction by E. F. Bleiler. "The absolute best of imaginative fiction," N. Y. Times. 335pp. 5⅜ x 8.   T605 Paperbound **$1.45**

SEVEN SCIENCE FICTION NOVELS, H. G. Wells. Full unabridged texts of 7 science-fiction novels of the master. Ranging from biology, physics, chemistry, astronomy, to sociology and other studies, Mr. Wells extrapolates whole worlds of strange and intriguing character. "One will have to go far to match this for entertainment, excitement, and sheer pleasure . . ." NEW YORK TIMES. Contents: The Time Machine, The Island of Dr. Moreau, The First Men in the Moon, The Invisible Man, The War of the Worlds, The Food of the Gods, In The Days of the Comet. 1015pp. 5⅜ x 8.   T264 Clothbound **$4.50**

THE PRISONER OF ZENDA and RUPERT OF HENTZAU, Anthony Hope. The first edition to contain the complete story of the English diplomat who becomes King for a Day in the ancient aristocratic Kingdom of Ruritania. Long a favorite of devotees of high adventure, romance, grand intigue. Intelligent thrills presented with verve and elegant excitement. Unabridged reprints. Two volumes bound as one. 14 illustrations by Charles Dana Gibson. 420pp. 5⅜ x 8.
T69 Paperbound **$1.35**

TWO LITTLE SAVAGES, Ernest Thompson Seton. A lively narrative of the adventures of two real boys who decide to go Indian, combined with a storehouse of survival information: how to make a fire without matches, use an axe expertly, smudge mosquitoes, distinguish animal tracks, make mocassins, bows and arrows, learn the stars, etc. A classic of nature and boyhood, certain to awaken nature-interest in any youngster—or oldster. Highly recommended to Scouts, hunters, campers, bird-watchers or even city-dwellers who like to learn about the ways of nature. 293 illustrations by the author. x + 286pp. 5⅜ x 8½.
T985 Paperbound **$1.50**

THREE MARTIAN NOVELS, Edgar Rice Burroughs. Complete unabridged reprinting, in one volume, of Thuvia, Maid of Mars; Chessmen of Mars; The Master Mind of Mars. Hours of science-fiction adventure by a modern master storyteller. Reset in large clear type for easy reading. 16 illustrations by J. Allen St. John. vi + 490 pp. 5⅜ x 8½.   T39 Paperbound **$1.75**

THE LAND THAT TIME FORGOT, and THE MOON MAID, Edgar Rice Burroughs. Two of Burroughs's rarest novels, considered by most authorities to be his best work. The first is adventure on a lost island where evolution is an individual matter and rapid, rather than slow and in terms of species; the second is the story of the first exploration of the Moon, the weird cultures that inhabit its interior, the conquest of the Earth by the Moon, and the millennia of struggle between the invaders and the earthmen. Packed full of thrills, thought-provoking. 5 illustrations by J. Allan St. John. 5⅜ x 8½.   T358 Paperbound **$2.00**
T1020 Clothbound **$3.75**

PIRATES OF VENUS, LOST ON VENUS, Edgar Rice Burroughs. These are the first two novels describing the adventures of Carson Napier on mysterious Venus. Thrilling adventures and exciting science-fiction situations among the towering jungles, monster-filled seas, and fantastic cities of the Second Planet. Complete and unabridged. Illustrations from original periodical publications. Illustrations by Matania. vi + 340pp. 5⅜ x 8½.
T1053 Paperbound **$1.75**

A PRINCESS OF MARS, A FIGHTING MAN OF MARS, Edgar Rice Burroughs. Two fantastic novels of Mars. "A Princess of Mars" explains how John Carter first came to Mars, and his adventures among the dying civilizations. "A Fighting Man of Mars", an independent novel set in the same adventurous environment, provides hours of thrills among lost cities and monsters. Illustrated by J. Allan St. John. 5⅜ x 8½.   T1055 Paperbound **$1.75**

Social Sciences

SOCIAL THOUGHT FROM LORE TO SCIENCE, H. E. Barnes and H. Becker. An immense survey of sociological thought and ways of viewing, studying, planning, and reforming society from earliest times to the present. Includes thought on society of preliterate peoples, ancient non-Western cultures, and every great movement in Europe, America, and modern Japan. Analyzes hundreds of great thinkers: Plato, Augustine, Bodin, Vico, Montesquieu, Herder, Comte, Marx, etc. Weighs the contributions of utopians, sophists, fascists and communists; economists, jurists, philosophers, ecclesiastics, and every 19th and 20th century school of scientific sociology, anthropology, and social psychology throughout the world. Combines topical, chronological, and regional approaches, treating the evolution of social thought as a process rather than as a series of mere topics. "Impressive accuracy, competence, and discrimination . . . easily the best single survey," Nation. Thoroughly revised, with new material up to 1960. 2 indexes. Over 2200 bibliographical notes. Three volume set. Total of 1586pp. 5⅜ x 8.

T901 Vol I Paperbound **$2.35**
T902 Vol II Paperbound **$2.35**
T903 Vol III Paperbound **$2.35**
The set **$7.05**

FOLKWAYS, William Graham Sumner. A classic of sociology, a searching and thorough examination of patterns of behaviour from primitive, ancient Greek and Judaic, Medieval Christian, African, Oriental, Melanesian, Australian, Islamic, to modern Western societies. Thousands of illustrations of social, sexual, and religious customs, mores, laws, and institutions. Hundreds of categories: Labor, Wealth, Abortion, Primitive Justice, Life Policy, Slavery, Cannibalism, Uncleanness and the Evil Eye, etc. Will extend the horizon of every reader by showing the relativism of his own culture. Prefatory note by A. G. Keller. Introduction by William Lyon Phelps. Bibliography. Index. xiii + 692pp. 5⅜ x 8. T508 Paperbound **$2.49**

PRIMITIVE RELIGION, P. Radin. A thorough treatment by a noted anthropologist of the nature and origin of man's belief in the supernatural and the influences that have shaped religious expression in primitive societies. Ranging from the Arunta, Ashanti, Aztec, Bushman, Crow, Fijian, etc., of Africa, Australia, Pacific Islands, the Arctic, North and South America, Prof. Radin integrates modern psychology, comparative religion, and economic thought with first-hand accounts gathered by himself and other scholars of primitive initiations, training of the shaman, and other fascinating topics. "Excellent," NATURE (London). Unabridged reissue of 1st edition. New author's preface. Bibliographic notes. Index. x + 322pp. 5⅜ x 8. T393 Paperbound **$1.85**

PRIMITIVE MAN AS PHILOSOPHER, P. Radin. A standard anthropological work covering primitive thought on such topics as the purpose of life, marital relations, freedom of thought, symbolism, death, resignation, the nature of reality, personality, gods, and many others. Drawn from factual material gathered from the Winnebago, Oglala Sioux, Maori, Baganda, Batak, Zuni, among others, it does not distort ideas by removing them from context but interprets strictly within the original framework. Extensive selections of original primitive documents. Bibliography. Index. xviii + 402pp. 5⅜ x 8. T392 Paperbound **$2.25**

A TREATISE ON SOCIOLOGY, THE MIND AND SOCIETY, Vilfredo Pareto. This treatise on human society is one of the great classics of modern sociology. First published in 1916, its careful catalogue of the innumerable manifestations of non-logical human conduct (Book One); the theory of "residues," leading to the premise that sentiment not logic determines human behavior (Book Two), and of "derivations," beliefs derived from desires (Book Three); and the general description of society made up of non-elite and elite, consisting of "foxes" who live by cunning and "lions" who live by force, stirred great controversy. But Pareto's passion for isolation and classification of elements and factors, and his allegiance to scientific method as the key tool for scrutinizing the human situation made his a truly twentieth-century mind and his work a catalytic influence on certain later social commentators. These four volumes (bound as two) require no special training to be appreciated and any reader who wishes to gain a complete understanding of modern sociological theory, regardless of special field of interest, will find them a must. Reprint of revised (corrected) printing of original edition. Translated by Andrew Bongiorno and Arthur Livingston. Index. Bibliography. Appendix containing index-summary of theorems. 48 diagrams. Four volumes bound as two. Total of 2063pp. 5⅜ x 8½. The set Clothbound **$15.00**

THE POLISH PEASANT IN EUROPE AND AMERICA, William I. Thomas, Florian Znaniecki. A seminal sociological study of peasant primary groups (family and community) and the disruptions produced by a new industrial system and immigration to America. The peasant's family, class system, religious and aesthetic attitudes, and economic life are minutely examined and analyzed in hundreds of pages of primary documentation, particularly letters between family members. The disorientation caused by new environments is scrutinized in detail (a 312-page autobiography of an immigrant is especially valuable and revealing) in an attempt to find common experiences and reactions. The famous "Methodological Note" sets forth the principles which guided the authors. When out of print this set has sold for as much as $50. 2nd revised edition. 2 vols. Vol. 1: xv + 1115pp. Vol. 2: 1135pp. Index. 6 x 9. T478 Clothbound 2 vol. set **$12.50**

Language Books and Records

GERMAN: HOW TO SPEAK AND WRITE IT. AN INFORMAL CONVERSATIONAL METHOD FOR SELF STUDY, Joseph Rosenberg. Eminently useful for self study because of concentration on elementary stages of learning. Also provides teachers with remarkable variety of aids: 28 full- and double-page sketches with pertinent items numbered and identified in German and English; German proverbs, jokes; grammar, idiom studies; extensive practice exercises. The most interesting introduction to German available, full of amusing illustrations, photographs of cities and landmarks in German-speaking cities, cultural information subtly woven into conversational material. Includes summary of grammar, guide to letter writing, study guide to German literature by Dr. Richard Friedenthal. Index. 400 illustrations. 384pp. 5⅜ x 8½.
T271 Paperbound **$2.00**

FRENCH: HOW TO SPEAK AND WRITE IT. AN INFORMAL CONVERSATIONAL METHOD FOR SELF STUDY, Joseph Lemaitre. Even the absolute beginner can acquire a solid foundation for further study from this delightful elementary course. Photographs, sketches and drawings, sparkling colloquial conversations on a wide variety of topics (including French culture and custom), French sayings and quips, are some of aids used to demonstrate rather than merely describe the language. Thorough yet surprisingly entertaining approach, excellent for teaching and for self study. Comprehensive analysis of pronunciation, practice exercises and appendices of verb tables, additional vocabulary, other useful material. Index. Appendix. 400 illustrations. 416pp. 5⅜ x 8½.
T268 Paperbound **$2.00**

DICTIONARY OF SPOKEN SPANISH, Spanish-English, English-Spanish. Compiled from spoken Spanish, emphasizing idiom and colloquial usage in both Castilian and Latin-American. More than 16,000 entries containing over 25,000 idioms—the largest list of idiomatic constructions ever published. Complete sentences given, indexed under single words—language in immediately useable form, for travellers, businessmen, students, etc. 25 page introduction provides rapid survey of sounds, grammar, syntax, with full consideration of irregular verbs. Especially apt in modern treatment of phrases and structure. 17 page glossary gives translations of geographical names, money values, numbers, national holidays, important street signs, useful expressions of high frequency, plus unique 7 page glossary of Spanish and Spanish-American foods and dishes. Originally published as War Department Technical Manual TM 30-900. iv + 513pp. 5⅜ x 8.
T495 Paperbound **$1.75**

SPEAK MY LANGUAGE: SPANISH FOR YOUNG BEGINNERS, M. Ahlman, Z. Gilbert. Records provide one of the best, and most entertaining, methods of introducing a foreign language to children. Within the framework of a train trip from Portugal to Spain, an English-speaking child is introduced to Spanish by a native companion. (Adapted from a successful radio program of the N. Y. State Educational Department.) Though a continuous story, there are ·a dozen specific categories of expressions, including greetings, numbers, time, weather, food, clothes, family members, etc. Drill is combined with poetry and contextual use. Authentic background music is heard. An accompanying book enables a reader to follow the records, and includes a vocabulary of over 350 recorded expressions. Two 10″ 33⅓ records, total of 40 minutes. Book. 40 illustrations. 69pp. 5¼ x 10½.
T890 The set **$4.95**

AN ENGLISH-FRENCH-GERMAN-SPANISH WORD FREQUENCY DICTIONARY, H. S. Eaton. An indispensable language study aid, this is a semantic frequency list of the 6000 most frequently used words in 4 languages—24,000 words in all. The lists, based on concepts rather than words alone, and containing all modern, exact, and idiomatic vocabulary, are arranged side by side to form a unique 4-language dictionary. A simple key indicates the importance of the individual words within each language. Over 200 pages of separate indexes for each language enable you to locate individual words at a glance. Will help language teachers and students, authors of textbooks, grammars, and language tests to compare concepts in the various languages and to concentrate on basic vocabulary, avoiding uncommon and obsolete words. 2 Appendixes. xxi + 441pp. 6½ x 9¼.
T738 Paperbound **$2.45**

NEW RUSSIAN-ENGLISH AND ENGLISH-RUSSIAN DICTIONARY, M. A. O'Brien. Over 70,000 entries in the new orthography! Many idiomatic uses and colloquialisms which form the basis of actual speech. Irregular verbs, perfective and imperfective aspects, regular and irregular sound changes, and other features. One of the few dictionaries where accent changes within the conjugation of verbs and the declension of nouns are fully indicated. "One of the best," Prof. E. J. Simmons, Cornell. First names, geographical terms, bibliography, etc. 738pp. 4½ x 6¼.
T208 Paperbound **$2.00**

96 MOST USEFUL PHRASES FOR TOURISTS AND STUDENTS in English, French, Spanish, German, Italian. A handy folder you'll want to carry with you. How to say "Excuse me," "How much is it?", "Write it down, please," etc., in four foreign languages. Copies limited, no more than 1 to a customer. **FREE**

CATALOGUE OF DOVER BOOKS

Say It language phrase books

These handy phrase books (128 to 196 pages each) make grammatical drills unnecessary for an elementary knowledge of a spoken foreign language. Covering most matters of travel and everyday life each volume contains:

Over 1000 phrases and sentences in immediately useful forms — foreign language plus English.

Modern usage designed for Americans. Specific phrases like, "Give me small change," and "Please call a taxi."

Simplified phonetic transcription you will be able to read at sight.

The only completely indexed phrase books on the market.

Covers scores of important situations: — Greetings, restaurants, sightseeing, useful expressions, etc.

These books are prepared by native linguists who are professors at Columbia, N.Y.U., Fordham and other great universities. Use them independently or with any other book or record course. They provide a supplementary living element that most other courses lack. Individual volumes in:

Russian 75¢	Italian 75¢	Spanish 75¢	German 75¢
Hebrew 75¢	Danish 75¢	Japanese 75¢	Swedish 75¢
Dutch 75¢	Esperanto 75¢	Modern Greek 75¢	Portuguese 75¢
Norwegian 75¢	Polish 75¢	French 75¢	Yiddish 75¢
Turkish 75¢		English for German-speaking people 75¢	
English for Italian-speaking people 75¢		English for Spanish-speaking people 75¢	

Large clear type. 128-196 pages each. 3½ x 5¼. Sturdy paper binding.

Listen and Learn language records

LISTEN & LEARN is the only language record course designed especially to meet your travel and everyday needs. It is available in separate sets for FRENCH, SPANISH, GERMAN, JAPANESE, RUSSIAN, MODERN GREEK, PORTUGUESE, ITALIAN and HEBREW, and each set contains three 33⅓ rpm long-playing records—1½ hours of recorded speech by eminent native speakers who are professors at Columbia, New York University, Queens College.

Check the following special features found only in LISTEN & LEARN:

- **Dual-language recording.** 812 selected phrases and sentences, over 3200 words, spoken first in English, then in their foreign language equivalents. A suitable pause follows each foreign phrase, allowing you time to repeat the expression. You learn by unconscious assimilation.

- **128 to 206-page manual** contains everything on the records, plus a simple phonetic pronunciation guide.

- **Indexed for convenience. The only set on the market** that is completely indexed. No more puzzling over where to find the phrase you need. Just look in the rear of the manual.

- **Practical.** No time wasted on material you can find in any grammar. LISTEN & LEARN covers central core material with phrase approach. Ideal for the person with limited learning time.

- **Living, modern expressions,** not found in other courses. Hygienic products, modern equipment, shopping—expressions used every day, like "nylon" and "air-conditioned."

- **Limited objective.** Everything you learn, no matter where you stop, is immediately useful. You have to finish other courses, wade through grammar and vocabulary drill, before they help you.

- **High-fidelity recording.** LISTEN & LEARN records equal in clarity and surface-silence any record on the market costing up to $6.

"Excellent . . . the spoken records . . . impress me as being among the very best on the market," **Prof. Mario Pei,** Dept. of Romance Languages, Columbia University. "Inexpensive and well-done . . . it would make an ideal present," CHICAGO SUNDAY TRIBUNE. "More genuinely helpful than anything of its kind which I have previously encountered," **Sidney Clark,** well-known author of "ALL THE BEST" travel books.

UNCONDITIONAL GUARANTEE. Try LISTEN & LEARN, then return it within 10 days for full refund if you are not satisfied.

Each set contains three twelve-inch 33⅓ records, manual, and album.

SPANISH	the set **$5.95**	GERMAN	the set **$5.95**
FRENCH	the set **$5.95**	ITALIAN	the set **$5.95**
RUSSIAN	the set **$5.95**	JAPANESE	the set **$5.95**
PORTUGUESE	the set **$5.95**	MODERN GREEK	the set **$5.95**
MODERN HEBREW	the set **$5.95**		

Literature, History of Literature

ARISTOTLE'S THEORY OF POETRY AND THE FINE ARTS, edited by S. H. Butcher. The celebrated Butcher translation of this great classic faced, page by page, with the complete Greek text. A 300 page introduction discussing Aristotle's ideas and their influence in the history of thought and literature, and covering art and nature, imitation as an aesthetic form, poetic truth, art and morality, tragedy, comedy, and similar topics. Modern Aristotelian criticism discussed by John Gassner. lxxvi + 421pp. 5⅜ x 8. T42 Paperbound **$2.00**

INTRODUCTIONS TO ENGLISH LITERATURE, edited by B. Dobrée. Goes far beyond ordinary histories, ranging from the 7th century up to 1914 (to the 1940's in some cases.) The first half of each volume is a specific detailed study of historical and economic background of the period and a general survey of poetry and prose, including trends of thought, influences, etc. The second and larger half is devoted to a detailed study of more than 5000 poets, novelists, dramatists; also economists, historians, biographers, religious writers, philosophers, travellers, and scientists of literary stature, with dates, lists of major works and their dates, keypoint critical bibliography, and evaluating comments. The most compendious bibliographic and literary aid within its price range.

Vol. I. THE BEGINNINGS OF ENGLISH LITERATURE TO SKELTON, (1509), W. L. Renwick, H. Orton. 450pp. 5⅛ x 7⅞. T75 Clothbound **$4.50**

Vol. II. THE ENGLISH RENAISSANCE, 1510-1688, V. de Sola Pinto. 381pp. 5⅛ x 7⅞. T76 Clothbound **$4.50**

Vol. III. AUGUSTANS AND ROMANTICS, 1689-1830, H. Dyson, J. Butt. 320pp. 5⅛ x 7⅞. T77 Clothbound **$4.50**

Vol. IV. THE VICTORIANS AND AFTER, 1830-1940's, E. Batho, B. Dobrée. 360pp. 5⅛ x 7⅞. T78 Clothbound **$4.50**

EPIC AND ROMANCE, W. P. Ker. Written by one of the foremost authorities on medieval literature, this is the standard survey of medieval epic and romance. It covers Teutonic epics, Icelandic sagas, Beowulf, French chansons de geste, the Roman de Troie, and many other important works of literature. It is an excellent account for a body of literature whose beauty and value has only recently come to be recognized. Index. xxiv + 398pp. 5⅜ x 8. T355 Paperbound **$2.00**

THE POPULAR BALLAD, F. B. Gummere. Most useful factual introduction; fund of descriptive material; quotes, cites over 260 ballads. Examines, from folkloristic view, structure; choral, ritual elements; meter, diction, fusion; effects of tradition, editors; almost every other aspect of border, riddle, kinship, sea, ribald, supernatural, etc., ballads. Bibliography. 2 indexes. 374pp. 5⅜ x 8. T548 Paperbound **$1.65**

MASTERS OF THE DRAMA, John Gassner. The most comprehensive history of the drama in print, covering drama in every important tradition from the Greeks to the Near East, China, Japan, Medieval Europe, England, Russia, Italy, Spain, Germany, and dozens of other drama producing nations. This unsurpassed reading and reference work encompasses more than 800 dramatists and over 2000 plays, with biographical material, plot summaries, theatre history, etc. "Has no competitors in its field," THEATRE ARTS. "Best of its kind in English," NEW REPUBLIC. Exhaustive 35 page bibliography. 77 photographs and drawings. Deluxe edition with reinforced cloth binding, headbands, stained top. xxii + 890pp. 5⅜ x 8. T100 Clothbound **$6.95**

THE DEVELOPMENT OF DRAMATIC ART, D. C. Stuart. The basic work on the growth of Western drama from primitive beginnings to Eugene O'Neill, covering over 2500 years. Not a mere listing or survey, but a thorough analysis of changes, origins of style, and influences in each period; dramatic conventions, social pressures, choice of material, plot devices, stock situations, etc.; secular and religious works of all nations and epochs. "Generous and thoroughly documented researches," Outlook. "Solid studies of influences and playwrights and periods," London Times. Index. Bibliography. xi + 679pp. 5⅜ x 8. T693 Paperbound **$2.75**

A SOURCE BOOK IN THEATRICAL HISTORY (SOURCES OF THEATRICAL HISTORY), A. M. Nagler. Over 2000 years of actors, directors, designers, critics, and spectators speak for themselves in this potpourri of writings selected from the great and formative periods of western drama. On-the-spot descriptions of masks, costumes, makeup, rehearsals, special effects, acting methods, backstage squabbles, theatres, etc. Contemporary glimpses of Molière rehearsing his company, an exhortation to a Roman audience to buy refreshments and keep quiet, Goethe's rules for actors, Belasco telling of $6500 he spent building a river, Restoration actors being told to avoid "lewd, obscene, or indecent postures," and much more. Each selection has an introduction by Prof. Nagler. This extraordinary, lively collection is ideal as a source of otherwise difficult to obtain material, as well as a fine book for browsing. Over 80 illustrations. 10 diagrams. xxiii + 611pp. 5⅜ x 8. T515 Paperbound **$2.75**

CATALOGUE OF DOVER BOOKS

WORLD DRAMA, B. H. Clark. The dramatic creativity of a score of ages and eras — all in two handy compact volumes. Over ⅓ of this material is unavailable in any other current edition! 46 plays from Ancient Greece, Rome, Medieval Europe, France, Germany, Italy, England, Russia, Scandinavia, India, China, Japan, etc. — including classic authors like Aeschylus, Sophocles, Euripides, Aristophanes, Plautus, Marlowe, Jonson, Farquhar, Goldsmith, Cervantes, Molière, Dumas, Goethe, Schiller, Ibsen, and many others. This creative collection avoids hackneyed material and includes only completely first-rate works which are relatively little known or difficult to obtain. "The most comprehensive collection of important plays from all literature available in English," SAT. REV. OF LITERATURE. Introduction. Reading lists. 2 volumes. 1364pp. 5⅜ x 8.
Vol. 1, T57 Paperbound **$2.25**
Vol. 2, T59 Paperbound **$2.25**

MASTERPIECES OF THE RUSSIAN DRAMA, edited with introduction by G. R. Noyes. This only comprehensive anthology of Russian drama ever published in English offers complete texts, in 1st-rate modern translations, of 12 plays covering 200 years. Vol. 1: "The Young Hopeful," Fonvisin; "Wit Works Woe," Griboyedov; "The Inspector General," Gogol; "A Month in the Country," Turgenev; "The Poor Bride," Ostrovsky; "A Bitter Fate," Pisemsky. Vol. 2: "The Death of Ivan the Terrible," Alexey Tolstoy "The Power of Darkness," Lev Tolstoy; "The Lower Depths," Gorky; "The Cherry Orchard," Chekhov; "Professor Storitsyn," Andreyev; "Mystery Bouffe," Mayakovsky. Bibliography. Total of 902pp. 5⅜ x 8.
Vol. 1 T647 Paperbound **$2.00**
Vol. 2 T648 Paperbound **$2.00**

EUGENE O'NEILL: THE MAN AND HIS PLAYS, B. H. Clark. Introduction to O'Neill's life and work. Clark analyzes each play from the early THE WEB to the recently produced MOON FOR THE MISBEGOTTEN and THE ICEMAN COMETH revealing the environmental and dramatic influences necessary for a complete understanding of these important works. Bibliography. Appendices. Index. ix + 182pp. 5⅜ x 8. T379 Paperbound **$1.25**

THE HEART OF THOREAU'S JOURNALS, edited by O. Shepard. The best general selection from Thoreau's voluminous (and rare) journals. This intimate record of thoughts and observations reveals the full Thoreau and his intellectual development more accurately than any of his published works: self-conflict between the scientific observer and the poet, reflections on transcendental philosophy, involvement in the tragedies of neighbors and national causes, etc. New preface, notes, introductions. xii + 228pp. 5⅜ x 8. T741 Paperbound **$1.45**

H. D. THOREAU: A WRITER'S JOURNAL, edited by L. Stapleton. A unique new selection from the Journals concentrating on Thoreau's growth as a conscious literary artist, the ideals and purposes of his art. Most of the material has never before appeared outside of the complete 14-volume edition. Contains vital insights on Thoreau's projected book on Concord, thoughts on the nature of men and government, indignation with slavery, sources of inspiration, goals in life. Index. xxxiii + 234pp. 5⅜ x 8. T678 Paperbound **$1.55**

THE HEART OF EMERSON'S JOURNALS, edited by Bliss Perry. Best of these revealing Journals, originally 10 volumes, presented in a one volume edition. Talks with Channing, Hawthorne, Thoreau, and Bronson Alcott; impressions of Webster, Everett, John Brown, and Lincoln; records of moments of sudden understanding, vision, and solitary ecstasy. "The essays do not reveal the power of Emerson's mind . . . as do these hasty and informal writings," N.Y. Times. Preface by Bliss Perry. Index. xiii + 357pp. 5⅜ x 8. T477 Paperbound **$1.85**

FOUNDERS OF THE MIDDLE AGES, E. K. Rand. This is the best non-technical discussion of the transformation of Latin pagan culture into medieval civilization. Covering such figures as Tertullian, Gregory, Jerome, Boethius, Augustine, the Neoplatonists, and many other literary men, educators, classicists, and humanists, this book is a storehouse of information presented clearly and simply for the intelligent non-specialist. "Thoughtful, beautifully written," AMERICAN HISTORICAL REVIEW. "Extraordinarily accurate," Richard McKeon, THE NATION. ix + 365pp. 5⅜ x 8. T369 Paperbound **$1.85**

PLAY-MAKING: A MANUAL OF CRAFTSMANSHIP, William Archer. With an extensive, new introduction by John Gassner, Yale Univ. The permanently essential requirements of solid play construction are set down in clear, practical language: theme, exposition, foreshadowing, tension, obligatory scene, peripety, dialogue, character, psychology, other topics. This book has been one of the most influential elements in the modern theatre, and almost everything said on the subject since is contained explicitly or implicitly within its covers. Bibliography. Index. xlii + 277pp. 5⅜ x 8. T651 Paperbound **$1.75**

HAMBURG DRAMATURGY, G. E. Lessing. One of the most brilliant of German playwrights of the eighteenth-century age of criticism analyzes the complex of theory and tradition that constitutes the world of theater. These 104 essays on aesthetic theory helped demolish the regime of French classicism, opening the door to psychological and social realism, romanticism. Subjects include the original functions of tragedy; drama as the rational world; the meaning of pity and fear, pity and fear as means for purgation and other Aristotelian concepts; genius and creative force; interdependence of poet's language and actor's interpretation; truth and authenticity; etc. A basic and enlightening study for anyone interested in aesthetics and ideas, from the philosopher to the theatergoer. Introduction by Prof. Victor Lange. xxii + 265pp. 4½ x 6⅜. T32 Paperbound **$1.45**

Philosophy, Religion

GUIDE TO PHILOSOPHY, C. E. M. Joad. A modern classic which examines many crucial problems which man has pondered through the ages: Does free will exist? Is there plan in the universe? How do we know and validate our knowledge? Such opposed solutions as subjective idealism and realism, chance and teleology, vitalism and logical positivism, are evaluated and the contributions of the great philosophers from the Greeks to moderns like Russell, Whitehead, and others, are considered in the context of each problem. "The finest introduction," BOSTON TRANSCRIPT. Index. Classified bibliography. 592pp. 5⅜ x 8.
T297 Paperbound **$2.00**

HISTORY OF ANCIENT PHILOSOPHY, W. Windelband. One of the clearest, most accurate comprehensive surveys of Greek and Roman philosophy. Discusses ancient philosophy in general, intellectual life in Greece in the 7th and 6th centuries B.C., Thales, Anaximander, Anaximenes, Heraclitus, the Eleatics, Empedocles, Anaxagoras, Leucippus, the Pythagoreans, the Sophists, Socrates, Democritus (20 pages), Plato (50 pages), Aristotle (70 pages), the Peripatetics, Stoics, Epicureans, Sceptics, Neo-platonists, Christian Apologists, etc. 2nd German edition translated by H. E. Cushman. xv + 393pp. 5⅜ x 8.
T357 Paperbound **$1.85**

ILLUSTRATIONS OF THE HISTORY OF MEDIEVAL THOUGHT AND LEARNING, R. L. Poole. Basic analysis of the thought and lives of the leading philosophers and ecclesiastics from the 8th to the 14th century—Abailard, Ockham, Wycliffe, Marsiglio of Padua, and many other great thinkers who carried the torch of Western culture and learning through the "Dark Ages": political, religious, and metaphysical views. Long a standard work for scholars and one of the best introductions to medieval thought for beginners. Index. 10 Appendices. xiii + 327pp. 5⅜ x 8.
T674 Paperbound **$1.85**

PHILOSOPHY AND CIVILIZATION IN THE MIDDLE AGES, M. de Wulf. This semi-popular survey covers aspects of medieval intellectual life such as religion, philosophy, science, the arts, etc. It also covers feudalism vs. Catholicism, rise of the universities, mendicant orders, monastic centers, and similar topics. Unabridged. Bibliography. Index. viii + 320pp. 5⅜ x 8.
T284 Paperbound **$1.85**

AN INTRODUCTION TO SCHOLASTIC PHILOSOPHY, Prof. M. de Wulf. Formerly entitled SCHOLASTICISM OLD AND NEW, this volume examines the central scholastic tradition from St. Anselm, Albertus Magnus, Thomas Aquinas, up to Suarez in the 17th century. The relation of scholasticism to ancient and medieval philosophy and science in general is clear and easily followed. The second part of the book considers the modern revival of scholasticism, the Louvain position, relations with Kantianism and Positivism. Unabridged. xvi + 271pp. 5⅜ x 8.
T296 Clothbound **$3.50**
T283 Paperbound **$1.75**

A HISTORY OF MODERN PHILOSOPHY, H. Höffding. An exceptionally clear and detailed coverage of western philosophy from the Renaissance to the end of the 19th century. Major and minor men such as Pomponazzi, Bodin, Boehme, Telesius, Bruno, Copernicus, da Vinci, Kepler, Galileo, Bacon, Descartes, Hobbes, Spinoza, Leibniz, Wolff, Locke, Newton, Berkeley, Hume, Erasmus, Montesquieu, Voltaire, Diderot, Rousseau, Lessing, Kant, Herder, Fichte, Schelling, Hegel, Schopenhauer, Comte, Mill, Darwin, Spencer, Hartmann, Lange, and many others, are discussed in terms of theory of knowledge, logic, cosmology, and psychology. Index. 2 volumes, total of 1159pp. 5⅜ x 8.
T117 Vol. 1, Paperbound **$2.00**
T118 Vol. 2, Paperbound **$2.00**

ARISTOTLE, A. E. Taylor. A brilliant, searching non-technical account of Aristotle and his thought written by a foremost Platonist. It covers the life and works of Aristotle; classification of the sciences; logic; first philosophy; matter and form; causes; motion and eternity; God; physics; metaphysics; and similar topics. Bibliography. New Index compiled for this edition. 128pp. 5⅜ x 8.
T280 Paperbound **$1.00**

THE SYSTEM OF THOMAS AQUINAS, M. de Wulf. Leading Neo-Thomist, one of founders of University of Louvain, gives concise exposition to central doctrines of Aquinas, as a means toward determining his value to modern philosophy, religion. Formerly "Medieval Philosophy Illustrated from the System of Thomas Aquinas." Trans. by E. Messenger. Introduction. 151pp. 5⅜ x 8.
T568 Paperbound **$1.25**

LEIBNIZ, H. W. Carr. Most stimulating middle-level coverage of basic philosophical thought of Leibniz. Easily understood discussion, analysis of major works: "Theodicy," "Principles of Nature and Grace," "Monadology"; Leibniz's influence; intellectual growth; correspondence; disputes with Bayle, Malebranche, Newton; importance of his thought today, with reinterpretation in modern terminology. "Power and mastery," London Times. Bibliography. Index. 226pp. 5⅜ x 8.
T624 Paperbound **$1.35**

CATALOGUE OF DOVER BOOKS

THE SENSE OF BEAUTY, G. Santayana. A revelation of the beauty of language as well as an important philosophic treatise, this work studies the "why, when, and how beauty appears, what conditions an object must fulfill to be beautiful, what elements of our nature make us sensible of beauty, and what the relation is between the constitution of the object and the excitement of our susceptibility." "It is doubtful if a better treatment of the subject has since been published," PEABODY JOURNAL. Index. ix + 275pp. 5⅜ x 8.
T238 Paperbound **$1.00**

PROBLEMS OF ETHICS, Moritz Schlick. The renowned leader of the "Vienna Circle" applies the logical positivist approach to a wide variety of ethical problems: the source and means of attaining knowledge, the formal and material characteristics of the good, moral norms and principles, absolute vs. relative values, free will and responsibility, comparative importance of pleasure and suffering as ethical values, etc. Disarmingly simple and straightforward despite complexity of subject. First English translation, authorized by author before his death, of a thirty-year old classic. Translated and with an introduction by David Rynin. Index. Foreword by Prof. George P. Adams. xxi + 209pp. 5⅜ x 8. T946 Paperbound **$1.45**

AN INTRODUCTION TO EXISTENTIALISM, Robert G. Olson. A new and indispensable guide to one of the major thought systems of our century, the movement that is central to the thinking of some of the most creative figures of the past hundred years. Stresses Heidegger and Sartre, with careful and objective examination of the existentialist position, values—freedom of choice, individual dignity, personal love, creative effort—and answers to the eternal questions of the human condition. Scholarly, unbiased, analytic, unlike most studies of this difficult subject, Prof. Olson's book is aimed at the student of philosophy as well as at the reader with no formal training who is looking for an absorbing, accessible, and thorough introduction to the basic texts. Index. xv + 221pp. 5⅜ x 8½. T55 Paperbound **$1.45**

SYMBOLIC LOGIC, C. I. Lewis and C. H. Langford. Since first publication in 1932, this has been among most frequently cited works on symbolic logic. Still one of the best introductions both for beginners and for mathematicians, philosophers. First part covers basic topics which easily lend themselves to beginning study. Second part is rigorous, thorough development of logistic method, examination of some of most difficult and abstract aspects of symbolic logic, including modal logic, logical paradoxes, many-valued logic, with Prof. Lewis' own contributions. 2nd revised (corrected) edition. 3 appendixes, one new to this edition. 524pp. 5⅜ x 8. S170 Paperbound **$2.00**

WHITEHEAD'S PHILOSOPHY OF CIVILIZATION, A. H. Johnson. A leading authority on Alfred North Whitehead synthesizes the great philosopher's thought on civilization, scattered throughout various writings, into unified whole. Analysis of Whitehead's general definition of civilization, his reflections on history and influences on its development, his religion, including his analysis of Christianity, concept of solitariness as first requirement of personal religion, and so on. Other chapters cover views on minority groups, society, civil liberties, education. Also critical comments on Whitehead's philosophy. Written with general reader in mind. A perceptive introduction to important area of the thought of a leading philosopher of our century. Revised index and bibliography. xii + 211pp. 5⅜ x 8½.
T996 Paperbound **$1.50**

WHITEHEAD'S THEORY OF REALITY, A. H. Johnson. Introductory outline of Whitehead's theory of actual entities, the heart of his philosophy of reality, followed by his views on nature of God, philosophy of mind, theory of value (truth, beauty, goodness and their opposites), analyses of other philosophers, attitude toward science. A perspicacious lucid introduction by author of dissertation on Whitehead, written under the subject's supervision at Harvard. Good basic view for beginning students of philosophy and for those who are simply interested in important contemporary ideas. Revised index and bibliography. xiii + 267pp. 5⅜ x 8½.
T989 Paperbound **$1.50**

MIND AND THE WORLD-ORDER, C. I. Lewis. Building upon the work of Peirce, James, and Dewey, Professor Lewis outlines a theory of knowledge in terms of "conceptual pragmatism." Dividing truth into abstract mathematical certainty and empirical truth, the author demonstrates that the traditional understanding of the a priori must be abandoned. Detailed analyses of philosophy, metaphysics, method, the "given" in experience, knowledge of objects, nature of the a priori, experience and order, and many others. Appendices. xiv + 446pp. 5⅜ x 8. T359 Paperbound **$2.25**

SCEPTICISM AND ANIMAL FAITH, G. Santayana. To eliminate difficulties in the traditional theory of knowledge, Santayana distinguishes between the independent existence of objects and the essence our mind attributes to them. Scepticism is thereby established as a form of belief, and animal faith is shown to be a necessary condition of knowledge. Belief, classical idealism, intuition, memory, symbols, literary psychology, and much more, discussed with unusual clarity and depth. Index. xii + 314pp. 5⅜ x 8. T235 Clothbound **$3.50**
T236 Paperbound **$1.50**

LANGUAGE AND MYTH, E. Cassirer. Analyzing the non-rational thought processes which go to make up culture, Cassirer demonstrates that beneath both language and myth there lies a dominant unconscious "grammar" of experience whose categories and canons are not those of logical thought. His analyses of seemingly diverse phenomena such as Indian metaphysics, the Melanesian "mana," the Naturphilosophie of Schelling, modern poetry, etc., are profound without being pedantic. Introduction and translation by Susanne Langer. Index. x + 103pp. 5⅜ x 8. T51 Paperbound **$1.25**

Americana

THE EYES OF DISCOVERY, J. Bakeless. A vivid reconstruction of how unspoiled America appeared to the first white men. Authentic and enlightening accounts of Hudson's landing in New York, Coronado's trek through the Southwest; scores of explorers, settlers, trappers, soldiers. America's pristine flora, fauna, and Indians in every region and state in fresh and unusual new aspects. "A fascinating view of what the land was like before the first highway went through," Time. 68 contemporary illustrations, 39 newly added in this edition. Index. Bibliography. x + 500pp. 5⅜ x 8.   T761 Paperbound **$2.00**

AUDUBON AND HIS JOURNALS, J. J. Audubon. A collection of fascinating accounts of Europe and America in the early 1800's through Audubon's own eyes. Includes the Missouri River Journals —an eventful trip through America's untouched heartland, the Labrador Journals, the European Journals, the famous "Episodes", and other rare Audubon material, including the descriptive chapters from the original letterpress edition of the "Ornithological Studies", omitted in all later editions. Indispensable for ornithologists, naturalists, and all lovers of Americana and adventure. 70-page biography by Audubon's granddaughter. 38 illustrations. Index. Total of 1106pp. 5⅜ x 8.   T675 Vol I Paperbound **$2.25**
T676 Vol II Paperbound **$2.25**
The set **$4.50**

TRAVELS OF WILLIAM BARTRAM, edited by Mark Van Doren. The first inexpensive illustrated edition of one of the 18th century's most delightful books is an excellent source of first-hand material on American geography, anthropology, and natural history. Many descriptions of early Indian tribes are our only source of information on them prior to the infiltration of the white man. "The mind of a scientist with the soul of a poet," John Livingston Lowes. 13 original illustrations and maps. Edited with an introduction by Mark Van Doren. 448pp. 5⅜ x 8.
T13 Paperbound **$2.00**

GARRETS AND PRETENDERS: A HISTORY OF BOHEMIANISM IN AMERICA, A. Parry. The colorful and fantastic history of American Bohemianism from Poe to Kerouac. This is the only complete record of hoboes, cranks, starving poets, and suicides. Here are Pfaff, Whitman, Crane, Bierce, Pound, and many others. New chapters by the author and by H. T. Moore bring this thorough and well-documented history down to the Beatniks. "An excellent account," N. Y. Times. Scores of cartoons, drawings, and caricatures. Bibliography. Index. xxviii + 421pp. 5⅝ x 8⅜.   T708 Paperbound **$1.95**

THE EXPLORATION OF THE COLORADO RIVER AND ITS CANYONS, J. W. Powell. The thrilling first-hand account of the expedition that filled in the last white space on the map of the United States. Rapids, famine, hostile Indians, and mutiny are among the perils encountered as the unknown Colorado Valley reveals its secrets. This is the only uncut version of Major Powell's classic of exploration that has been printed in the last 60 years. Includes later reflections and subsequent expedition. 250 illustrations, new map. 400pp. 5⅝ x 8⅜.
T94 Paperbound **$2.00**

THE JOURNAL OF HENRY D. THOREAU, Edited by Bradford Torrey and Francis H. Allen. Henry Thoreau is not only one of the most important figures in American literature and social thought; his voluminous journals (from which his books emerged as selections and crystalliza-tions) constitute both the longest, most sensitive record of personal internal development and a most penetrating description of a historical moment in American culture. This present set, which was first issued in fourteen volumes, contains Thoreau's entire journals from 1837 to 1862, with the exception of the lost years which were found only recently. We are reissuing it, complete and unabridged, with a new introduction by Walter Harding, Secretary of the Thoreau Society. Fourteen volumes reissued in two volumes. Foreword by Henry Seidel Canby. Total of 1888pp. 8⅜ x 12¼.   T312-3 Two volume set, Clothbound **$20.00**

GAMES AND SONGS OF AMERICAN CHILDREN, collected by William Wells Newell. A remarkable collection of 190 games with songs that accompany many of them; cross references to show similarities, differences among them; variations; musical notation for 38 songs. Textual dis-cussions show relations with folk-drama and other aspects of folk tradition. Grouped into categories for ready comparative study: Love-games, histories, playing at work, human life, bird and beast, mythology, guessing-games, etc. New introduction covers relations of songs and dances to timeless heritage of folklore, biographical sketch of Newell, other pertinent data. A good source of inspiration for those in charge of groups of children and a valuable reference for anthropologists, sociologists, psychiatrists. Introduction by Carl Withers. New indexes of first lines, games. 5⅜ x 8½. xii + 242pp.   T354 Paperbound **$1.65**

CATALOGUE OF DOVER BOOKS

GARDNER'S PHOTOGRAPHIC SKETCH BOOK OF THE CIVIL WAR, Alexander Gardner. The first published collection of Civil War photographs, by one of the two or three most famous photographers of the era, outstandingly reproduced from the original positives. Scenes of crucial battles: Appomattox, Manassas, Mechanicsville, Bull Run, Yorktown, Fredericksburg, etc. Gettysburg immediately after retirement of forces. Battle ruins at Richmond, Petersburg, Gaines'Mill. Prisons, arsenals, a slave pen, fortifications, headquarters, pontoon bridges, soldiers, a field hospital. A unique glimpse into the realities of one of the bloodiest wars in history, with an introductory text to each picture by Gardner himself. Until this edition, there were only five known copies in libraries, and fewer in private hands, one of which sold at auction in 1952 for $425. Introduction by E. F. Bleiler. 100 full page 7 x 10 photographs (original size). 224pp. 8½ x 10¾.　　　　　　　　　　　　　　　T476 Clothbound **$6.00**

A BIBLIOGRAPHY OF NORTH AMERICAN FOLKLORE AND FOLKSONG, Charles Haywood, Ph.D. The only book that brings together bibliographic information on so wide a range of folklore material. Lists practically everything published about American folksongs, ballads, dances, folk beliefs and practices, popular music, tales, similar material—more than 35,000 items of books, articles, periodicals, monographs, music publications, phonograph records. Each entry complete with author, title, date and place of publication, arranger and performer of particular examples of folk music, many with Dr. Haywood's valuable criticism, evaluation. Volume I, "The American People," is complete listing of general and regional studies, titles of tales and songs of Negro and non-English speaking groups and where to find them, Occupational Bibliography including sections listing sources of information, folk material on cowboys, riverboat men, 49ers, American characters like Mike Fink, Frankie and Johnnie, John Henry, many more. Volume II, "The American Indian," tells where to find information on dances, myths, songs, ritual of more than 250 tribes in U.S., Canada. A monumental product of 10 years' labor, carefully classified for easy use. "All students of this subject . . . will find themselves in debt to Professor Haywood," Stith Thompson, in American Anthropologist. ". . . a most useful and excellent work," Duncan Emrich, Chief Folklore Section, Library of Congress, in "Notes." Corrected, enlarged republication of 1951 edition. New Preface. New index of composers, arrangers, performers. General index of more than 15,000 items. Two volumes. Total of 1301pp. 6⅛ x 9¼.　　　　T797-798 Clothbound **$12.50**

INCIDENTS OF TRAVEL IN YUCATAN, John L. Stephens. One of first white men to penetrate interior of Yucatan tells the thrilling story of his discoveries of 44 cities, remains of once-powerful Maya civilization. Compelling text combines narrative power with historical significance as it takes you through heat, dust, storms of Yucatan; native festivals with brutal bull fights; great ruined temples atop man-made mounds. Countless idols, sculptures, tombs, examples of Mayan taste for rich ornamentation, from gateways to personal trinkets, accurately illustrated, discussed in text. Will appeal to those interested in ancient civilizations, and those who like stories of exploration, discovery, adventure. Republication of last (1843) edition. 124 illustrations by English artist, F. Catherwood. Appendix on Mayan architecture, chronology. Two volume set. Total of xxviii + 927pp.

Vol I T926 Paperbound **$2.00**
Vol II T927 Paperbound **$2.00**
The set **$4.00**

A GENIUS IN THE FAMILY, Hiram Percy Maxim. Sir Hiram Stevens Maxim was known to the public as the inventive genius who created the Maxim gun, automatic sprinkler, and a heavier-than-air plane that got off the ground in 1894. Here, his son reminisces—this is by no means a formal biography—about the exciting and often downright scandalous private life of his brilliant, eccentric father. A warm and winning portrait of a prankish, mischievous, impious personality, a genuine character. The style is fresh and direct, the effect is unadulterated pleasure. "A book of charm and lasting humor . . . belongs on the 'must read' list of all fathers," New York Times. "A truly gorgeous affair," New Statesman and Nation. 17 illustrations, 16 specially for this edition. viii + 108pp. 5⅜ x 8½.

T948 Paperbound **$1.00**

HORSELESS CARRIAGE DAYS, Hiram P. Maxim. The best account of an important technological revolution by one of its leading figures. The delightful and rewarding story of the author's experiments with the exact combustibility of gasoline, stopping and starting mechanisms, carriage design, and engines. Captures remarkably well the flavor of an age of scoffers and rival inventors not above sabotage; of noisy, uncontrollable gasoline vehicles and incredible mobile steam kettles. ". . . historic information and light humor are combined to furnish highly entertaining reading," New York Times. 56 photographs, 12 specially for this edition. xi + 175pp. 5⅜ x 8½.　　　　　　　　　　　　　　　　　T964 Paperbound **$1.35**

BODY, BOOTS AND BRITCHES: FOLKTALES, BALLADS AND SPEECH FROM COUNTRY NEW YORK, Harold W. Thompson. A unique collection, discussion of songs, stories, anecdotes, proverbs handed down orally from Scotch-Irish grandfathers, German nurse-maids, Negro workmen, gathered from all over Upper New York State. Tall tales by and about lumbermen and pirates, canalers and injun-fighters, tragic and comic ballads, scores of sayings and proverbs all tied together by an informative, delightful narrative by former president of New York Historical Society. ". . . a sparkling homespun tapestry that every lover of Americana will want to have around the house," Carl Carmer, New York Times. Republication of 1939 edition. 20 line-drawings. Index. Appendix (Sources of material, bibliography). 530pp. 5⅜ x 8½.　　　　　　　　　　　　　　　　　　　　　T411 Paperbound **$2.00**

Art, History of Art, Antiques, Graphic Arts, Handcrafts

ART STUDENTS' ANATOMY, E. J. Farris. Outstanding art anatomy that uses chiefly living objects for its illustrations. 71 photos of undraped men, women, children are accompanied by carefully labeled matching sketches to illustrate the skeletal system, articulations and movements, bony landmarks, the muscular system, skin, fasciae, fat, etc. 9 x-ray photos show movement of joints. Undraped models are shown in such actions as serving in tennis, drawing a bow in archery, playing football, dancing, preparing to spring and to dive. Also discussed and illustrated are proportions, age and sex differences, the anatomy of the smile, etc. 8 plates by the great early 18th century anatomic illustrator Siegfried Albinus are also included. Glossary. 158 figures, 7 in color. x + 159pp. 5⅝ x 8⅜. T744 Paperbound **$1.50**

AN ATLAS OF ANATOMY FOR ARTISTS, F Schider. A new 3rd edition of this standard text enlarged by 52 new illustrations of hands, anatomical studies by Cloquet, and expressive life studies of the body by Barcsay. 189 clear, detailed plates offer you precise information of impeccable accuracy. 29 plates show all aspects of the skeleton, with closeups of special areas, while 54 full-page plates, mostly in two colors, give human musculature as seen from four different points of view, with cutaways for important portions of the body. 14 full-page plates provide photographs of hand forms, eyelids, female breasts, and indicate the location of muscles upon models. 59 additional plates show how great artists of the past utilized human anatomy. They reproduce sketches and finished work by such artists as Michelangelo, Leonardo da Vinci, Goya, and 15 others. This is a lifetime reference work which will be one of the most important books in any artist's library. "The standard reference tool," AMERICAN LIBRARY ASSOCIATION. "Excellent," AMERICAN ARTIST. Third enlarged edition. 189 plates, 647 illustrations. xxvi + 192pp. 7⅞ x 10⅝. T241 Clothbound **$6.00**

AN ATLAS OF ANIMAL ANATOMY FOR ARTISTS, W. Ellenberger, H. Baum, H. Dittrich. The largest, richest animal anatomy for artists available in English. 99 detailed anatomical plates of such animals as the horse, dog, cat, lion, deer, seal, kangaroo, flying squirrel, cow, bull, goat, monkey, hare, and bat. Surface features are clearly indicated, while progressive beneath-the-skin pictures show musculature, tendons, and bone structure. Rest and action are exhibited in terms of musculature and skeletal structure and detailed cross-sections are given for heads and important features. The animals chosen are representative of specific families so that a study of these anatomies will provide knowledge of hundreds of related species. "Highly recommended as one of the very few books on the subject worthy of being used as an authoritative guide," DESIGN. "Gives a fundamental knowledge," AMERICAN ARTIST. Second revised, enlarged edition with new plates from Cuvier, Stubbs, etc. 288 illustrations. 153pp. 11⅜ x 9. T82 Clothbound **$6.00**

THE HUMAN FIGURE IN MOTION, Eadweard Muybridge. The largest selection in print of Muybridge's famous high-speed action photos of the human figure in motion. 4789 photographs illustrate 162 different actions: men, women, children—mostly undraped—are shown walking, running, carrying various objects, sitting, lying down, climbing, throwing, arising, and performing over 150 other actions. Some actions are shown in as many as 150 photographs each. All in all there are more than 500 action strips in this enormous volume, series shots taken at shutter speeds of as high as 1/6000th of a second! These are not posed shots, but true stopped motion. They show bone and muscle in situations that the human eye is not fast enough to capture. Earlier, smaller editions of these prints have brought $40 and more on the out-of-print market. "A must for artists," ART IN FOCUS. "An unparalleled dictionary of action for all artists," AMERICAN ARTIST. 390 full-page plates, with 4789 photographs. Printed on heavy glossy stock. Reinforced binding with headbands. xxi + 390pp. 7⅞ x 10⅝. T204 Clothbound **$10.00**

ANIMALS IN MOTION, Eadweard Muybridge. This is the largest collection of animal action photos in print. 34 different animals (horses, mules, oxen, goats, camels, pigs, cats, guanacos, lions, gnus, deer, monkeys, eagles—and 21 others) in 132 characteristic actions. The horse alone is shown in more than 40 different actions. All 3919 photographs are taken in series at speeds up to 1/6000th of a second. The secrets of leg motion, spinal patterns, head movements, strains and contortions shown nowhere else are captured. You will see exactly how a lion sets his foot down; how an elephant's knees are like a human's—and how they differ; the position of a kangaroo's legs in mid-leap; how an ostrich's head bobs; details of the flight of birds—and thousands of facets of motion only the fastest cameras can catch. Photographed from domestic animals and animals in the Philadelphia zoo, it contains neither semiposed artificial shots nor distorted telephoto shots taken under adverse conditions. Artists, biologists, decorators, cartoonists, will find this book indispensable for understanding animals in motion. "A really marvelous series of plates," NATURE (London). "The dry plate's most spectacular early use was by Eadweard Muybridge," LIFE. 3919 photographs; 380 full pages of plates. 440pp. Printed on heavy glossy paper. Deluxe binding with headbands. 7⅞ x 10⅝. T203 Clothbound **$10.00**

CATALOGUE OF DOVER BOOKS

THE 100 GREATEST ADVERTISEMENTS, WHO WROTE THEM AND WHAT THEY DID, J. L. Watkins.
100 (plus 13 added for this edition) of most successful ads ever to appear. "Do You Make These Mistakes in English," "They laughed when I sat down," "A Hog Can Cross the Country," "The Man in the Hathaway Shirt," over 100 more ads that changed habits of a nation, gave new expressions to the language, built reputations. Also salient facts behind ads, often in words of their creators. "Useful . . . valuable . . . enlightening," Printers' Ink. 2nd revised edition. Introduction. Foreword by Raymond Rubicam. Index. 130 illustrations. 252pp. 7¾ x 10¾.   T540 Paperbound **$2.25**

THE DIDEROT PICTORIAL ENCYCLOPEDIA OF TRADES AND INDUSTRY, MANUFACTURING AND THE TECHNICAL ARTS IN PLATES SELECTED FROM "L'ENCYCLOPEDIE OU DICTIONNAIRE RAISONNE DES SCIENCES, DES ARTS, ET DES METIERS" OF DENIS DIDEROT, edited with text by C. Gillispie. The first modern selection of plates from the high point of 18th century French engraving, Diderot's famous Encyclopedia. Over 2000 illustrations on 485 full-page plates, most of them original size, illustrating the trades and industries of one of the most fascinating periods of modern history, 18th century France. These magnificent engravings provide an invaluable source of fresh, copyright-free material to artists and illustrators, a lively and accurate social document to students of cultures, an outstanding find to the lover of fine engravings. The plates teem with life, with men, women, and children performing all of the thousands of operations necessary to the trades before and during the early stages of the industrial revolution. Plates are in sequence, and show general operations, closeups of difficult operations, and details of complex machinery. Such important and interesting trades and industries are illustrated as sowing, harvesting, beekeeping, cheesemaking, operating windmills, milling flour, charcoal burning, tobacco processing, indigo, fishing, arts of war, salt extraction, mining, smelting iron, casting iron steel, extracting mercury, zinc, sulphur, copper, etc., slating, tinning, silverplating, gilding, making gunpowder, cannons, bells, shoeing horses, tanning, papermaking, printing, dying, and more than 40 other categories. Besides being a work of remarkable beauty and skill, this is also one of the largest collections of working figures in print. 920pp. 9 x 12. Heavy library cloth.   T421 Two volume set **$18.50**

THE HANDBOOK OF PLANT AND FLORAL ORNAMENT, R. G. Hatton. One of the truly great collections of plant drawings for reproduction: 1200 different figures of flowering or fruiting plants—line drawings that will reproduce excellently. Selected from superb woodcuts and copperplate engravings appearing mostly in 16th and 17th century herbals including the fabulously rare "Kreuter Büch" (Bock) "Cruijde Boeck" (Dodoens), etc. Plants classified according to botanical groups. Also excellent reading for anyone interested in home gardening or any phase of horticulture. Formerly "The Craftsman's Plant-Book: or Figures of Plants." Introductions. Over 1200 illustrations. Index. 548pp. 6⅛ x 9¼.   T649 Paperbound **$2.98**

HANDBOOK OF ORNAMENT, F. S. Meyer. One of the largest collections of copyright-free traditional art in print. It contains over 3300 line cuts from Greek, Roman, Medieval, Islamic, Renaissance, Baroque, 18th and 19th century sources. 180 plates illustrate elements of design with networks, Gothic tracery, geometric elements, flower and animal motifs, etc., while 100 plates illustrate decorative objects: chairs, thrones, daises, cabinets, crowns, weapons, utensils, vases, jewelry, armor, heraldry, bottles, altars, and scores of other objects. Indispensable for artists, illustrators, designers, handicrafters, etc. Full text. 3300 illustrations. xiv + 548pp. 5⅜ x 8.   T302 Paperbound **$2.25**

COSTUMES OF THE GREEKS AND ROMANS, Thomas Hope. Authentic costumes from all walks of life in Roman, Greek civilizations, including Phrygia, Egypt, Persia, Parthia, Etruria, in finely drawn, detailed engravings by Thomas Hope (1770-1831). Scores of additional engravings of ancient musical instruments, furniture, jewelry, sarcophagi, other adjuncts to ancient life. All carefully copied from ancient vases and statuary. Textual introduction by author. Art and advertising personnel, costume and stage designers, students of fashion design will find these copyright-free engravings a source of ideas and inspiration and a valuable reference. Republication of 1st (1812) edition. 300 full-page plates, over 700 illustrations. xliv + 300pp. 5⅝ x 8⅜.   T21 Paperbound **$2.00**

PRINCIPLES OF ART HISTORY, H. Wölfflin. Analyzing such terms as "baroque," "classic," "neoclassic," "primitive," "picturesque," and 164 different works by artists like Botticelli, van Cleve, Dürer, Hobbema, Holbein, Hals, Rembrandt, Titian, Brueghel, Vermeer, and many others, the author establishes the classifications of art history and style on a firm, concrete basis. This classic of art criticism shows what really occurred between the 14th century primitives and the sophistication of the 18th century in terms of basic attitudes and philosophies. "A remarkable lesson in the art of seeing," SAT. REV. OF LITERATURE. Translated from the 7th German edition. 150 illustrations. 254pp. 6⅛ x 9¼.   T276 Paperbound **$2.00**

AFRICAN SCULPTURE, Ladislas Segy. First publication of a new book by the author of critically acclaimed AFRICAN SCULPTURE SPEAKS. It contains 163 full-page plates illustrating masks, fertility figures, ceremonial objects, etc., representing the culture of 50 tribes of West and Central Africa. Over 85% of these works of art have never been illustrated before, and each is an authentic and fascinating tribal artifact. A 34-page introduction explains the anthropological, psychological, and artistic values of African sculpture. "Mr. Segy is one of its top authorities," NEW YORKER. 164 full-page photographic plates. Bibliography. 244pp. 6 x 9.   T396 Paperbound **$2.00**

DESIGN MOTIFS OF ANCIENT MEXICO, J. Enciso. This unique collection of pre-Columbian stamps for textiles and pottery contains 766 superb designs from Aztec, Olmec, Totonac, Maya, and Toltec origins. Plumed serpents, calendrical elements, wind gods, animals, flowers, demons, dancers, monsters, abstract ornament, and other designs. More than 90% of these illustrations are completely unobtainable elsewhere. Use this work to bring new barbaric beauty into your crafts or drawing. Originally $17.50. Printed in three colors. 766 illustrations, thousands of motifs. 192pp. 7⅞ x 10¾. T84 Paperbound **$1.85**

DECORATIVE ART OF THE SOUTHWEST INDIANS, D. S. Sides. A magnificent album of authentic designs (both pre- and post-Conquest) from the pottery, textiles, and basketry of the Navaho, Hopi, Mohave, Santo Domingo, and over 20 other Southwestern groups. Designs include birds, clouds, butterflies, quadrupeds, geometric forms, etc. A valuable book for folklorists, and a treasury for artists, designers, advertisers, and craftsmen, who may use without payment or permission any of the vigorous, colorful, and strongly rhythmic designs. Aesthetic and archeological notes. 50 plates. Bibliography of over 50 items. xviii + 101pp. 5⅝ x 8⅜. T139 Paperbound **$1.00**

PAINTING IN THE FAR EAST, Laurence Binyon. Excellent introduction by one of greatest authorities on subject studies 1500 years of oriental art (China, Japan; also Tibet, Persia), over 250 painters. Examines works, schools, influence of Wu Tao-tzu, Kanaoka, Toba Sojo, Masanobu, Okio, etc.; early traditions; Kamakura epoch; the Great Decorators; T'ang Dynasty; Matabei, beginnings of genre; Japanese woodcut, color print; much more, all chronological, in cultural context. 42 photos. Bibliography. 317pp. 6 x 9¼. T520 Paperbound **$2.00**

ON THE LAWS OF JAPANESE PAINTING, H. Bowie. This unusual book, based on 9 years of profound study-experience in the Late Kano art of Japan, remains the most authentic guide in English to the spirit and technique of Japanese painting. A wealth of interesting and useful data on control of the brush; practise exercises; manufacture of ink, brushes, colors; the use of various lines and dots to express moods. It is the best possible substitute for a series of lessons from a great oriental master. 66 plates with 220 illustrations. Index. xv + 177pp. 6⅛ x 9¼. T30 Paperbound **$1.95**

THE MATERIALS AND TECHNIQUES OF MEDIEVAL PAINTING, D. V. Thompson. Based on years of study of medieval manuscripts and laboratory analysis of medieval paintings, this book discusses carriers and grounds, binding media, pigments, metals used in painting, etc. Considers relative merits of painting al fresco and al secco, the procession of coloring materials, burnishing, and many other matters. Preface by Bernard Berenson. Index. 239pp. 5⅜ x 8. T327 Paperbound **$1.85**

THE CRAFTSMAN'S HANDBOOK, Cennino Cennini. This is considered the finest English translation of IL LIBRO DELL' ARTE, a 15th century Florentine introduction to art technique. It is both fascinating reading and a wonderful mirror of another culture for artists, art students, historians, social scientists, or anyone interested in details of life some 500 years ago. While it is not an exact recipe book, it gives directions for such matters as tinting papers, gilding stone, preparation of various hues of black, and many other useful but nearly forgotten facets of the painter's art. As a human document reflecting the ideas of a practising medieval artist it is particularly important. 4 illustrations. xxvii + 142pp. D. V. Thompson translator. 6⅛ x 9¼. T54 Paperbound **$1.35**

VASARI ON TECHNIQUE, G. Vasari. Pupil of Michelangelo and outstanding biographer of the Renaissance artists, Vasari also wrote this priceless treatise on the technical methods of the painters, architects, and sculptors of his day. This is the only English translation of this practical, informative, and highly readable work. Scholars, artists, and general readers will welcome these authentic discussions of marble statues, bronze casting, fresco painting, oil painting, engraving, stained glass, rustic fountains and grottoes, etc. Introduction and notes by G. B. Brown. Index. 18 plates, 11 figures. xxiv + 328pp. 5⅜ x 8. T717 Paperbound **$2.00**

METHODS AND MATERIALS OF PAINTING OF THE GREAT SCHOOLS AND MASTERS, C. L. Eastlake. A vast, complete, and authentic reconstruction of the secret techniques of the masters of painting, collected from hundreds of forgotten manuscripts by the eminent President of the British Royal Academy: Greek, Roman, and medieval techniques; fresco and tempera; varnishes and encaustics; the secrets of Leonardo, Van Eyck, Raphael, and many others. Art historians, students, teachers, critics, and laymen will gain new insights into the creation of the great masterpieces; while artists and craftsmen will have a treasury of valuable techniques. Index. Two volume set. Total of 1025pp. 5⅜ x 8. T718 Paperbound **$2.00**
T719 Paperbound **$2.00**
The set **$4.00**

BYZANTINE ART AND ARCHAEOLOGY, O. M. Dalton. Still the most thorough work in English—both in breadth and in depth—on the astounding multiplicity of Byzantine art forms throughout Europe, North Africa, and Western Asia from the 4th to the 15th century. Analyzes hundreds of individual pieces from over 160 public and private museums, libraries, and collections all over the world. Full treatment of Byzantine sculpture, painting, mosaic, jewelry, textiles, etc., including historical development, symbolism, and aesthetics. Chapters on iconography and ornament. Indispensable for study of Christian symbolism and medieval art. 457 illustrations, many full-page. Bibliography of over 2500 references. 4 Indexes. xx + 727pp. 6⅛ x 9¼. T776 Clothbound **$8.50**

History, Political Science

THE POLITICAL THOUGHT OF PLATO AND ARISTOTLE, E. Barker. One of the clearest and most accurate expositions of the corpus of Greek political thought. This standard source contains exhaustive analyses of the "Republic" and other Platonic dialogues and Aristotle's "Politics" and "Ethics," and discusses the origin of these ideas in Greece, contributions of other Greek theorists, and modifications of Greek ideas by thinkers from Aquinas to Hegel. "Must" reading for anyone interested in the history of Western thought. Index. Chronological Table of Events. 2 Appendixes. xxiv + 560pp. 5⅜ x 8.   T521 Paperbound **$1.85**

THE IDEA OF PROGRESS, J. B. Bury. Practically unknown before the Reformation, the idea of progress has since become one of the central concepts of western civilization. Prof. Bury analyzes its evolution in the thought of Greece, Rome, the Middle Ages, the Renaissance, to its flowering in all branches of science, religion, philosophy, industry, art, and literature, during and following the 16th century. Introduction by Charles Beard. Index. xl + 357pp. 5⅜ x 8.   T40 Paperbound **$2.00**

THE ANCIENT GREEK HISTORIANS, J. B. Bury. This well known, easily read work covers the entire field of classical historians from the early writers to Herodotus, Thucydides, Xenophon, through Poseidonius and such Romans as Tacitus, Cato, Caesar, Livy. Scores of writers are studied biographically, in style, sources, accuracy, structure, historical concepts, and influences. Recent discoveries such as the Oxyrhinchus papyri are referred to, as well as such great scholars as Nissen, Gomperz, Cornford, etc. "Totally unblemished by pedantry." Outlook. "The best account in English," Dutcher, A Guide to Historical Lit. Bibliography, Index. x + 281pp. 5⅜ x 8.   T397 Paperbound **$1.50**

HISTORY OF THE LATER ROMAN EMPIRE, J. B. Bury. This standard work by the leading Byzantine scholar of our time discusses the later Roman and early Byzantine empires from 395 A.D. through the death of Justinian in 565, in their political, social, cultural, theological, and military aspects. Contemporary documents are quoted in full, making this the most complete reconstruction of the period and a fit successor to Gibbon's "Decline and Fall." "Most unlikely that it will ever be superseded," Glanville Downey, Dumbarton Oaks Research Lib. Geneological tables. 5 maps. Bibliography. Index. 2 volumes total of 965pp. 5⅜ x 8. T398, 399 Two volume set, Paperbound **$4.00**

A HISTORY OF ANCIENT GEOGRAPHY, E. H. Bunbury. Standard study, in English, of ancient geography; never equalled for scope, detail. First full account of history of geography from Greeks' first world picture based on mariners, through Ptolemy. Discusses every important map, discovery, figure, travel expedition, war, conjecture, narrative, bearing on subject. Chapters on Homeric geography, Herodotus, Alexander expedition, Strabo, Pliny, Ptolemy, would stand alone as exhaustive monographs. Includes minor geographers, men not usually regarded in this context: Hecataeus, Pytheas, Hipparchus, Artemidorus, Marinus of Tyre, etc. Uses information gleaned from military campaigns such as Punic Wars, Hannibal's passage of Alps, campaigns of Lucullus, Pompey, Caesar's wars, the Trojan War. New introduction by W. H. Stahl, Brooklyn College. Bibliography. Index. 20 maps. 1426pp. 5⅜ x 8. T570-1, clothbound, 2-volume set **$12.50**

POLITICAL PARTIES, Robert Michels. Classic of social science, reference point for all later work, deals with nature of leadership in social organization on government and trade union levels. Probing tendency of oligarchy to replace democracy, it studies need for leadership, desire for organization, psychological motivations, vested interests, hero worship, reaction of leaders to power, press relations, many other aspects. Trans. by E. & C. Paul. Introduction. 447pp. 5⅜ x 8.   T569 Paperbound **$2.00**

A HISTORY OF HISTORICAL WRITING, Harry Elmer Barnes. Virtually the only adequate survey of the whole course of historical writing in a single volume. Surveys developments from the beginnings of historiographies in the ancient Near East and the Classical World, up through the Cold War. Covers major historians in detail, shows interrelationship with cultural background, makes clear individual contributions, evaluates and estimates importance; also enormously rich upon minor authors and thinkers who are usually passed over. Packed with scholarship and learning, clear, easily written. Indispensable to every student of history. Revised and enlarged up to 1961. Index and bibliography. xv + 442pp. 5⅜ x 8½. T104 Paperbound **$2.25**

Prices subject to change without notice.

Dover publishes books on art, music, philosophy, literature, languages, history, social sciences, psychology, handcrafts, orientalia, puzzles and entertainments, chess, pets and gardens, books explaining science, intermediate and higher mathematics, mathematical physics, engineering, biological sciences, earth sciences, classics of science, etc. Write to:

Dept. catrr.
Dover Publications, Inc.
180 Varick Street, N.Y. 14, N.Y.